SURVIVAL

the Reptile

Rajan Sankaran with Meghna Shah

Volume-I

Homoeopathic Medical Publishers
Mumbai, India

Printed in India

First edition: 2010

ISBN: 978-81-906316-8-6

Cover Design: Cheryl Feng

On the cover: *Morelia viridis* (Green tree python)

Printed by: Parksons Graphics
Off New Link Road, Andheri (West), Mumbai - 400 053

Published by :

Homoeopathic Medical Publishers
201 Dinar, 20, Station Road, Santacruz (W), Mumbai - 400 054, INDIA
E-mail: spirit@vsnl.com
Website: www.rajansankaran.com

Homeopathy 1936

THE CHARACTERISTICS OF INDIVIDUAL ANIMALS IN LIFE AND IN THE REMEDIES

By H. A. ROBERTS, M.D. (Derby, Conn.)

(Emphasis by the authors')

"We know less of the personal habits of the snakes than of some of the other animals from which we derive remedies. However, it is characteristic of all the snake venoms that in the provings there is the excessive sensitiveness to touch. The snake is an antagonist of every living creature; he avoids all contacts with other creatures, except for food, when his is the offensive attitude. The snake does not coil to strike at haphazard; there is a regularity to this posture in many snakes. The provings of the remedies prepared from the snake venoms invariably develop in the direction of the symptoms, the same direction as the snake takes in coiling. For instance, the *Lachesis* always coils from left to right; *Lachesis* symptoms, in the provings, start on the left side and move toward the right, with the aggravation usually on the left.

He continues...

"It is characteristic of the snake venoms, in their provings, that there is always the element of fear - the fear of enemies, suspicion. *Lachesis* fears that someone is behind her, and dreads sitting so that someone might injure her in the back; she cannot endure having her back toward anyone else in the room. *Crotalus horridus*, the rattlesnake, imagines himself surrounded by enemies. *Elaps* (*Micrurus corallinus*, the painted coral snake — authors) has a fear of being alone, but does not wish to be spoken to. *Cenchris* (*Agkistrodon contortrix*, the copperhead — authors) has such a nervous apprehension that it causes the patient to tremble and the teeth to chatter, with the belief that his enemies are plotting against him."

"Even as each patient presents to us individual characteristics, so each remedy has a personality of its own which is delineated in the symptomatology produced through careful provings. Just as each person's individuality is most clearly shown by his mental reactions, or by his habits and eccentricities which reflect his mental attitude, so the raising of any animal substance to a potency form reflects the true spirits of the creature from which it was derived, and allows us to compare these symptomatic findings of the racial peculiarities of the creature with the mental symptoms developed in our patients."

"This is a field which has yielded but a small part of its possibilities. *If we could know more of the habits of these creatures from which our animal remedies are derived, we would use them with far greater accuracy,* for we might then know better the individual peculiarities which we often see reflected in our sick patients. If, on the other hand, many of these animal remedies were better or more completely proved, we might well infer from the symptoms produced much more of the natural history of these creatures who have so great a part in the healing art."

Contents

Foreword

The recent decade has brought exciting innovations and ideas to homeopathy. Extending far beyond the merely theoretical, this wave of understanding has brought profound insight which has served as an unalloyed asset to clinical practice. One of the most exciting trends has been the use of botanical, chemical and zoological groupings or families to facilitate understanding of homeopathic remedies' actions and usage. What started some years ago has blossomed into an amazing understanding of the inner workings, not only of homeopathy, but of Nature herself.

On any journey it is worthwhile to look back from where one came, reflecting on the route taken. Now is such an occasion. Like many others of my homeopathic generation, when I first began studying in the mid-1980s, learning materia medica was a laborious job of memorizing baskets full of unrelated symptoms. It was rare to the point of eccentricity to see anything written that united all of a remedy's symptoms into a coherent and understandable whole. A century earlier, E. A Farrington [1847-1885] spoke what we all were experiencing, that the materia medica was 'a mass of symptoms seeming to have no connection at all.'

Whereas we all knew that homeopathy regarded a person as a united whole being, that was far from true when regarding remedies. Even in those early days that disconnect seemed incongruent to some, including myself. Somewhere in the early 1990s faint rumblings began to occur. Leaves had started to twitch and people held onto their hats as the breeze of new ideas was picking up speed. The variety of new thoughts and ideas had a common theme, which was that an orderly and systematic understanding of the materia medica was possible. Far from the notion that a remedy was a stand-alone, independent conglomeration of symptoms, pioneering and innovative thinkers put forth the concept that remedies naturally congregated in groups or families with shared symptoms, themes and actions. This seeming revolution in thought was opening the front door to a gust of new, more effective and practical approaches to the materia medica and homeopathic prescribing. The winds of change had risen.

'Everything old is new again' as the adage goes, and this is certainly true with the new trends. I said 'seeming revolution' above because the idea of remedies having family associations has been around for a long time. Again, I refer to Farrington who maintained there were 'underlying laws which string together the materia medica into one consistent whole.' He specifically spoke of families. 'Now, then, you will find that drugs hold certain relations to each other. The first I have called the family relation, derived from their similarity in origin. When drugs belong to the same family they must of necessity have a similar action.' Despite the valuable insight, Farrington's ideas never took hold at the time.

It is often not enough to have a great idea to make it work. The idea must be cradled in a context that supports it. History is replete with examples of an idea dying on the vine because there was no context from which the idea could feed and flourish. My favourite example of this is the discovery of penicillin, ostensibly by A. Fleming in 1928. Few know that the same observation made by Fleming, that a mould would eradicate purulent processes, was made by several others in the mid 1800s. Nothing became of these observations because there was no context. Germs had not been 'invented' yet. Once they were, then something to stop them had a place. As both movie directors and politicians often say, 'Timing is everything.'

The re-invention or re-appreciation of the 'concept' of remedies in the same family sharing similar actions and symptoms has come about because of the accumulation of clinical experience and observations. In other words, the need had developed. It does not do justice to these ideas to call them concepts. They are not mental constructs born from theoretical musings, wishful thinking, fanciful and inventive projection or blind adherence to a framework that feeds self-fulfilling confirmation. They are the antithesis of that. Reproducible observations in real patients with real diseases experiencing real cures is the bedrock of the new ideas. We are afforded a glimpse into the inner workings of Nature.

Leading the way in this renaissance of understanding is Rajan Sankaran. Over the last few decades, he has pioneered the practical application of homeopathic remedy family ideas. As long ago as 1993 in his book Substance of Homeopathy, these ideas were clearly explained. He has never been one to accept anything solely theoretical. Every notion must be minced, ground and pulverized in the crucible of clinical experience. The trash is well and truly separated from the treasure. When he presents the homeopathic community the fruits of his ever-creative, ever-active fertile mind, they are never in the

8

form of untested hypotheses. If an idea has passed muster with Rajan, it can be incorporated in anyone's clinic with confidence. I am not in any way implying suborning anyone's own intelligent questioning, experience or discussion to anything Rajan has done. I can only state on behalf of myself and many others that he has served as a reliable trail blazer for the homeopathic community allowing the rest of us to forge our own paths in the wake of the clearings he has provided.

There is a reason that the observations that remedies in the same botanical, chemical and zoological groupings or families have similar actions have taken the homeopathic community by storm! These ideas work to help the clinician do a better job of helping their patients. It is that simple. Many prominent homeopaths not only use these ideas, but also have added valuable information to the materia medica based on this foundation.

This historical preamble has been for the purpose of providing a context as well as bringing us up to date with the current work. Again, Rajan's perceptive understanding of the basic idea of families has allowed him to take additional steps farther. Whereas the notion that all animals share commonalities in symptoms and even that all reptiles or arachnids share family characteristics has been successfully incorporated into the homeopathic thinking and daily practice of many for some years now. This current book details the next step beyond families into the delineation of subfamilies. Rajan's experience has lead him to the understanding that groupings such as reptiles or even the subset of snakes, helpful as they are, do not tell the whole story. Between the large family group and the individual species, there are other divisions that reveal extremely useful information about similarities and differences among the members. This book takes us into the world of reptiles and the various zoological subdivisions to reveal that those groups are also homeopathic divisions of such immense practical usefulness that, once understood, it will be unlikely to prescribe with confidence without taking them into consideration.

Speaking of the existing materia medica, this book bursts the seams on those confines. Simply browsing through the book, any homeopath will be intrigued by the vast array of reptiles that can and are being used in homeopathy. Rajan has taken our palette of the few and expanded that to the many and varied, giving us far more possibilities to prescribe correctly. Gone now are the days in which homeopaths must perpetuate the habit, borne of necessity, to fit the patient into the limited list of remedy possibilities at hand. The patients' nuances of expression and distinct symptoms can more accurately and precisely be matched to the ever-expanding cornucopia of remedies. With a firm foundation in clinical practice, supplemented with zoological data, provings, known symptoms and other information, Rajan offers not only clear and practical information on which to prescribe the additional remedies featured in this book, but family and subfamily understanding that opens the door to many additional remedies, limited only my Nature herself.

Linda Johnston, M.D.
Thousand Oaks, CA
February 2010

The recent expansion of homeopathy into the natural worlds has brought many advantages. It has also unearthed some glaring problems, which are all generally under the heading of 'inaccurate categorization'. If homeopaths are going to rely on zoological or botanical information to advance the materia medica, it must, first and foremost, be accurate. Though exactness and precision has always been desirable, in the past it was not as crucial as it is today. It does not take much digging into the materia medica or even just in the listings of remedies to find numerous mistakes in the form of incorrect names, inaccurate assigning of families and species, ambiguous provings and even simple misspellings!

I have spent the better part of the past 15 years delving into this topic. Over the years, I have run into a startling number of mistakes, some of which directly affect a clinician's ability to prescribe correctly. There is a domino effect that starts with small inaccuracies which lead to slip-ups which then lead to glaring errors. The final result is an unsolved case or worse. This problem should not be underestimated. Though most know me through my books on materia medica, woven into those texts are a vast number of corrections. As the utility of remedy family information reaches greater and greater depths, so too should the accuracy of the information. One great advantage to a book like this is that these past errors can be set right. Rajan has taken pains to make sure all the technical and zoological information is both up to date and accurate. This alone is a great service to the existing materia medica.

My work on materia medica through research into the natural world has yielded more than error correction. It has become blatantly obvious that there are profound consistencies and correlations between natural phenomena, survival strategies and adaptations, habitat, toxicological or phytochemical properties and other zoological or botanical parameters and the homeopathic uses of animal and plant remedies. The value of this also should not be underestimated. It is of great importance for the advance of homeopathic science that all of this information be systemised to enhance the understanding of the materia medica. This book does just that for the reptiles.

Frans Vermeulen
Thousand Oaks, CA
February 2010

12

Preface

I wish to emphasis that the sensation method is not different from classical homoeopathy. I continue to hold my strong background and training in classical homoeopathy as the foundation of my practice, research, and writings. The repertory and materia medica continue to be the cornerstone of my practice and my work. All my research and innovations aim to deepen and widen the scope of classical homoeopathy and are not meant in any way to negate, bypass or replace it. In every one of my books I have repeatedly emphasized this point and have cautioned my students, cautioned the readers, not to veer from our established foundations.

What, then, is the originality of my work? First of all what is the intention? The intention has always been to make our task of remedy selection simpler, more consistent, more definite and more predictable. The method that I used was to see if there are patterns in the materia medica that could be identified and utilized.

The idea was to find patterns within the various kingdoms. Even a cursory look at the materia medica's remedies in terms of plant, animal and mineral — looking for patterns — begins to vibrate with something interesting.

For example, if we consider the plant remedies like *Ignatia, Pulsatilla* and *Staphysagria* — what can we say that the people who need them have in common? We can say that they are extremely sensitive people, extremely reactive people.

If we look at three well-known mineral remedies — let's say *Natrum muriaticum, Argentum nitricum* and *Baryta carbonicum* — what do we see common? We see that these remedies perceive a problem in relationships, performance and capability. We see that they have as their main issue not the sensitivity and reactivity of the plant remedies but, rather, the feeling that something is lacking or lost.

If we look at three animal remedies — let's say *Lachesis, Lac caninum* and *Apis mellifica* — what do we see in common? We see issues of jealousy, competition and hierarchy.

These three patterns — sensitivity, survival and structure — correspond to what we observe in nature in plants, animals and minerals, respectively. The plants and, by extension, plant remedies have to do with sensitivity and adaptability. Minerals and mineral remedies have to do with the formation and breaking of structure. Animals and thus the remedies made from them have to do with competition and survival.

This was the beginning of my study of the kingdoms. This kingdom approach to homoeopathy figures out how the patterns observed within a group of remedies can be applied in the clinical setting to find a patient's remedy.

Though the understanding of disease will always advance, my approach to the patient and the disease — the homoeopathic method as practiced by me — actually integrates new ideas quite seamlessly, for knowledge of remedy and of kingdom, of symptoms and of systems, complement each other and take the homoeopath to a point where there is no difference.

When we study *Lachesis* from our materia medica and we read such symptoms as sensitivity around the throat, tongue darting in and out, extrasensory perception, sensitivity to extremes of heat and cold, etc., are we not hearing the voice of the snake? The knowledge of *Lachesis* from our materia medica helps us to understand snakes; similarly an understanding of snakes helps us see *Lachesis* more clearly and we can see it as a part of a group of reptiles. By considering a remedy source as a member of a related group, we are naturally led to consider the nuances that differentiate the group's members, and this allows a more intricate discrimination of related, close remedies. Thus, the possibility for a closer prescription increases, and our remedy selection is much more exact.

This applies in equal measure to plant families and the study of the rows and columns of the periodic table of the mineral kingdom. The study of individual remedies gives us the idea of the whole group to which they belong and this understanding does enhance, broaden and deepen our understanding of other remedies of the group, both well-known and lesser known. This exponentially expands the scope of remedy choice, understanding and selection.

With these advancements we are now able to deliver a truly homoeopathic cure to many more than we could earlier. I see this work as a deepening and widening of traditional homeopathy and not as a replacement to it. A firm foundation in the Repertory, the Materia Medica and the Organon of Medicine is at the basis of this. Without such a foundation a new student can be carried away. With such a foundation, he will find this work very useful. The cases in this volume represent the way I work, using the new with the old and seeing them as one.

- Rajan Sankaran
Mumbai, India
2010

About the Authors

Rajan Sankaran, M.D. (Hom), F.S. Hom (England) has been practicing Homoeopathy since 1981. He is known as an original thinker, and has introduced many concepts in Homoeopathy.

He has authored several books, namely *The Spirit of Homoeopathy, The Substance of Homoeopathy, The Soul of Remedies, Provings, The System of Homoeopathy, An Insight into Plants (three volumes), The Sensation in Homoeopathy, The Other Song, Sankaran's Schema, Sensation Refined, Structure (two volumes), Survival – the Mollusc* and has also helped develop the software *VitalQuest.* Many of his books have been translated in several languages.

Rajan Sankaran lives and practices in the Juhu area of Mumbai, and teaches worldwide.

Meghna Shah, B.H.M.S. worked in the Mumbai homoeopathic hospital after receiving her degree in 2000; since 2001 she has been a physician in Dr. Sankaran's clinic. She has organized video and live seminars of Dr. Rajan Sankaran, and has been instrumental in starting the *'insight-alliance homoeopathic'* webgroup. She has worked with Dr. Sankaran on the books *Sankaran's Schema, Structure- Experiences with the Mineral Kingdom* and *The Other Song*—which have all been highly appreciated and translated into many languages. She is currently working on *Survival - the Arachnida.*

She has spent three years researching the reptiles for this book, including a stay at the Reptile Park in Chennai, where she observed them firsthand and consulted the park's herpetologists.

16

Contributors

Anne Schadde has been practicing homoeopathy since 1984 in Munich, Germany. She is studying with Dr. Rajan Sankaran since 1990. She gives seminars in Germany, USA, Israel. She has conducted provings of *Ozone, Lapis lazuli, Lithium carbonicum, Ginkgo biloba, Lignum aquilaria agallocha* and *Cypraea eglantina* (Cowrie snail). Her provings have been published in: *Ozone* (1997) and *Listening to Stone, Wood and Shell* (2004).

April Bowen is practicing homoeopathy since 2004 and currently leads an NCH-affiliated study group, is the Co-chair of the San Diego, Association of Classical Homoeopaths (SACH), mentors students, and gives lectures. She is a frequent contributor to Insight Alliance discussion forum. She thoroughly enjoys her family practice, where her patients continue to teach and inspire her.

Ashok Borkar, B.H.M.S. completed graduation from Smt. C. M. Patel Homoeopathic Medical College (Mumbai), in 1990. Worked for a year as a resident physician in the Government Homoeopathic Hospital (Mumbai). Started practice as a Homoeopathic physician in Goa in 1991. Was a visiting lecturer of Organon and Philosophy in Shri Kamakshdevi Homoeopathic Medical College, Goa from 2000 to 2003. Regularly conducts seminars in Goa and Karnataka. Conducted CME (continuing medical education) in Goa. Underwent teacher's training course in the Sensation method taught by Homoeopathic Research and Charities (Dr. Rajan Sankaran and group). Taught in the "Advanced course in Sensation method" held in Mumbai in August 2008 and August 2009. Conducts courses in Sensation method for Homoeopathic physicians of Goa and Karnataka on a regular basis.

Bart Lambert has been practicing homoeopathy since 1990 in Kortrijk, Belgium. Bart is a member of "Samosa", Belgium study group. He is the organizer of the European Clinical Seminars (7 so far). Bart also invites Indian colleagues to give seminars in Kortrijk. He teaches along with Bert Lefevre in Antwerp, Belgium, and for the VSU, the School of Homoeopathy in Belgium. He has also started teaching the sensation method in Poznan, Poland, in 2008, and will continue this year.

Ben Ta'ati serves as a core faculty member of the American Medical College of Homeopathy and Chairman for its department of Case Taking and Case Analysis. Ben's full time practice owes its resounding success to Dr. Rajan Sankaran and his team.

Bill Mann has practiced in the healing arts since 1981. Later, he became licensed to practice traditional Chinese Medicine and Acupuncture. During this time, he was introduced to homoeopathy and completed studies at the Hahnemann College of Homoeopathy. While there, he was introduced to the work of Dr. Rajan Sankaran in 1993 and attended numerous seminars with him since then, including the Bombay clinical workshops in India for International homoeopaths. Bill has lectured at many homoeopathic schools and conferences, and helped establish schools like the Desert Institute School of Classical Homoeopathy and the Homoeopathic Academy of Southern California. In 2004, he founded the California Center for Homoeopathic Education (CCHE) and now exclusively teaches the Vital Sensation method.

Bob and Judyth Ullman

Bob is the author or co-author of seven books on Homoeopathy including the best-selling *Ritalin-Free Kids*. He has been in practice since 1981 and is the co-founder of The Northwest Center for Homoeopathic Medicine in Edmonds, Washington. U.S.A.

Judyth is the author or co-author of seven books on Homoeopathy including the best-selling *Ritalin-Free Kids* and author of *Whole Woman Homoeopathy*. She has been in practice since 1983 and is the co-founder of The Northwest Center for Homoeopathic Medicine in Edmonds, Washington. U.S.A.

Craig Wright, M.Tech.Hom (TN), PCH (UK), MSc (Herb.Med) (Wales) completed a Master's Degree in Homoeopathy at Technikon Natal (now Durban University of Technology) in 1999, where he had lectured and practiced before moving to the UK in that year. He furthered his studies by obtaining a postgraduate diploma from the Dynamis School for Advanced Homoeopathic Studies and completed a PG Dip and MSc in Herbal Medicine at the Scottish School of Herbal Medicine & University of Wales. Craig returned to South Africa in late 2009 and is now practicing in Cape Town, and continues to teach homoeopathy and herbal medicine in London, Scotland & Spain and co-ordinates the MSc programme for the Scottish School. Also the editor of the Scottish Journal of Herbal Medicine, Craig is particularly interested in integrating different medicine systems to find a unique solution to a patient's problems and in researching the medicinal properties of South African plants.

Gurmej Virk, PhD, RSHom. has gained a PhD from Sheffield University, England, in 1992. He teaches at colleges in the UK. He founded the Aroga School in 2006 with his partner Dawn Price, and the two of them are also co-founders of *The Source,* an International Newsletter dedicated to sharing knowledge and advancements in the Sensation Method.

Ingrid Van de Vel is from Belgium. She started studying Homoeopathy in 1998 at VSU, Belgium and started her practice in 1999. Since 2001 she got inspired by the work of Rajan Sankaran. She is one of the founders of "Synapsis", which organizes the seminars with Rajan Sankaran. She is organizing along with Bert Lefevre the study group "Samosa". She has been giving guest lectures in Europe.

Jacques Echard, M.D. lives and practices in Toulouse, France. He organizes and teaches classical homoeopathy in several seminars and discussion groups. He organizes Rajan Sankaran seminars in France and also his video seminar's there.

Jeff Baker practices homoeopathy on the island of Maui in Hawaii. A strong proponent of Dr. Rajan Sankaran's work, Jeff has organized and/or presented dozens of seminars throughout the USA on the sensation method.

Joanne Greenland has a full time homoeopathic practice in Jindivick, Victoria, Australia. She teaches the 2nd year component of homoeopathy to classical students and also the 'contemporary homoeopathy' component to the 4th year students. Joanne is writing a book on 'Understanding the meaning of disease'. Joanne offers post graduate workshops teaching this understanding.

Jonathan Shore graduated from medical school in 1968 and has practiced homoeopathy since 1976. He has taught extensively both in North and South America, Europe, Southern Africa, Australia and New Zealand. At this time he maintains a small private practice in Novato California.

Juergen Becker a senior homoepath from Freiburg Germany was one of the first to break free from the traditional confines of homoeopathy. He worked on fairy tales, symbols, mythology and on the phenomenon of synchronicity. He also worked on dreams, dream provings and recently he has been working with newer method of potentising remedies called the C4 potencies which he reports brings out far deeper levels of the remedies message. He is the author of several books in the german language, which include monographs on some remedies and a voluminous book on his latest discoveries on the C4 potency called Neue Welten der Homöopathie und der Kräfte des Lebens.

Laurie Dack enjoys a full time Homoeopathic practice in Vancouver, Canada. Her study and practice of Homoeopathy have taken her to Europe, India and the U.S. over the past 19 years. She now teaches in Canada and the U.S.A.

Linda Johnston, M.D. graduated from the University of Washington Medical School in 1979, and began practising medicine in Los Angeles in 1981. Her homoeopathic practice commenced five years later. She has authored the book *Everyday Miracles: Homoeopathy in Action* and numerous articles. She also gives lectures, interviews and case presentations.

Melinda Leeson is a Florida-licensed Doctor of Oriental Medicine with extensive training and practice in acupuncture, herbology, oriental food therapy, and classical homeopathy. She founded Nature's Own Wellness in 2000 to serve as an alternative integrative health care clinic combining both Eastern and Western healing modalities. She assisted Todd Rowe in his proving of Alligator by supplying the substance via Micheal Quinn.

Michael Rutledge-Blessin started studying homoeopathy in 2000 and was introduced to the sensation method by Detlef Schreiber. He is doing research on plant families and runs his own practice since 2005 in Hamburg.

Miriam Heffer, RCHom. has been practicing classical homoeopathy since 1995. She lives in Israel and practices from her clinic in Jerusalem. She has followed closely the teachings of Dr. Sankaran since she first read his book *The Spirit of Homoeopathy*. She has presented his Video Courses in Jerusalem and teaches in private and study groups.

Nancy Herrick has been practicing homoeopathy since 1975. Director of the New Hahnemann Medical Clinic, she also teaches classical homoeopathy to professional medical practitioners at Hahnemann College of Homoeopathy. She has been lecturing throughout the world for over twenty years. She is the author of two books on provings: *Sacred Plants, Human Voices* and *Animal Mind, Human Voices.*

Pratibha Dalvi, B.H.M.S. (India), RCHom (NZ) has been practicing since 1994 first in Mumbai and now in Auckland, New Zealand. She is a Senior lecturer at The South Pacific College of Natural Therapies and teaches Practice oriented differentiations and Role of Homeopathy in Asthma all over New Zealand. She conducts Sankaran's video courses in Auckland.

Reinhard Flick, M.D. born 1954, homoeopathic practitioner in Vienna since 1985, member of the teacher's staff of ÖGHM (Austrian Association of Homoeopathic Medicine), vice president of ÖGHM. He has been very active in proving remedies like *Mater perlarum, Kalium sulphuricum, Natrum phosphoricum, Vipera berus, Formica rufa, Vespa crabro, Magnesium bromatum, Magnesium iodatum, Salvia officinalis, Carboneum sulphuratum, Samarium, Gadollynium metallicum* and *Coccinella septempunctata*. He has contributed numerous publications in Documenta Homoeopathica, Homoeopathic Links and Homöopathie in Österreich; also lectures at Congresses of LHMI in 1998, 2000, 2003 and 2005, lectures and seminars in Austria, Germany and Slovenia.

Robert Gramlich, M.D. completed his M.D. at USC School of Medicine in 1994 and his residency in Family Practice at UCLA in 1997. He began study and practice of homoeopathy in 1993 and has a clinic in Los Angeles.

Sigrid Lindemann has been practicing classical homeopathy in Auroville, an intentional community in South India, since 1997, and has been studying with the Bombay Group since 1999. She is teaching the Sensation method in Germany in 3 days seminar since 2004: bird remedies, carbon group and ocean remedies. Besides teaching with video and live cases she develops interactive teaching methods, training in perception skills and case taking exercises.

Sonja Doyle started studying homoeopathy at the CLH, Belgium in 1992 straight after completing medical studies. She has since enjoyed travelling across 3 continents following the seminars of many international teachers, most from the Bombay school. She runs a full time practice in Brussels and is member of the Samosa study group in Belgium.

Staria Manos, C.C.H., RSHom (NA) graduated from Homoeopathic Academy of Southern California in June 2004. Currently practicing Homoeopathy in San Diego and Murrieta California, USA.

Sudhir Baldota, M.D. has been practicing homeopathy since 1991 in Mumbai. He has been one of the core teachers of the Mumbai group. He is also a trustee of the Homoeopathic Research and Charities. His active involvement in teaching at the HRC is since 1993. He teaches both nationally and internationally in countries like Ireland, Holland, Germany, U.S.A, Canada, Slovakia, Australia, United Kingdom. Along with Dr. Rajan Sankaran he has co-authored the book *Survival-the Mollusc.* He now practices and teaches in Winterthur (Switzerland) (www.sternsicht.com).

Sujit Chatterjee has been practicing Homoeopathy since 1983. He is one of the core teachers of the Bombay School of Homoeopathy. He has conducted provings of remedies like *Uranium nitrate, Ficus religiosa, Ficus indica* and *Chocolate.* Dr. Chatterjee has given several international seminars in countries including the USA, Canada, Switzerland, Austria, Germany, and the UK.

Sunil Anand is best known for his approach in pediatric cases. He is practicing since 1982 and has taught at D.S. Homoeopathic Medical College where he was head of the Pediatric clinic in Homoeopathy.

Susan Sonz, C.C.H. is the Director of the New York School of Homoeopathy and principal instructor. Susan publishes articles regularly for national journals, serves on the national board of the Council for Homoeopathic Education (C.H.E.) and is the President of the New York State Homoeopathic Association (NYSHA). Susan lives and practices in New York City.

Susanne Sieben is practicing homoeopathy since 1995. Since 2001 she is studying with Dr. Rajan Sankaran and is practicing in her own homoeopathic clinic in Mannheim, Germany. She gave the Sankaran video course in Germany and gives seminars where she is teaching the Sensation method. She has also conducted a proving of the Sea anemone *(Stoichactis Kenti).*

Tim Shannon, N.D. is a licensed Naturopathic Physician in private practice in Portland Oregon. He serves as an adjunct faculty at the National College of Naturopathic Medicine in Portland. Dr. Shannon specializes in the treatment of mental, emotional, and behavioral health. He uses classical homoeopathy to treat a wide range of mental health complaints: ADHD, OCD, ODD, Tourette's Syndrome, Depression, Anxiety, Eating disorders, PTSD, Bi polar, & Schizophrenia, etc. He publishes case studies regularly as well as utilizing video technology to illustrate and teach good patient care. His primary mentor since 1997 is Massimo Mangialavori.

Todd Rowe is a licensed homoeopathic physician in Phoenix Arizona. He is the president and founder of the American Medical College of Homoeopathy. He is the director of the Society for the Establishment of Research in Classical Homoeopathy. He has conducted 15 provings, mostly focusing on local flora and fauna. Most recently he has published *The Desert World: A Homoeopathic Exploration,* which summarizes many of these provings. Other books include *The Homoeopathic Journey* and *Homoeopathic Methodology.* His current project is the formation of a full-time homoeopathic medical school, in Phoenix, Arizona.

Uta Santos-König has been practicing homoeopathy since 1987 in Vienna. Being also Jungian psychotherapist one of her main interests has been the work on dreams in remedy provings as well as with patients. For 10 years she has been following Massimo Mangialavori's approach. Comparing the different homoeopathic schools and finding many contradictions, her main interest lately has been comparative homoeopathic epistemology and the role of the prescriber.

24

Acknowledgement

We would like to thank some of our dear friends and colleagues who have helped us in creating this work.

Our editors Susan Cortes, April Bowen, Samuel and Lila Flagler and Abhijit Nanavati for their skill in trimming this book. Also to Mugdha Sovani who worked on the final corrections.

Cheryl Feng for designing the cover page which speaks for itself.

We would also like to thank the pharmacies: Helios, Remedia, Freeman and Hahnemann laboratories for assisting in compiling the list of reptile remedies.

Linda Johnston and Frans Vermulen for agreeing to contribute the foreword.

We would also like to express our gratitude to the Chennai Crocodile Park (India), and for all their extended support, which enabled us to go there and get a first-hand experience on the reptiles.

Our sincere gratitude to Parksons Graphics, India for all their efforts in printing this book.

We also extend our sincere thanks to the staff of Homoepathic Medical Publishers (HMP) (Mumbai, India) for their contribution.

We would also like to thank all our patients for their trust in us, which has always helped us refine our method.

And last but not least, our thanks to our dear friend Sudhir Baldota for his support.

26

Introduction

Inquiry into the Case

The best use of this book, and indeed the whole series, is possible only with a clear understanding of the concepts on which the entire body of work is founded. These concepts are elucidated in my earlier works: *The Sensation in Homoeopathy, Sensation Refined* and *The Other Song*. It would be advantageous to summarize these concepts again.

During the process of case-taking we begin with an inquiry into any one aspect of the patient's case: the chief complaint, a situation, a dream, etc. Then we traverse through the levels of *how he experiences* that aspect. These levels are Name, Fact, Emotion, Delusion, Sensation, Energy Pattern, and the Seventh Level. For example, a patient says that her ailment started after she felt let down or betrayed by a very close friend. First we can find out what the facts of the situation are. Then we probe into her feelings that she experienced. It could be anger, hurt, etc. On further inquiry into the feelings, we can see how she perceives this situation. For example: a carpet pulled from under her feet, or a stab in the back, etc.

If we take this inquiry further, into the actual experience of the patient in that imagined situation, we will see that there is a complete physical and mental inner experience. It is an experience that is the center of all experiences, and all aspects of the patient's being. This inquiry into the experience of the patient should not be an intellectual exercise. In fact, there must be no mind involved if we are to apprehend *the patient's* experience. This is because the mind interprets, analyzes, and classifies. It imposes its own viewpoint and experience, and does not simply experience what is true for the patient. The deepest levels of the case are reached when the mind of the patient, as well as that of the homoeopath, is temporarily suspended. One has to get into a mode of a "witness", without using any kind of reasoning or logic.

Allow the patient to simply go into the experience, in a kind of meditative journey. In that very moment he experiences the complete totality of physical and mental sensations.

The trick is to get the patient to speak from the bedrock manner in which he experiences the world, by asking, *"Tell me just a little bit more."* From this point will arise words, gestures, and patterns that are completely illogical, unreasonable, and unconnected to his actual situation. These words and gestures are strange and peculiar, and yet very, very individual and consistent. They will reveal a pattern and a consistent inner story. This pattern that is revealed will equate or reflect a pattern of something else in nature, be it an animal, a mineral, or a plant.

On deeper inquiry, and on going deeper into the experience, specific details of this pattern will emerge unconsciously from the patient. Such a pattern will indicate the specific subkingdom or genus of substance that is being channeled through by the patient. It will seem as if you are hearing the voice of something else, a parallel song, speaking from within the patient. This other song, this pattern, this reflection of some substance in nature, is the face of the patient's disease. When the disease is faced with a remedy that has the same song, it is then healed.

How do we get there?

This process of case-taking, this inquiry process, this meditative journey, is the heart of this approach. The case-taking process itself may allow the patient to look deeply into what is troubling him and gain insight into himself, which in itself is an important step towards healing. However, its real focus is to accurately pinpoint the kingdom, subkingdom, and the source of the patient's constant pattern of disturbance, so the remedy that will accomplish the healing process can be identified and prescribed. It is important to know that in the case-taking process, words from the level of kingdom, subkingdom, and source may not come out in that sequence. They often will come up intermingled or jumbled with each other. It is important not to play a guessing game with the words that come. We should clearly know the level at which the patient is mentioning those words. For example, just because the patient prominently mentions a dream about, or an aversion to, snakes, we cannot assume that he needs a snake remedy. To simply jump to the idea that the patient needs a snake remedy because he has mentioned snakes, and then finagle[1] the rest of what he says to fit the characteristics of snakes, would be absolutely wrong! One needs to understand this very clearly: A single reaction to snakes, (e.g., dreams, aversion to), occurs at the delusion level and does not necessarily indicate that the patient's remedy will be a snake, or any reptile. In order to determine if the patient *habitually maintains* the pattern of reptiles (snakes), one needs to reach the level of the

---

1. Fingale: to get or acheive by trickery, craftiness, or perruasion, wangle, manipulate

patient's *constant experience* to see whether at that level, again and again, in all types of events, ideas, and circumstances, the patient holds to a reptilian pattern of action and response. If he does **not**, he will **not need** a reptile remedy. In fact, our emphasis should be not to classify the patient, but to delve deeper and deeper into the experience.

So one would ask, *"Tell me about your aversion to snakes."* We then need to be very alert to which words or gestures the patient uses with respect to snakes. For example: he may say snakes are very slimy. When you ask about the experience of slimy, the patient may go on to something completely unconnected with snakes. For example: he might say, slimy means slippery, dirty, yucky! And you ask him to tell more. He further says it is so disgusting that you would not like it to come close to you, lest it touch and infect you. So to avoid this you prefer to be away from it, be in your shell, it should not touch you. Be in this protective covering that protects you not only from this but from all other external potential harm. And when he does this he makes a gesture of a shell. In this case the patient might then need a remedy from the second row of the periodic table. This is the row that correlates to the human experience of the fetus in the womb. Then you see all the other aspects of the patient come to the same experience. This will include his fears, his hobbies, etc. Underlying all his varied expressions is the experience of a fetus in the womb, not ready to face the world. This is a very crucial point in case-taking, as it's the level where one makes maximum mistakes. One needs to understand that **the energy of the patient has to match with the energy of the source.**

Sensation — and the sublevels
Sensation is:

> that basic core experience of a person,
> that which dominates one's life,
> that which pervades all his actions and reactions.

It is the level where we are free from the filter of the human being, and we see it as it is. It is the level where the energy starts speaking directly! It is the point where what most powerfully affects the patient as he gives his case seems complete nonsense, when we start hearing two distinct songs — the human and nonhuman. This energy can be a plant, mineral, or animal. There are other possibilities as well: nosodes, imponderables, and man-made substances, but the remedies of most of the patients that a homoeopath will see usually come from the plant, mineral, and animal kingdoms.

This level of sensation can be further differentiated into three levels:

> *Sensation A-Kingdom*
> *Sensation B-Subkingdom*
> *Sensation C-Source*

There will be a set of expressions that point to a particular kingdom: for example, the animal, mineral, or plant kingdom. There will be a set of expressions that indicate a subkingdom: for example, the reptilian, the anacardiacean, or the third row of the periodic table. Then there will be a set of words that indicate the source. A careful understanding and differentiation of these sublevels is vital in concluding upon a remedy.

Recognizing the source language

- *Knowing the attributes*

At sensation level C one might come across words or gestures that are very strange, but which actually show the physical qualities of the source: color, size, shape, consistency, temperament, defense strategy, etc. For example, one patient spoke about her experience in a situation where she felt *pinned down, weighed upon, grasping and stifled.* I then asked her:

D: Describe *stifling, grasping.*
P: One trying to get up but stifling, can't.

Claustrophobic, stifling, can't lift, can't get up.

D: What means *stifling,* just the word.
P: Stifling, you can't get up. Stifling for me is like my head can get up.

Helplessness.

It's like stifled, you can't breathe in a sense. The body can't breathe, except head. **Head is different, body different.** Head can move, body can't.

D: Describe *head is different and body is different.*
P: Head has got light on it, it is fine, it is moving around, but the body is tied. Head is looking at the body which is weighed down. Helpless, helpless.

D: Describe *head is looking at the body which is weighed down.*
P: Yeah it's like…the body is like…it's like a separate part, different.

D: Little bit more *the body is a separate part.*
P: Supposedly the body is rotting, do you know that terrible, horrible thing to say but it feels like ….the body is looking, the head looks fine but the body is like…

31

D: Little bit more *the head is fine but the body is rotting.*

P: Body looks good but it's rotted. Head is fine full of light and energy but **body is rotting, black, gangrenous** kind of thing. Feels like gangrene for some strange reasons. I don't know what gangrene is but feels like it, rotting.

D: Little bit more about *rotting.*

P: **Rotting, blackish.**

D: Little bit more describe this more.

P: **Decomposing.**

D: Describe all the qualities of this *rotting* and *decomposing.*

P: **Ugly, ugly, ugly.**

D: Describe *ugly.*

P: **Gross rotten flesh.**

D: What comes to your mind when you say that?

P: Right now it is not so bad, but initially **it was very dark...**

D: *Dark?*

P: **Body is dark, really dark, blackish dark, greenish dark.**

D: Describe *greenish dark.*

P: Dark greenish, blackish...more of a shade of black actually. Dark green.

D: Describe the *greenish dark* a little bit more.

P: It is sort of greeny...darkish greenish. A green dark moss, that sort of green type of thing. So I associated with that I guess, the stool, but dark green. Not so much dark green but before it was blacky, dark green, it was more black. But then this dark green thing came in I don't know. May be its not right. I don't know. But it was not pleasant.

This was a surprise turn of events for me. So far I was sure about the kingdom (animal) and the subkingdom (reptile-snake). But the words *black* and *green* were very significant, as they were said with emphasis and came completely out of context. They neither seem to indicate the kingdom or the subkingdom.

These are source words that:

- *indicate a physical quality of a substance*
- *point to a specific quality that is characteristic of a substance*

The source words neither indicate nor are connected to the kingdom or to the subkingdom. They should be used for the ultimate differentiation of a substance or species after one has established the kingdom and the subkingdom.

Here *black* or *green* has nothing to do with reptiles or snakes in general. They simply indicate a physical quality or a physical characteristic of the source. One has to be alert for such words which occur so much out of context and which are not part of a pattern. This patient who described the colors green and black required the remedy *Dendroaspis polylepis* (black mamba). Later on, when we checked about the mamba snakes, we saw that they come in two colors: green and black. Since she emphasized *black* more than *green*, I gave her the remedy from the black mamba. (The detailed case appears later in the book.)

- **The source will have it all**

In case-taking we observe expressions of the kingdom, subkingdom, class, family and species scattered haphazardly, as the patient gives his case. For example, in an octopus case, the patient could talk about the experience of being within a shell, and exhibit the energy of withdrawing inside it even though octopuses lack a shell. This is because the sensibility of a shell is such a strong general issue with the molluscs. Further, they will also exhibit specific features and energy patterns of a cephalopod and an octopus.

- **Gestures and the source**

Any gesture or energy pattern that carries maximum energy is indicative of the source only, and nothing else. We will illustrate an example. Oftentimes students or even practitioners get confused between the carnivorous remedy *Drosera rotundifolia* and the insect remedies, when we hear the words 'trapped' and 'caught'. When these sensation words are accompanied with a gesture of both the hands coming closer and closing in, it reflects the energy of the *Drosera* plant in nature and not an insect.

In animal cases, this significant gesture is indicative of the aggressor. When a gesture or an idea is expressed from a victim's stance, on exploring the case further, one can see that it's often the same thing that the patient wishes to do to others. So it is either someone doing to him, or him doing to someone. All the energy patterns always indicate the source. It cannot be anything else. For example, in a *Python* case they say squeezed and coiled from a victim mode. When you take this further, you will see that it's the same thing that it would do to others, when in an aggressor mode.

Every peculiar aspect, every important word and gesture of the patient can be seen within the phenomena of that particular source. Then we can be sure of that source as the remedy.

This is the basic perception, the fundamental reality. Beyond the facts, emotions, and images, it's the most fundamental perception. The deeper you perceive, the clearer the remedy, and the more consistent and better the results.

We need to be prepared to enter into the vast area of the unknown. The whole success depends on the ability to stay in the unknown and just explore what there is, instead of trying to classify it without understanding the depth of the case. Just unearthing, it's pure archaeology. Bring it out as it is!

* * * * *

The use of this book is a complement to the understanding of the concepts. It's also a highly useful book, which has been constructed to make the application of the concepts much simpler.

Recognizing the Animal Song

(This chapter is an expanded version from the book *'Survival-the Mollusc'*.) In this chapter we will study how animal behaviour patterns manifest in humans who need a remedy from the animal kingdom.

The three kingdoms

When we talk about the kingdoms we know that the basic issue in…

- Animals is *survival*
- Minerals is *structure*
- Plants is *sensitivity*

The issue in animals is survival, i.e., *the survival of the fittest.* This is a phrase coined by nineteenth-century English social philosopher Herbert Spencer, and subsequently applied to the work of Charles Darwin, which characterises the animal kingdom.

Survival in the animal kingdom characterises a *competitive* situation of:

- me versus myself/others
- the stronger versus the weaker
- the victim versus the aggressor
- the predator versus the prey
- attack and defense

In animals it's about a process, where something is happening to someone. It's a process from birth to death; of a survival pattern comprising animals' characteristic behavior, of a mating process, and of modes of defense and attack. These have evolved in each individual species to help them survive successfully in their individual environment. Therefore in animal cases, we don't see one sensation and its opposite (like we see in the plant kingdom), or a lack or loss of a structure (like in the mineral kingdom). Here we see many sensations with energy patterns.

On further observation, one can see that the animal energy pattern will comprise *one prominent sensation, with many smaller ones alongside it.* The prominent one will represent the most characteristic movement of that animal. The smaller ones will represent different other aspects, such as its attack or defense mechanism, its sexuality, etc. For example in a black mamba *(Dendroaspis polylepis)* case, the prominent sensation is speed, in a rush, fast, quick. This also reflects the black mamba snake's ability to run at great speed, and to attack with rapidity.

The following is an example of how the process is expressed in the case of an animal remedy.

The patient said she had a headache. When asked to describe the headache, she started to show her hands coming closer to each other, half-clawing, and she said, 'It rocks my brain.' At that point the whole language changed. When asked about the rocking, she said, 'It takes me over. It is slowly getting tighter and tighter.' When asked to describe 'tighter and tighter', she replied, 'I want it to burst open'. Then she said, 'I feel very light, as if I have no limbs.' So the whole process, in all its different facets, of a caterpillar in a cocoon on the verge of metamorphosing into a butterfly, was described. She did very well on *Limenitis bredowii californica,* the California sister butterfly.

Issues of the animal kingdom

Animals have diverse forms of lifestyle which include: anatomical characteristics, physiological functions, dwelling, locomotion, life cycle and reproduction, sexual conduct, emotions and behavior, and methods of attack and defense. We need to understand how these features can be translated as human expressions.

• **Predation: Victim and Aggressor**

Predation is a biological interaction where a predator (a heterotroph that is hunting) feeds on its prey (the organism that is attacked). Predators may or may not kill their prey prior to feeding on them, but the act of predation always results in the death of the prey.

In a way, all animals are predators and all animals are prey. The main understanding is not whether it is predator or prey, but what is the energy pattern that the patient is showing and to which kingdom does he belong. He may call it 'victim', or alternatively, he may call it 'aggressor'.

For example, the person may say, 'I want to choke someone,' or, 'I want to choke him.' The moment he describes the choke with a hand gesture, he will unerringly demonstrate his own source. It doesn't make a difference what he calls it.

The theme of victim and aggressor has many forms of expression, and the practitioner needs to take the case well in order to be truly sure. The patient may say, *"The illness is getting the better of me,"* or *"It takes me over,"* or *"My throat pain is killing me."* There is the theme of *me versus you or me versus somebody.* The practitioner should be alert to the patients expressing the idea that *he is stronger and I am weaker,* or *somebody 'is doing this to me'.* There is a sense of *one versus the other.* There are also issues of *conflicts with others.* The energy patterns and hand gestures show one thing doing something to another.

The patients with animal energy often perceive their problems in terms of *comparison.* Their constant internal source of discomfort, if voiced, would sound something like the following:

'If I can get the better of, beat, or eliminate the other person, then I am okay.'

'If I am more successful than the other person, then I am okay.'

'If I am better liked than the other person, then I am okay.'

'If I am more physically attractive than the other person, then I am okay.'

In other words, to the animal-energy patient, it's not her inherent strength or ability that is the problem (as in a mineral patient), rather, it's her comparative attributes or acquisitions. *Do I have it compared to the other person?* So there is a sense of *competition* and *one-upmanship. Jealousy* is often a natural outgrowth of the animal-energy patient's pathological attitude.

Another variation of the victim-aggressor theme is *'I versus myself'.* There are *issues of conflicts* with oneself and with others. The plant reacts to the outside, while the mineral experiences a lack in oneself. But the animal, somehow, has a distinct character, a distinct whole identity. Therefore, its energy within the human causes the experience of two separate distinct identities within the self, causing a *split* within the self. Hence there is a sense of one versus one's own self. There is a sense of duality.

Here the patient might say:

'I feel I am not good.'

'I feel I shouldn't have done that.'

'I don't know what part of me makes me do that.'

'I am so tempted to do that, but something stops me. I don't know what.'

The need to survive also leads to *malice* or being *revengeful*. This comes from a sense of 'It is you versus me.' So 'If you hurt me, I will hurt you.' The intent to harm another often seen as an undercurrent in those with animal energy, finds expression in words and actions. Malice or revenge leads to forms of *aggression* or *violent* behavior which can be expressed impulsively, (e.g., spider remedies) or calculatingly (e.g., snake remedies).

With such a basic animal need to survive, actions are not dictated by a sense of what is right and what is wrong *(lack of morality)*. *A sense of right and wrong, which is essentially a human construct, is generally not found in the animal kingdom.* At a deeper level, the issue of survival dictates to the animal. If it thinks it can get away with something that it needs for its survival, it will do it, and not be disturbed by its 'rightness' or 'wrongness' in a moral sense. Remember, it's an issue of 'survival of the fittest'!

We can see that animal remedy people either engage in amoral animal behavior themselves, such as: cheating, betraying, back stabbing, lying, etc. Or they are sensitive to such behavior around them, and the people who perpetrate it. Those who perpetrate violence and cruelty with power fascinate people with animal energy. This is at a very deep level. Images of violence in revenge for harm, for example, can occur in their delusion and fantasy. These images will give them great pleasure. At the everyday level, however, they can be very moral, ethical, and conscientious.

The final issue is, therefore, one of who will "best" whom, for *survival.*

Some human expressions of victim/aggressor sensations:

Take advantage of, exploited, ill-used, put-upon, victimised
Oppressed, dominated, bullied, subjugated, conquered
Manipulate, influence and control to one's advantage
Picked on, better than me, don't like me, told what to do
Excluded, left out, ignored, criticized
Treat badly, punish unjustly, unfairly
Being used by another to accomplish something
Previously used or owned by another
Pounce on me/them

- **Fight for supremacy: Territoriality (Hierarchy) and Mating rights (Sexuality)**

  ▵ **Territoriality: Hierarchy**

  In animals that live in groups, there is competition or an inevitable conflict for supremacy for the most valued resources, for food and a mate. Conflict over social supremacy in animals often leads to violent fights.

  Human expressions of social supremacy are:
  Superior/inferior,
  Somebody above/somebody below
  High/low
  Dominant, powerful or stronger/weaker or powerless

  Deeper to these human terms lies the sense that 'somebody who is above me is doing this to me.' Again, this could be accompanied by a hand gesture.

  ▵ **Mating rights: Sexuality**

  Reproduction is the most important phase for animal proliferation. For this reason, we observe complex mating rituals like: use of colors, making sounds, various body gestures, etc. Hence *sexuality* and *attractiveness* are important issues in animal cases. They could either wear bright, attractive colors or behave in a way that will attract notice. There could be a flirtatious aspect, which could be crude or subtle. There are also themes of being unattractive, which may make them withdraw. There may be a feeling of dirtiness or disgust about oneself. Their pathology could make them feel unattractive.

  The fight for supremacy is also to win over a female. This is why males compete with each other during the mating season. The winner gains access to a female, which ensures the survival of his progeny.

  A few human expressions that reflect the
  sexual nature in animal cases:
  Attract
  Attention seeking
  Allure
  Draw

Pull towards you
Appeal to
Charm
Entice
Tempt
Look attractive

Often animal remedies make interesting patients. They tend to get presented in seminars more frequently because they are livelier. There is a certain animation in these cases!

One should be aware that there are plant and mineral remedies that share these qualities. The Liliaceae plants, for example, exhibit themes and concerns involving attractiveness. *Veratrum album, Crocus sativa,* and *Paris quadrifolia* seek attention. Certain cases of Solanaceae can make the story very vivid. Ranunculaceae has its sensitivity. *Hyoscyamus* has its sexuality. *Phosphorus*, with its communicativeness, or *Fluoric acid* with its flirtatiousness, can also make lively presentations.

However, when you go into the depth of their sensation, it will be seen that the survival and sexuality in them is a part of something else. For example, in the *Hyoscyamus,* the sexuality strips down at the deepest level to a fear of losing the partner, which in turn provokes its sensitivity to very fearful things. That sensitivity is the basis, and the sexuality is the expression of it. Similarly, in Liliaceae the attractiveness arises from a sensitivity to being included or excluded, which causes the case to look like an animal remedy. These cases will ultimately lack other important animal energy features as comparison, victim/aggressor, attack and defense, etc. *Phosphorus* has, at the deepest level, the need to develop an identity different from his own family. So he starts being a little indifferent to his family, and starts having more friends. That is the underlying basis of his communicativeness issue.

- **Survival skills: Methods of attack and defense in animals**

Animals generally fight for:

- Self-defense (the 'cornered-rat' syndrome)
- Protecting young ones from danger
- To gain access over valued resources (mate, food, territory)

When an animal is forced to deploy its weapons, i.e., when it attacks, it is capable of causing damage, pain, and injury. The aim is to incapacitate the rival or at least force it to retreat. Each animal has a specific mode of attack: to chase/pursue, ambush attack, pounce, grab suddenly with the claws, etc. Similarly each animal has specific means of defense: changing colors, camouflage, mimicry, withdrawal into a shell, etc.

Over the ages, the species evolved abilities for defense from that sort of attack for higher rates of survival. Each group is distinguished from the other in the *peculiar nature of attack* they experience, as well as how they perform it. The type of *defense mechanism* they adopt against attack is determined by each species.

Similarly, a patient will express both the aspects. He will talk from the victim mode, as well as the aggressor mode, of the species he needs as a remedy. The *victim and the aggressor are two sides of the same state.* The victim has the seed of the aggressor and vice versa. For example, the person needing a snake, particularly the pythons or the boas, experiences the symptom of being 'constricted or squeezed', which is what it does to its victim as well.

△ **General methods of attack in the animal kingdom**

Carnivorous animals attack their prey in a wide variety of ways that depend upon their evolution, habitat, anatomical characteristics and mode of living. Some of these actions are frequently described as 'pouncing', 'catching', 'gripping', and 'grabbing'. The details of the manners in which they pursue and obtain their prey vary too widely to be succinctly described here. However, the classification method is the best way to understand the techniques, which are specific to phylum, order, family, genus, and even species. Each consecutive group is a subset of the previous one.

△ **General methods of defense in the animal kingdom**

It is similarly so with defences. Primary defences include hiding, escaping, and using physical or chemical defense. A few defense modes are as follows:

- *Crypsis and immobility:* Coloration or shape that resembles random features of the animal's environment. Cryptic colors and remaining motionless allow the animal to, for example, blend in with fallen leaves or appear to be a rock. Remaining still also allows it to escape detection by sight hunters.

41

- *Camouflage:* The colour of the animal blends with or matches the background of its habitat, making it difficult for the predator to distinguish it. It requires only that the animal remain still, to avoid detection.

- *Deceptive markings:* Such as large fake eyes, can startle predators, or various skin coloration and patterns, etc.

- *Mimicry:* To mimic the appearance of a dangerous species, can warn off potential predators.

- *Aposematism:* The animal adopts a very bright colouration that warns the predator that it is not tasty or that it is poisonous.

- *Vocalization:* The producing of sounds to scare away the predator. Hissing in snakes for example.

- *Threat displays:* Exhibitions of aggression, or size increase, to scare away the attacker.

There is a large array of defensive techniques, and each genus and species may additionally evolve techniques very peculiar to itself. For example, if a battle gets really fierce, the octopus has the ability to 'cut off' one of its arms and leave it behind. This phenomenon is called *autotomy.* The arm grows back again later. Autotomy is also observed in lizards.

The world of the animal is full of challenges. They come from other animals, but also from the environment (freezing temperature, drought, etc.). Each species has specific adaptations to its environment. For example, unable to generate body heat, the cold-blooded reptiles bask in the sun and hibernate in extreme cold.

- **Living in groups**
Social life in animals is probably a complex and effective survival strategy. It may be regarded as a sort of symbiosis among individuals of the same species: a society composed of individuals belonging to the same species (referred to as a herd, flock, etc.) living within well-defined rules of food management, role assignments, and reciprocal dependence. It would not be uncommon to hear the patient speak in terms of the dichotomy of *staying within a group versus being an individual.*

- **Communication**

  Animals exhibit different means of communication; they are able to talk to each other in their language. Communication is vital to obtaining food, defense or attracting a potential mate. This can be expressed, and also observed as human expressions, via:

  - *Vocalization:* This is like the warning cries in monkeys, hissing in snakes, etc.

  - *Display of a body part or distinct body movement (gestures):* Like spreading the hood in the cobra, waggle-dance in the bees, etc.

  - *Colors:* Such as changing colors in the chameleon, displaying bright colors, or camouflage in the octopus, etc.

- **Restriction and Freedom**

  Along with the sense of being victimised by a circumstance or another person, there is a sense of a loss of one's freedom to be oneself and express oneself. There is a feeling of being **caged** and **trapped,** and a desire to be **free.** This sensation, connected with liberty from being victimised, exists in almost all the animals, but is most marked among birds. With birds, the sensation of freedom is spontaneously and strongly associated with flying, wide-open spaces, without boundaries, high places, etc. We can also see the opposite sensations like light/heavy, caught/free, etc. In domesticated animals, the issue of freedom also exists. Domestic animal remedy patients may also express the *opposite.* These patients may display a pattern of habitually getting themselves into situations where they are trapped or restricted. However, the other specific issues of the families may be more prominent. For example, in dogs, the issue of needing to please (the master) and to be loyal is most marked.

  The feeling of restriction and freedom can also be observed in shelled animals like the molluscs and tortoise, with respect to their shell or carapace. On one hand, the shell acts as a protective shield, but within that shell they feel restricted and lack the freedom of movement enjoyed by non-shelled animals. Hence follows the duality: 'Shall I remain within, or shall I emerge out of this?'

- **Mobility**

  All animals are motile, unlike plants and minerals. They need to move. In animal cases we see prominence of features that reflect various forms of locomotion, like speed, run, slither, climb, swim, etc.

- **Music**

  There is a sense of rhythm in most animals. Many of them make sounds to attract and to communicate with one another. Many dance and move rhythmically, for example, the horse. Most animal patients react to music in some way or other. Among all the animals, the Arachnida (spiders) particularly, are very distinctive in their sensitivity to music, especially rhythm.

- **Connection with the source**

  The patient will sometimes, in the course of deep and nonleading case-taking, express a spontaneous fear or fascination with or aversion to a particular species of animal or its habitat. For example, snake remedies often dream of snakes or express a fascination with snakes. Mollusc remedies express an attraction for and/or a connection with the seashore and the sea.

  In the course of case-taking, the patient with animal energy may mention words that belong to several species in a class, or even words from several classes in a phylum. Further nonleading questioning will show more clearly the particular genus.

  The important thing is that an *entire constellation of words* of the subgroup should exist. By chasing up what appears not to fit, ultimately clarity can be obtained.

  Let us assume that after deep case-taking, perceiving the energy pattern, and understanding the fundamental issues in the patient's life, we perceive that it is an animal remedy. At that point in time, if the patient has not spontaneously identified an animal source within him/herself, then we would need to identify it.

Miasm in the animal kingdom

Normally, when we understand all the qualities of the animal, we don't have to worry about the miasm. It is almost automatically covered. In a plant case understanding the miasm is an important differentiating tool between all the known remedies in that particular family. In an animal case it's more important to understand the kingdom, the subkingdom, and the source. Still, the miasm is a very good indicator of where to look. For example, consider the remedy *Lac leoninum,* which is under the syphilitic miasm. The lion has qualities of complete destruction. It will not back off, and it will fight to the finish. Dogs and cats fight too, but it is not necessarily a fight to the finish. Miasmatically, it is of a lesser degree. In the animal remedies, the concept of miasm can help us to understand the depth or degree of desperation in a particular source.

We don't need to be rigid about matching miasms in an animal case. In the animal world we know that certain families belong to a particular miasm, with exceptions of course. When we know these exceptions, we mention them. If we don't know the miasm associated with a particular animal remedy, we can infer it over time by seeing enough patients who need this remedy when their miasm is clear.

The Importance of Classification

The important words and themes expressed by the patient in the course of deep and nonleading case-taking are the guideposts to finding the remedy. They are the words of the source that we are looking for. These *source words* can sometimes be found in the provings, but more certainly in the zoological information about the source itself.

We find that *sources closely related to one another in the natural world express similar sensations.* Thus we realise the importance of studying groups of natural objects and organisms. The knowledge of zoology, botany, and chemistry therefore becomes an important tool in this search. The internet, encyclopaedias, and the wildlife television channels are among the most valuable sources of our knowledge in that regard.

The already existing classification of the natural world, systematised on the basis of evolutionary history and anatomical as well as physiological similarity, is a useful guide to understanding the characteristics of each group of animal remedy sources.

The kingdom is the highest taxonomic category into which natural objects are classified. We consider three: the animal, the plant, and the mineral. Carolus Linnaeus, the scientist who established the most influential taxonomic system of classifying living organisms, grouped plants and animals in categories of descending specificity based on their common characteristics. Hence he created phylum, class, order, family, genus and species. As we go from above downwards, the common characteristics across each subgroup become narrower, more specific, and the organisms resemble each other more closely. As scientists continued the work of classifying more and more organisms, they added additional subgroups such as superorder and superfamily. Linnaeus also instituted the binomial system of naming, in which the first name is that of the genus, while the second is that of the species. Initially plants were named in this manner. Later, animals too were similarly named.

In this series of books of the animal kingdom, we use established taxonomical classification as a guideline to study the qualities of each subkingdom. We are then able to study the qualities of each animal within the classes and subclasses. At this point we must mention that what these books present is but a fraction of the knowledge that exists about the animal kingdom. This in itself is probably a fraction of the knowledge that is possible. There is so much that we will never know and cannot reach in several lifetimes. How then can we effectively help more of our patients today? By truly listening to the patient, to the nonsense, and to the nonhuman words and ideas that he expresses, we can determine what remedy he is speaking and prescribe it, even if we have minimal knowledge of that particular plant, animal, or mineral.

There is an encouraging reflection. If it is only the exact source that works to cure, we could cure only one out of ten thousand patients. Yet with the limited knowledge and remedies we have, we are still able to help patients. How is this working? The only possible reason for this, is perhaps that it is not necessary to give the *exact source* in order to achieve a result. Results happen when we are *close enough* to the source. The closer we get, the better. Therefore, it's important that we at least attempt to distinguish one animal category (subclass or genus) from another.

Studying animal remedies according to their natural classifications, within Linnaean taxonomy, yields unrealized knowledge of this complex kingdom. Discrepancies or uncertainty of name and even animal will inevitably arise. Taxonomy is a constantly evolving science, and many of the scientific names used for animal remedies in homoeopathy have today been replaced by others. Sometimes it can even be difficult to tell exactly which species or subspecies was used for a remedy. For example, the homoeopathic name for the remedy made from the venom of the cottonmouth snake is *Cenchris contortrix*, yet in modern taxonomy, this snake is called *Agkistrodon contortrix*. Similarly, the remedy *Crotalus cascavella*, whose source homoeopathy identifies as the Brazilian rattlesnake, is in current taxonomy *Crotalus durissus*. This neotropical rattlesnake has *Crotalus durissus cascavella* among its subspecies.

Such issues of name and animal can be clarified to a reasonable certainty by consulting taxonomic sources, which list, often by year and taxonomist, names formerly used for a species. Homoeopathic pharmacies worldwide are invaluable sources of information about the animal remedies they offer. Some pharmacies list remedies by both their homoeopathic and modern names.

This highlights the need to bring more remedies into the Materia Medica so that we potentise more sources, especially those directly mentioned by the patient at the deepest level. We can then add at least one substance from each subclass to the Materia Medica.

Fortunately, this is presently happening at a very rapid pace. In the last few years we have added many remedies to our storehouse of knowledge, especially from animal sources. Provings have also taken place of many remedies. Homoeopaths Jeremy Sherr, Jonathan Shore, Anne Schadde, Jürgen Hansel, Nancy Herrick, and others have introduced valuable remedies such as: *Salmon, Falcon peregrine, Lac loxodonta* and *Cypraea eglantina* (Cowry snail).

With a plethora of information coming in, one can get lost or confused without a clear map or classification. These books are an attempt to provide a first map. It is an attempt to make a comprehensive system, so that arbitrariness, intuition, and guesswork are left with little role to play in our practice.

They are the first step in that direction, and they are far from being complete and final. We hope the information in these books will be of help in practice.

In these books we suggest some presumed important aspects of the currently available source information. As we begin to get cases worldwide, we may find that for any given remedy some characteristics are not as important as we had thought. We may notice other ones becoming prominent and being confirmed in provings. Only further provings and cases will help to clarify and confirm these issues, and thus take our understanding forward.

The Scheme of this Book

This book begins with preliminary chapters on the approach to case-taking and the rationale behind a classification-based study of natural sources of homoeopathic remedies. There is then a general introduction to the animal kingdom and an introduction to the **class** Reptilia. Then follow the sections on each of the four reptilian **orders:**

- Testudines (tortoises, turtles and terrapins)
- Crocodylia (crocodiles, alligators, caimans and gharials)
- Squamata (snakes, lizards and amphisbaenians)
- Sphenodontida/Rhynchocephalia (tuataras)

These are followed by a section on dinosaurs.

Each chapter begins with an introduction to the general order. Within each order is presented information on those families, genera, and species from which homoeopathic remedies are available. This information includes: the natural habitat, general anatomy, life cycle, reproduction, behavior, and method of attack and defense for each family, genus, and species.

Latin names are used to denote each species. The use of Latin names allows one to identify a species, and differentiate between that species and any other species. It also gives an idea of the relationship of that species to other animals. The more closely related two organisms appear to be, the more likely taxonomists have placed them, at the very least, in the same family, if not in the same subfamily or same genus. Since we don't have remedies from all families, we sometimes have to resort to prescribing at the superfamily or subfamily or genus level. In such situations, prescriptions based on the same taxonomic tree, is likely to benefit the patient, even though the exact remedy his case calls for is unavailable.

Following the zoological information on each family, genus, and species, we have presented the possible human expressions derived from it. Information presented about the animals will include the characteristics of their body parts (e.g. color patterns, characteristic appendages, etc.), functions, specific behavioral patterns and specific methods of their attack and defense. Information presented about the way these animal characteristics manifest in human patients will include the important source and sensation words. It will also include processes which describe an adaptation and possible synonyms of that. These expressions can be seen in cases at Levels 5 (Sensation) and 6 (Energy). It is important to understand that the specific source, specie specific words, will emerge only at sensation level C3. Here one has to be extremely discreet in differentiating the kingdom, subkingdom, order, family and the source words. Sensation level C3 is where the patient talks in non-human-specific expressions, which mingle with the specific energy of the source. This is the remedy that he needs. For example, in a *Naja naja* (Indian cobra) case one might see the patient use a vertical forearm and curved hand gesture to express the energy pattern of the cobra's characteristic defensive posture—fore third of the body raised vertically off the ground, hood expanded via extension of the long, movable ribs that unfurl the loose skin of the neck—and at the same time threaten to attack an opponent who tries to come too close, saying, 'Dare you come close. Stay away.' The words of the patient in this example are very representative of the *Naja naja* snake's behavior in nature. All of these features are included in the expressions of this snake. The specific expressions of each remedy are also combined with the available homoeopathic information from materia medica, repertories, provings, and cases wherever possible.

To conclude, in each section there are schematic representations that differentiate the species within that particular order. Where natural symmetry exists, small comparisons are made between orders as well.

We also request the reader to first carefully understand the natural behavior of an animal, and then proceed to read the homoeopathic derivation. This will give a more complete picture and a better understanding of the different species.

Many cases in the book were taken some time ago, when there were probably fewer remedies available, particularly from the lesser-known orders of reptiles such as the tortoise and lizards. The patients of the older cases may not have been prescribed the correct remedy, because the salient features of their cases could have been missed. This was at a time when homoeopathy lacked information about the features of their correct remedies, and a better match could have been made. A failure to correctly identify an animal remedy could be attributable either to a paucity of information of genera and species below a known remedy, or a lack of availability of the basic remedies of an animal order. As our case-taking method has evolved, we now try to get into our cases at a very deep level. We are able to go to that depth where we can tap the source language of the remedy that the patient is expressing. Therefore it is possible that we might appreciate the different levels of sensation A, B, & C more clearly in our recent cases. There are still many things that we have learned and can still learn from our older cases.

In this book we have tried to connect many characteristic symptoms from materia medica with the natural behavior of that particular species, although in few remedies this was not possible.

The list of remedies has been updated with assistance from: Freeman's Homoeopathic Pharmacy, Hahnemann Laboratories, Inc., Helios Homoeopathic Pharmacy, Roy and Co. (in Mumbai), Remedia Homoeopathy, and the Wichmann provings (list of remedies).

In using this method to take cases, we now see patients expressing the language of many new remedies. Over time there will be additions to the remedies mentioned in this book.

Possibly significant 'source words' are highlighted throughout the descriptive text in the book. Possible source words, delineated in the class or genus, are *not to be considered final.* They are only suggestions for further confirmation through cases and provings. A lot of work has gone into doing the research and understanding each order, genus, and species. There is still more to be unveiled, as the animal kingdom in general is so fascinating, many details about its members is yet unknown. There are still many things yet to be unearthed. Any additional information, that adds value to the book, is more than welcome.

Brown bold = Specific to animal kingdom and reptiles.

Black bold = Specific to an order and family.

SMALL CAPITALS = Specific to a genus or species.

Under expressions of patients presented for each remedy:

Possible source words and expressions derived from the species' natural history = regular font.

Characteristic behavior of the species, confirmed from the materia medica = *italics.*

Characteristic symptom obtained only from the materia medica and not connected to the source = *brown italics.*

The interviewer is represented by either the first-name initial,

or D = doctor, or H = homoeopath.

P = the patient.

hg/HG = hand gesture.

The text of most of the cases is condensed and grammatically altered for easier reading. Gesture descriptions are placed within parentheses. Cases are interspersed with the respective presenter's comments in italics. A detailed analysis follows the case. Cases also include the authors' comments within brackets in brown font followed by their analysis at the end.

An Overview of Reptiles

The main idea of this chapter is to bring the reader into the world of reptiles so that he will recognize in a patient the reptilian outlook on the world. This includes: actions dictated by body make-up, revelling in their environment, idiosyncratic habits, and survival vigilance. The four main reptilian orders are covered, along with the families and the species within each order. This immersion into the reptilian world is the best way for a reader (who may have little or no knowledge of reptiles) to come to an applicable understanding of such a vast subject.

What is a reptile?

Reptiles are air-breathing vertebrates that have tough skins covered with scales. They are ectothermic, or cold-blooded. This means they must continually access warm or cool spots in their environment to maintain a survivable temperature, because they do not generate internal heat (unlike mammals). Thus reptiles inhabit every corner of the planet except the places of extreme cold, like the Antarctic.

The living reptiles are classified into four orders:

- Testudines (tortoise, turtles, and terrapins)

- Crocodylia (crocodiles and alligators)

- Squamata (snakes, lizards, and amphisbaenians)

- Rhynchocephalia (tuataras)

To grasp the reptilian nature is to understand reptiles' constant dichotomous conflict between staying warm and staying safe. Their cold-bloodedness makes it mandatory that in order to bask, they venture away from safe hideaways and out into open sunlit areas where they are vulnerable to predation. To obtain the heat vital to every function of their survival—locomotion, finding food, mating, and escape—reptiles must risk their safety. Reptiles come out into the open to bask, only under optimal temperature, but when the circumstances become unsuitable, they hide in their retreats or hibernate (in the winter).

Reptiles' cold-bloodedness requires that they constantly conserve energy— and the simplest way to achieve this is to avoid prolonged exertion. The characteristically reptilian sudden burst of activity (either to attack or defend), is actually a method of energy preservation, because it allows the task to be accomplished so suddenly and dramatically, as to curtail the need for further action/exertion. Reptiles tend to perform sudden changes: an ambush from a hidden position, or a change in form, behavior, shape, or color. The concepts of sudden change and surprise attack from a hidden position, are very important parts of the reptilian nature. After its burst of action, the reptile usually runs and hides (escape/avoidance behavior), because reptiles always feel at a disadvantage and incapable of a face-to-face fight; hence they mostly remain hidden and camouflaged.

Reptiles are very deceptive, because their survival depends on their ability to remain hidden or go unnoticed. They don't reveal their true selves. They need to camouflage, as they very often seem incapable of a fierce attack. Many times, the victim of a reptilian ambush attack is caught utterly off guard, with no time even to react.

If provoked further or cornered, after all their different strategies for defending themselves have failed, reptiles can become extremely aggressive. They will strike and bite. This nth degree anger and violence are very important — the concept is expressed in patients via such extreme forms as killing, death, murder, complete destruction, etc. In fact, most of the snakes are very syphilitic in nature (the syphilis miasm outlook is one of despair, hopelessness, impossibility, and destruction).

Reptiles can be very aggressive and get into fights over territories and mating rights. However, this passion does not carry over to their offspring, as reptiles are extremely indifferent parents (with few exceptions). In patients this lack of maternal love and affection often shows up as independence from a very young age, or preoccupation with parental relationships.

After we establish these reptilian characteristics, then we need to proceed and differentiate the four main orders:
- Testudines (tortoises and turtles)
- Crocodilians (crocodiles and alligators)
- Squamata (snakes, lizards, and amphisbaenians)
- Rhynchocephalia (tuataras)

Here each order will manifest or express further the common reptilian features in its own unique way. Each order has evolved in its own characteristic way and has adopted specific methods to survive. Similarly, in humans with reptilian traits, they will also display the different nuances in their behavior.

Testudines (tortoises and turtles)

The order testudines includes all the tortoises and turtles. Tortoises are easily recognised with their unique bony armor: the hard shell that encloses the soft parts of the body. The main function of the shell is to provide protection from the outside threat. The main feeling in testudines in seeking this protection is: **a need to disappear, to remain hidden and to camouflage.** The testudines, with such a heavy weight on their back and with a limited form of locomotion (except the fast-moving sea turtles), feel extremely defenceless. When in danger they withdraw into their shell for safety and will remain hidden until harm is out of its way. So the main conflict in them is to either be **hidden inside the shell while remaining absolutely still and motionless,** or to **emerge out, move ahead,** and **make progress.**

A tortoise is primarily a land-based reptile, with short club-shaped elephantine feet and a dome-shaped shell which gives rise to the slow-moving and awkward gait on land. Tortoises are generally herbivores and docile, but highly sexual. They lack any means to defend themselves, so they simply withdraw into their shell for safety.

Turtles differ from tortoises in various ways. Turtles can be semiaquatic or marine/sea turtles. The semiaquatic turtles are amphibious by nature. They can move on the ground as well as live in the water, whereas the marine/ sea turtles come onto land only to lay eggs. But all turtles and tortoises need to breathe air, so even aquatic and sea turtles must surface. The semiaquatic turtle has sharp claws for digging and burrowing, whereas the sea turtle's feet are like flippers that help them swim with ease. In fact the sea turtles can even migrate long distances.

In the turtles there is also an ambiguous feeling about their mobility — they can be extremely fast and swift in the water, but on land they drag themselves.

The other differentiating feature between turtles and tortoises is shell structure. A turtle's shell is not as bony and complete as the tortoise's. The turtle shell is flatter, and more streamlined. In some instances the turtle shell is only partially developed. This anatomical difference has evolved to support the turtles' aquatic lifestyle. Hence turtles can only partially withdraw into their shell. In fact, the sea turtles are absolutely nonretractile! Thus, with a streamlined or truncated shell that compromises protection (i.e., the heavy armor of the tortoise's shell) in favor of sleekness, turtles have developed different modes of attack and defense: like snapping, quickly sliding into the water, swimming away swiftly, etc. Turtles have evolved to be more aggressive than the tortoise. Also, the fact that in their aquatic lifestyle they are more exposed to larger predators like sharks and killer whales makes them more prone to severe injuries.

Crocodilians (crocodiles and alligators)

Crocodilians are amphibious reptiles, with lizard-like appearance and carnivorous habits. They are the **largest** and the **heaviest** of the reptiles, and one of the few animals on earth that inspire awe in humans. They have powerful and expandable jaws, and sharp conical teeth. Their unique body form allows them to be suspended in water, **partly hidden and submerged,** except for their eyes and nostrils which are exposed. Crocodilians are extremely **territorial.** Unlike most reptiles, they show a good deal of parental care towards their eggs and newborns.

In fact we all have this inherent fear to go near a waterside if we know that crocodiles live there. They could be **hidden beneath the surface,** absolutely **silent and motionless.** In no time they could **suddenly explode, out of the seemingly quiet surface, dragging you, and pulling you with such force, that no amount of struggle or measure can release you from that powerful grip.** You are simply **cut, minced, and crushed** into pieces. This **extreme violence and destruction** is also an indication of their syphilitic nature. Crocodilians are therefore dangerous, extremely powerful and feared creatures, not only amongst the reptiles but amongst all animals.

Another important attribute in the crocodile unlike a land creature which can roam freely, or a sea creature which can swim freely inside the water, is that their area is limited. Crocodilians need land to bask, water to live and air to breathe. Therefore, it can live only in a specified area; and it cannot go outside a specified radius. It has to wait for the creature to come in order to attack. **So it is extremely powerful, but in a very small, limited territory.** If you go within the territory then you are in danger but if you avoid that territory it can't do anything to you.

Within the crocodilians there are differences between the alligators and the crocodiles. The alligators are much more affectionate towards their children and can ferociously guard their nesting sites. They are also extremely vocal, and they make refuge holes called 'gator holes'. Alligators are also less aggressive than the crocodiles.

Snakes

Snakes are the most evolved and sophisticated of all reptiles. The two most characteristic features of the snakes are their **limblessness** and **poison glands.** The vital element in snakes is an ability to survive in the absence of limbs. They have a remarkable ability to overcome this handicap. Despite being limbless, snakes occupy a wide range of habitat and are very capable in their movement. They can crawl over the land, dig underground burrows, climb treetops, swim over and under water, and even glide through the air.

Out of the approximately 2,700 species of snakes on the planet, fewer than 600 are venomous. Snakes pick up scent particles from their surroundings through their forked tongue and transfer it to the Jacobson's organs (openings of which are located in the roof of the mouth). From there the information is processed further. In general snakes have three-dimensional movement of their skull bones, compared to the two-dimensional movement in lizards. Therefore, snakes are able to swallow much larger prey, even twice their size, than lizards can! The prey is swallowed whole, even if it is alive and struggling. Snakes lack ears; hence they are deaf. However they have excellent senses of smell and taste, and they can sense vibrations transmitted through the ground while they are resting. They have immovable eyelids. They are able to shed their skin in a single piece.

Snakes are generally defenceless creatures and their first form of reaction to any attack is to run away and escape. They only attack when threatened, and their best form of attack is to **bite. Apart from biting, snakes have adopted such methods of defense as camouflage, mimicking, squirting, adopting defensive postures like spreading the hood (in the cobra), and hissing.** Before swallowing their prey whole, the dangerous snakes first **kill by either envenomation or constriction.** The harmless snakes simply snatch their prey.

The two main snake infraorders are: Alethinophidia and Scolecophidia.

The former is the more diverse group, consisting of most of the other snakes. The latter are blind snakes.

The Colubridae family of snakes makes up about two-thirds of all snakes in the world, most of which are not poisonous. The garter snakes are common, nonpoisonous colubrid snakes that live in diverse habitats—from marshes to mountains—although they always prefer to be near water, such as ditches, ponds, lakes, and rivers. Other commonly known nonpoisonous colubrid snakes include black snakes, racers, and king snakes. These snakes can be speedy and aggressive, quick to bite, but not poisonous. They often have a constricting ability. Colubrid snakes often mimic the poisonous snakes.

Boas and pythons come from the family Boidae, which includes some of the largest snakes in the world. Boas and pythons are known for squeezing their prey until it suffocates, and then swallowing it whole. These large snakes often lie in wait next to watering sources, and then attack the animals that come to drink. The main difference between the two is that boas give birth to live young ones, whereas pythons lay eggs. Pythons are also known to nurture their eggs (a maternal instinct) by coiling around them and providing them heat by shivering. This movement is intended to liberate heat, rather than to accomplish motion.

Venomous snakes are the most dangerous of all. They include snakes from the Elapidae and Viperidae families.

The Elapidae family includes the cobras, coral snakes, mamba snakes, etc. The Viperidae family is further divided into the subfamilies Viperinae (true or pitless vipers) and Crotalinae (pit vipers). Pit vipers are named for the small pits located just behind their nostrils that detect infrared radiation. These pits alert them to the heat of warm-blooded creatures that might make a good meal. This organ is absent in the pitless vipers. The Crotalinae snakes are the most sophisticated and dangerous snakes and include: the copperhead *(Agkistrodon contortrix* or *Cenchris contortrix),* water moccasin *(Agkistrodon piscivorus),* rattlesnake *(Crotalus* group of snakes),* bushmaster, *(Lachesis),* etc. The function of these pit organs is possibly reflected in human, as clairvoyance. *Lachesis* is one of the Crotalinae snakes that is very well known for clairvoyance from our materia media. The Viperinae snakes include the deadly adders, of which the *Bitis gabonica rhinoceros* (gaboon viper) is the king of camouflage, with its intricate patterns which blend beautifully where it lies!

The elapid snakes have the important themes of 'injury' and 'desire to be alone'. The elapids' solitary nature contrasts with the viperids' tendency to gather in groups for wintering, mating, and clustering near spots with conditions ideal for egg laying (females). Therefore, in the case of a patient involved in mafia groups, terrorist activity, and gang wars— with proscribed activity where a group of people is involved, the Viperidae snakes should come to mind. Patients whose remedy is from the Elapidae family are more likely to be solitary—like the cobra or the mamba snakes.

Elapid snakes bite their prey and hang on, because their neurotoxic venom works so quickly, that the prey is unlikely to struggle sufficiently to injure them. However the viperid snakes stab and swiftly leave the prey, because their hemotoxic venom requires time to work, and they cannot risk injury by remaining attached to their struggling victim. With the help of their pit organs they will later track the poisoned animal. All the snakes swallow their prey whole, starting from the head, so the victim's limbs do not become wedged.

Lizards

Lizards are the most commonly seen of all the reptiles. They form a large and varied group which is not easy to define. A typical lizard has a long, slender and elongated body with scales, four well-developed feet, a tail and movable eyelids. We often see them stuck to the wall, watchful of their surroundings — and at the slightest hint of danger they simply dart off in their typical zigzag motion. This is characteristic of a lizard: **agility** and **speed.** We often see lizards exhaling and inhaling, while they are trying to puff their bodies, so that they appear larger and bigger than they are. Lizards bluff or show off — **a false façade of strength to distract or scare** their predator. Here, **autotomy**—the ability to lose their tail, is a common feature of lizards. Patients who require a lizard remedy may be concerned with **colors:** favorite colors, detested colors, the idea of "changing color" to suit the situation, etc. There are many exceptions to these generalizations.

Two suborders in lizards are Iguania and Scleroglossa. The Iguanias include the iguana, chameleon, calotes, and frilled lizards. They have a specialized means for capturing prey with their tongue, by grasping, and here the chameleons beat the rest. Therefore they are able to capture only visible prey. The Iguanias are also known for their specialized ornamentation: crests, spines, exotic coloration, and visual signals such as head-bobbing and push ups. They are very good climbers and can also swim. They are also very territorial and exhibit many social rituals.

Whereas the Scleroglossa capture prey with their movable jaws, coupled with their sensitive chemosensory apparatus and active foraging. Hence they are able to capture hidden prey. These are the geckos, heloderma, monitor lizards, skinks (that look more typically lizardlike), etc.

Of the iguanas, the chameleons are the most familiar, due to their exceptional ability to change colors. However little did we know that this ability to change colors is not just to defend themselves, but to reflect their different moods.

The geckos are popularly known as the acrobats, with their ability to climb smooth, vertical surfaces and hang upside down. They are also very vocal and primarily nocturnal. The genus Heloderma consists of the only two species of venomous lizards *(Heloderma suspectum* and *Heloderma horridum)*. The monitor lizards are called the 'king of lizards' or 'land crocodiles' due to their large size, powerful musculature, and sharp claws and teeth. They are the most powerful, aggressive and ferocious amongst all of the lizards.

Amphisbaenians

They are also called the 'worm lizards', but they are neither worms nor lizards. They have worm-like cylindrical bodies, with annular scales, and most of them are legless (like the snakes). They move in a peculiar accordion-like or concertina-like movement, but they have a special ability to move both ways. They have thick and heavy skulls with which they burrow and make their own tunnels — as they primarily live underground lives in their burrows. They only emerge when it rains.

* * * * *

We know that all reptiles have underlying feelings of needing to remain concealed, being at a disadvantage, hidden violence, sudden change of form, attacking from a hidden position, deception, violence, etc. Each order will have different shades or gradations of these themes. There could be a very strong prominence of one feature, where it completely stands out. For example in testudines the feeling of being defenceless and weak is very strong and then we see the need to retract inside their protective shell. This will differentiate them from snakes, crocodiles and lizards. Snakes, being limbless, also feel at a disadvantage, but they have their own characteristic ways of attack/defense i.e. by being venomous or by constriction. Lizards are more adept in being agile, alert and to stun their predator by suddenly changing their behavior by changing color or amputating their tail (autotomy), etc.; and crocodiles are specialised by their sudden burst of violent activity from a completely silent position.

Thereby, we can understand that reptiles have evolved into an impressive spectrum of shapes and sizes: from the shell-covered turtles and tortoises, to the long, sinuous snakes, to the swiftly moving lizards, to the heavy bodied crocodiles; along with a wide variety of strategies to survive. Here we can summarise their characteristics:

Tortoises, turtles and terrapins (Testudines)	Crocodiles, alligators, caimans and gharials (Crocodylia)	Snakes, lizards and amphisbaenians (Squamata)	Tuataras (Sphenodontida/ Rhynchocephalia)
About 313 species. Scales modified into a shell Four legs. They have no teeth; instead have a horny beak which covers their jaw.	About 23 species. Large bodies with bony, plate-like armor in the skin along their backs. Heavy, powerful, and expandable jaws, lined with pointed teeth capable of killing.	About 5079 species of lizards, 168 amphisbaenians and 2700 species of snakes. Skin covered with platelike, tubercular, or flat scales that can be overlapping or juxtaposed.	Two species found on island off coast of New Zealand. More active in cooler temperatures than other reptiles. Come out from their burrows at night to feed on insects and other small animals.

Tortoises, turtles and terrapins (Testudines)	Crocodiles, alligators, caimans and gharials (Crocodylia)	Snakes, lizards and amphisbaenians (Squamata)	Tuataras (Sphenodontida/ Rhynchocephalia)
Turtles live near or under water. They only come onto the land to lay eggs and to the surface of the water to breathe. While tortoises (sometimes called land turtles) live on land.	Long, powerful tails and short legs. A unique body form that allows them to be suspended in water — partly hidden and submerged, except for their eyes and nostrils which are exposed.	Live in habitats around the globe that are diverse in terms of both climate and terrain. Easy mobility and flexibility of jaw. Snakes and few lizards have a forked or notched tongue.	Species have dwindled to two, possibly due to losing competition with true lizards during later Mesozoic era and onwards. Active at night; spend days in burrow or basking at burrow entrance.
The land-based tortoises pull their head, legs and tail into the shell for protection.	Nest attendance and parental care of young is commonly seen.	**Snakes:** Snakes are limbless, though some have remnants of tiny legs near their tails. No eyelids or ear openings.	
Whereas the aquatic turtles, with their compromised ability to pull inside the shell, either snap or slide into the water, or swim away swiftly.	Territoriality. Stronger male dominates and fights aggressively for dominance and mating rights.	They have an immovable covering of transparent scales which protects the eyes.	
No parental care of young. Highly sexual.	Terrifying ability to explode into sudden violent activity — completely unexpected in such an otherwise lethargic-seeming creature. Lie-in-wait, ambush predators.	Active foraging or camouflage and ambush attack. Cannot tear, they can only bite or constrict. Snakes swallow prey whole, headfirst, and then retreat to a safe place to digest the meal	

Tortoises, turtles and terrapins (Testudines)	Crocodiles, alligators, caimans and gharials (Crocodylia)	Snakes, lizards and amphisbaenians (Squamata)	Tuataras (Sphenodontida/ Rhynchocephalia)
	Hold prey underwater until it drowns, then drag it away to eat by tearing off large pieces by rolling it in what is called the crocodile "death roll".	slowly. Some snakes can dislocate jaws to swallow prey larger than they themselves are. Most dangerous are the venomous and constrictor. Strikes are fast and accurate. **Lizards:** Most lizards have four legs, while some are limbless. Stun their prey, shake vigorously, bite and tear. Ability to catch fast-moving prey. Fast-moving (most species) and agile. Characteristics of locomotion-ability to cling to vertical surfaces. Communication through highly stereotyped behaviors – using colors (e.g., camouflage or enhancing colors) and various body morphology (e.g., tail autotomy to	

Tortoises, turtles and terrapins (Testudines)	Crocodiles, alligators, caimans and gharials (Crocodylia)	Snakes, lizards and amphisbaenians (Squamata)	Tuataras (Sphenodontida/ Rhynchocephalia)
		distract an onlooker's attention, enlarging throat flaps to bluff or appear bigger than they are, etc). These visual signals include aggression between rival males and courtship rituals between the sexes.	
		Amphisbaenians: They resemble the worms, with no limbs in most species or very small front legs, but have annular scales. Inhabit underground tunnels and burrows. They have specialized means for underground hearing. Tears off chunks of flesh from prey by spinning body while gripping with mouth. Can move in both directions.	

(Note: Number of species (except snakes) according to J. Craig Venter Institute's reptile database and snakes number according to David Attenborough's 'Wildlife Specials – Serpent'.)

List of Homoeopathic Reptile Remedies

() – Homoeopathic abbreviations

[] – Common names

Snakes

Agkistrodon contortrix or *Cenchris contortrix* (Cench.) [Southern copperhead]

Agkistrodon piscivorus [cottonmouth, water mocassin]

Atropoides nummifer olmec [jumping pitviper]

Bitis arietans (Biti-a.) [puff adder, Clotho arictans]

Bitis caudalis [horned adder]

Bitis gabonica rhinoceros [gaboon viper, butterfly adder]

Bitis nasicornis [rhinoceros viper]

Boa constrictor [common boa; sometimes called red-tailed boa]

Boa constrictor adipis [adipis=fat] [fat of common boa]

Bothrops atrox (Both-a.) [common lancehead, fer-de-lance]

Bothrops columbiensis or *Bothrops colombiensis* [Southern American snake]

Bothrops jararaca [Jararaca]

Bothrops lanceolatus (Both-l.) [Martinique lancehead]

Bungarus caeruleus (Bung-c.) [Common krait, Indian krait]

Bungarus fasciatus (Bung-f.) [Banded krait]

Cerastes cerastes [desert viper, Sahara horned viper]

Crotalus cascavella or *Crotalus durissus* (Crot-c.) [Neotropical rattlesnake, South American rattlesnake]

Crotalus crotalus atrox [Western diamondback rattlesnake]

Crotalus horridus (Crot-h.) [Timber rattlesnake]

Crotalus viridis viridis or *Crotalus viridus viridus* [western rattlesnake, Prairie rattlesnake]

Cyclagras gigas or *Hydrodynastes gigas* [false water cobra]

Daboia russelli (Dab-r.) [Russell's viper]

Daboia russelli siamensis or *Vipera russelli siamensis* [Eastern russell's viper]

Deinagkistrodon acutus [sharp-nosed viper, snorkel viper, hundred pacer]

Dendroaspis polylepis (Dend-p.) [black mamba]

Dendroaspis viridis [Western green mamba]

Elaphe guttata [corn snake, rat snake]

Elaps corallinus or *Micrurus corallinus* (Elaps) [coral snakes]

Eunectes notaeus [yellow anaconda]

Hemachatus haemachatus [Rinkhals, ring-necked spitting cobra]

Hydrophis cyanocinctus (Hydro-c.) [sea snake]

Lachesis muta (Lach.) [South American bushmaster, Surucucu, Verrugosa]

Lampropeltis getula californiae [California king snake]

Lampropeltis triangulum [milk snake]

Laticauda colubrina [banded sea krait]

Macrovipera lebetina [blunt-nosed viper, Lebetine viper, Levant viper]

Morelia spilota variegata [Carpet python, North-west carpet python]

Morelia viridis [Green tree python]

Naja annulifera anchietae or *Naja anchietae* (Naja-a.) [Banded cobra, Anchieta's cobra]

Naja haje [Egyptian cobra, Aspis]

Naja kaouthia or *Naja naja kaouthia* [Monocled cobra]

Naja mossambica pallida or *Naja pallida* [Mozambique spitting cobra]

Naja nigricollis [black-necked cobra, spitting cobra]

Naja nivea (Naja-n.) [Cape cobra]

Naja tripudians or *Naja naja* (Naja) [Indian cobra, spectacled cobra]

Natrix natrix [grass snake]

Notechis scutatus (Note-s.) [black tiger snake]

Ophiophagus hannah [King cobra]

Oxyuranus microlepidotus (Oxyu-m.) [inland taipan]

Oxyuranus scutellatus canni (Oxyu-s.) [Taipan]

Python molurus or Python (Divya) [Indian python, Indian rock python]

Python regius (Pyth.) [Royal python, Ball python]

Thamnophis sirtalis sirtalis [common garter snake, garden snake]

Trimeresurus flavoviridis [Habu snake]

Trimeresurus mucrosquamatus [brown spotted viper]

Trimeresurus puniceus [flat-nosed pitviper]

Trimeresurus purpureomaculatus [mangrove pit viper, shore pitviper, Cryptelytrops purpureomaculatus]

Trimeresurus stejnegeri [Chinese tree viper]

Trimeresurus wagleri (Trim.) [Wagler's pit viper, Tropidolaemus wagleri]

Vipera ammodyles meridionalis [Eastern sand viper]

Vipera aspis (Vip-a.) [aspis, asp adder, European asp]

Vipera berus (Vip.) [adder, European adder, Vipera torva]

Vipera redi (Vip-r.) [Italian viper]

Vipera xanthina [rock viper, coastal viper, Ottoman viper, Bornmueller's viper]

Tortoises and turtles

Chrysemys scripta elegans or *Trachemys scripta elegans* [red-eared slider]

Eretmochelys imbricata [hawksbill sea turtle]

Geochelone sulcata [African spurred tortoise]

Lepidochelys olivacea [olive ridley sea turtle]

Ovum *Chelydra serpentina* [egg of common snapping turtle]

Terrapene carolina [box turtle]

Testudo hermanni [shell of Hermann's tortoise]

Testudo hermanni [blood of Hermann's tortoise]

Crocodiles and alligators

Alligator mississippiensis (Alli-m.) [American alligator, Mississippi alligator]

Crocodylus acutus [American crocodile]

Crocodylus niloticus [Nile crocodile]

Crocodylus novaeguineae [New Guinea crocodile]

Lizards

Anguis fragilis [Slow worm]

Calotes versicolor [Bloodsucker]

Chamaeleo zeylanicus or Chamaeleon (Divya) [Indian chameleon]

Chlamydosaurus kingii [Frilled neck lizard]

Furcifer oustaleti [Oustalet's chameleon, Malagasy giant chameleon]

Heloderma horridum [Mexican beaded lizard]

Heloderma suspectum (Helo.) [Gila monster]

Iguana iguana [Green iguana]

Varanus komodoensis [Komodo dragon, Monitor lizard]

Lacerta agilis (Lacer.) [Sand lizard, Green lizard]

Lacerta vivipara [Common lizard]

Lizard (Divya) [species unidentified]

Pogona vitticeps [Central bearded dragon]

Sceloporus occidentalis [Western fence lizard, Blue-bellies]

Amphisbaenians

Amphisbaena alba [white-bellied worm lizard]

Amphisbaena vermicularis (Amph.)

Dinosaurs

Maiasaura lapidea (Maia-l.) [fossilized Maiasaura peeblesorum]

Tyrannosaurus rex (T-rex.) [fossilized Tyrannosaurus rex]

Reptiles

70

Introduction

The mysterious and the misunderstood ... the feared and the revered
Reptiles are one of the most wonderful and diverse creatures on earth, varying in their size, shape, color and behavior. Traditionally speaking they comprise a large and wide-ranging group of air-breathing vertebrates (animals with a backbone). This includes the alligators, crocodiles, lizards, snakes, turtles and tortoises, as well as the less obvious forms such as the tuataras and amphisbaenians; not forgetting the extinct, related forms like the dinosaurs.

But strictly speaking, reptiles are not that easy to define, because phylogenetically they don't have an isolated evolutionary lineage as do the birds. One reptile doesn't look very much like the other. Lizards run about on their four legs. Snakes don't have any legs and they slither away. Crocodiles resemble the giant lizards and partly even the dinosaurs, with their big and powerful jaws. Turtles and tortoises live protected under a hard bony shell. They are all reptiles!!

The word 'reptile' is derived from the Latin word *'repere'* which means **'to creep'**. This commonly reminds one of snakes and lizards. Interestingly, *'repere'* also means a **'groveling or despised'** person.

Reptiles have a spectacular history. They have been around for almost 300 million years, and during the age of the dinosaurs, they ruled the earth. Those days are long gone, and even those giants have vanished. Still some 6,500 species of reptiles still manage to thrive today. Even now they cover a range of species from the colorful tree snakes to the huge dragon-like lizards and the man-eating crocodiles. Considering the constraints of their limited body forms and cold-bloodedness, reptiles have an astonishing array of lifestyles and survival strategies. And the ways in which reptiles mate and move are equally broad; with parental care, courtship, territoriality, and migration rivaling the complex social structure and behavioral interaction of the birds and mammals. They have all evolved to fit the environment and are one of the most successful and prolific groups of creatures on the planet. Clearly we have much more to learn about these wonderful and mysterious animals.

There are very few animals that are surrounded with as much mythology and disinformation as reptiles. Snakes in particular are the subject of many exaggerated claims, perhaps due to the fear and fascination in which they are held. And most of these extraordinary facts are related to reptilian longevity.

The oldest known reptile of all was a Madagascan tortoise presented to the Tongan royal family in either 1773 or 1777. Whichever date is correct, it lived until 1965, making it at least 188 years old! Only in recent years, modern research has been able to disprove many misconceptions and the misguided theories about reptiles being the most repelling and unfriendly sort. In fact, these cold-blooded, scaly creatures inhabit every continent, nearly every corner of the planet, including most of the oceans, with the exception of most of the Arctic and Antarctica. Though, they have an incredible capability to cope with the harshest environments, and have an ability to go for prolonged periods without food.

These creepy crawly creatures have managed to sneak into a broad range of habitat, from the bottom of ponds and lakes to the high tree lines, where they all walk or crawl, slither or swim, leap or lunge, or some even spend their life under a shell; all in their own unique ways. Thus reptiles are one of the most fascinating subjects in nature, both in fiction and in scientific study.

Evolution

Reptiles, impressive as they are, just aren't what they used to be in comparison to the largest of their evolutionary ancestors. Even the biggest of today's lizards don't match up to some of their predecessors, the hugest of the dinosaurs. Those mighty monsters from the past were all reptiles too! The evolutionary history of reptiles stretches far into ancient times. The oldest fossilized reptilian remains are those of a reptile that lived over 320 million years ago, while the amphibians are even older; some fossils date back over 375 million years.

The ancestral lineage of both reptiles and amphibians arose during the Carboniferous period, about 300-350 million years ago. Although the amphibians continued to evolve successfully (and are still evolving today), the reptiles were able to move away from the lakes and swamps to which the amphibians were tied due to their breeding requirements, and colonized the land completely. Reptiles evolved to occupy an intermediate position in the evolutionary development between amphibians and warm-blooded vertebrates, i.e., the birds and mammals and over time the reptiles diverged from their ancestors in two significant respects:

- They developed a dry, horny and tough skin covered with platelike, tubercular, or flat scales that can be overlapping or juxtaposed (as opposed to hair or feathers).

- And secondly, they also evolved a shelled, amniotic egg, in which the embryo developed within a sac of water, protecting it from the environment.

The advantage of scales and shelled eggs is that these characteristics enable reptiles to complete their entire life cycle (including reproduction and giving birth to young ones) on land in a dry environment, unlike the amphibians and the fish which need water to reproduce.

The differences between reptiles and amphibians are generally more obvious than their similarities, although their joint study under the name "herpetology" (from the Greek *herpeton,* meaning a creeping or crawling thing) is a scientific tradition dating back nearly two centuries.

Classification

Scientists divide the animal kingdom into several major groups for classification purposes. By far the largest group is the invertebrates: it contains about 95 percent of the millions of known species of animals, including sponges, crustaceans and insects. Reptiles are vertebrates which belong to a group of animals characterized by having a bony backbone, a flexible but strong support column of articulated sections (vertebrae) to which the other body structures are attached. Vertebrates also include amphibians, fishes, birds and mammals.

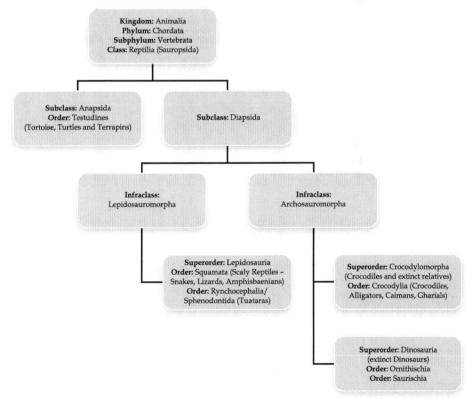

Broadly speaking reptilia are chiefly represented by four orders:

- Testudines (Tortoises, turtles and terrapins)
- Crocodylia (Crocodiles, alligators, caimans and gharials)
- Squamata (Snakes, lizards and amphisbaenians)
- Rhynchocephalia/Sphenodontida (Tuataras)

Thermal regulation: Cold-blooded reptiles

One significant factor in the behavior of reptiles is their inability to produce sufficient internal metabolic heat to maintain a constant body temperature, as do almost all birds and mammals. For this reason they are termed as "cold-blooded creatures" or "ectotherms". Their temperature is dictated by the temperature of the air or water surrounding them. Though some reptiles are able to generate enough heat to raise their temperature for a specific purpose for limited periods; for example, female pythons while brooding their eggs.

Without the sun's heat, a reptile's body stops working properly. They need heat to help them digest their food, facilitate locomotion, and enable escape from predators. Thus maintaining an optimum body temperature is the key to a reptile's survival and an integral part of its nature.

That is one prime reason that we see these sun-loving creatures virtually everywhere, except in most Arctic areas or in Antarctica. Cold-bloodedness greatly limits their ability to live and breed in colder climates, with the consequence they are most abundant in tropical and warm, temperate regions. Their body stops working when it gets too cold, and also when it gets too warm. In extreme cold they become very sluggish, which makes them an easy prey. To prevent this from happening there are many things they do to regulate their temperature, and if required keep it at a higher level.

Cold-bloodedness in reptiles does not literally mean they are emotionally 'cold-blooded'. In fact many of them show remarkable maternal instincts and very affectionate courtship rituals.

Cold-bloodedness (or poikilothermism) in reptiles has some advantages over the warm-bloodedness (or homoiothermism) in birds and mammals. Reptiles can simply "shut down" when the conditions are unsuitable; for example when it is too cold or food is scarce. Therefore they do not have to use up large amounts of stored energy to keep themselves warm. They are able to cope quite well even with a drop in temperature. In mammals the slightest fluctuation in temperature can be potentially serious. As a result mammals need a constant supply of food to produce energy (a contrast to the situation of reptiles of the same size, who can manage with much less food for prolonged periods of time).

Another advantage of cold-bloodedness is its tendency, via fluctuating temperature, to inhibit the growth of bacteria and parasites.

Methods adopted for temperature regulation

Basking

Reptiles slowly emerge from where they have spent the night to bask in the sun, absorbing or soaking the rays through their skin. Once they have warmed up enough, they move around, looking for food. Sometimes they also flatten their body to increase the surface area receiving the warmth. Their body continues to stay warm for a while, even after it moves into the shade. Overheating is as much a danger as

Tortoise basking with its head emerged out of the shell

becoming too cold; both extremes can occur in the case of desert-dwellers. When overheated they will retreat to a shady area to lower their body temperature, as they habitually do during the hottest part of the day. Therefore we understand that basking in the sun is a vital function to a reptile's survival.

Basking in a group

Many reptiles, like the armadillo lizard (*Cordylus cataphractus*), bask in groups. One advantage of this is that as a result there are many more eyes looking for any potential danger. And if one lizard sights a hungry bird, it will immediately dart for cover, and the others will follow suit immediately.

Basking in females

Female lizards' basking involves more than regulation of temperature and metabolic processes. Female lizards that bask optimally have longer, heavier, and livelier offspring. It is thought that female basking during gestation speeds up the gestational process slightly, resulting in healthier offspring. Sometimes dominant lizards will restrict other lizards' access to basking spots. A female lizard seeking an optimal spot for maternal basking may be chased off by a dominant male, although a subordinate male may not pose as much of a threat.

Hibernation

Hibernation in reptiles, often called 'brumation', occurs when, in response to lower temperatures, the metabolic processes of these cold-blooded critters slow down and they hide in burrows, rock crevices, caves or leaf litter to wait out the cold weather where they can go completely unnoticed. Many species of snakes, lizards, turtles and tortoises in temperate and desert regions retreat underground during the harsh winter months, where they are protected from freezing conditions by slightly warmer surroundings there. Some do so by digging burrows into the ground or slipping into a crack between two rocks. They stay there until the weather warms up.

Some species utilize burrows made by other animals or cavities in the base of tree stumps. Some species are known to hibernate in large groups, while some species of snake such as rattlesnakes are known to form large hibernation balls which may contain dozens of individuals. Unlike mammals that fatten before going into dens for hibernation, reptiles will instinctively fast before going into brumation. During brumation reptiles do not live off fat stores as do mammals such as bears; rather, the brumating reptile's body processes just slow down. It is important for a reptile's digestive system to be free of food before its metabolic processes slow down during its cold weather brumation, because any undigested food could putrefy and sicken or kill the reptile.

Reptiles don't need to use reserve food energy to keep themselves warm, and they have a much lower overall energy requirement than endothermic/ warm-blooded animals such as mammals and can thus maintain a much lower metabolic rate. This is one reason that many reptiles are able to hibernate for long periods without needing food to keep them alive; their internal body processes can be slowed down so far that they can survive without food for many months. However, they are still active and still awake, though very sluggish. Also, for many reptiles, hibernation is necessary for breeding. The cooling period stimulates ovulation and the production of sperms and regulates thyroid function. Brumation is also important for healthy immune system.

Reptiles that live in desert and semidesert habitats sometimes enter an inactive state during dry periods when food becomes scarce, called 'aestivation' that resembles hibernation, so that their survival can be optimized by reducing evaporative water loss and limiting metabolic response to extreme temperature, until the arrival of rain and/or cooler temperature.

Generalized anatomy

Even though today's reptiles don't reach the enormous size of some of their dinosaur ancestors, they still vary enormously in size and structure. This reflects the adaptations suited to almost every conceivable habitat, throughout the tropical and temperate regions of the world. For example, the anacondas can grow to between 26 to 36 feet (8 to 11 m) in length. At the other end of the scale, the smallest reptiles are geckos; some don't grow any longer than around 1 inch (2.5 cm). That even fits on your finger tip!!

Skin and scales

The most easily visible and differentiating sign of a reptile is the scaly skin that covers most of its body. The outer layer of their skin is thickened to form scales, composed of keratin; some areas are further thickened to form tubercles and crests. In many reptiles small bones develop in the skin just below

Scales

the surface. These dermal bones, or osteoderms, add strength and protection to the skin and make it even more impervious to water loss. Reptiles' ability to staunch water loss, and thereby go without water for long periods, is the prime reason that they are able to thrive in the warm, desert environments favored by their cold-bloodedness. These scales also form a barrier that protects them from abrasion, as well as attacks from predators and parasites. Skin color and color changes are largely determined by pigment cells just below the outer layers of skin. Having the scales is a key factor for reptiles' survival.

A lizard in a close-up view displaying the scaly skin

Reptiles' protective scales have various growth modes. Snakes' and lizards' scales don't get bigger as the animal grows. Instead, old scales and skin are shed or molted very often and are replaced by new ones. Snakes slough their skin in one piece, while the lizards shed it in chunks or flakes. Crocodilians

lose bits of their surface scales continuously in flakes or small sheets, as new keratinous layers are pushed up, while the osteoderms below the surface scales are enlarged via growth rings. Turtles' and tortoise's shells have underlying fused bony plates covered by scales called scutes. Made of keratin, the scutes enlarge by either being retained and adding growth rings, or becoming thicker and larger as new layers of keratin are added from beneath.

Snake shedding its skin

Body structure

The basic skeletal structure has become highly modified in reptiles. An extreme adaptation is found in turtles, in which the greater part of the vertebral column, the ribs, and the limb girdles has become fused with the dermal bones to form a protective shell. But in general the skeletal system in reptiles is considerably sturdier than that of an amphibian, making them more suited to life on land.

Unlike those of mammals and birds, a reptile's limbs support the body from the side, which gives them a sprawling gait when they move. Snakes, together with most amphisbaenians and some lizards, are without functional legs. Subsequently each group of reptiles developed its own particular variations on this major pattern in accord with the general adaptive trends of the group.

Many reptiles developed joints (in addition to the hinge for the lower jaw) within the skull, permitting at least slight movement of one part relative to others. The capacity for such movement within the skull, called kinesis, enables an animal to increase the gape of the mouth and thus is an adaptation for swallowing large objects.

Teeth in reptiles vary greatly in form and structure, from simple blunt teeth used to grasp and partially crush prey, to those with broad grinding surfaces or sharp shearing edges. Perhaps the most specialized are the fangs of snakes that have evolved grooves or hollows, making them efficient venom-delivering hypodermic needles.

The reptiles' tongue is an important adjunct to the teeth and jaws in catching prey. It is usually very muscular, flexible and extrusible, and is often sticky with mucus, in order to adhere to prey such as insects. It is also used to manipulate food within the mouth. In some groups of reptiles, such as monitor lizards and snakes, the tongue has become a specialized sense organ which senses and locates prey, but otherwise is not directly involved in the capturing of prey.

Internal organs

The soft structures of reptiles are similar to those of other vertebrate animals. A trachea leads from the glottis to paired lungs. Reptiles require aerial respiration, which means they breathe without having to go back to the water or receive oxygen through the skin like amphibians. Having lungs means they are able to survive on land. Most species have two lungs, but some snakes have only one (mostly the left lung has been lost during the course of evolution). In some aquatic species the lungs may be reduced or absent and they absorb all the oxygen they need through their skin. In many sea snakes the lung now extends forward along the length of the trachea and is involved in regulating the snake's buoyancy when diving.

The circulatory system of most reptiles, while less complex than that of the crocodiles (as well as birds and mammals), is efficient enough for these ectothermic creatures. Being cold-blooded, they do not have the perpetually high oxygen requirements that support the metabolic processes used by birds and mammals to maintain a constant body temperature. The heart of reptiles has only three chambers: two auricles or atria, and a partially divided ventricle. This means that the pulmonary and systemic blood systems are not entirely separated, and there is the possibility of some mixing of oxygenated and deoxygenated blood.

The digestive system of reptiles varies among the species, according to the kind of food the animal eats. Reptiles that feed mainly on animals, or on such animal products as eggs, have a fairly simple stomach and a short intestine. Such reptiles include *Boa constrictors* and Gila monsters. Species that eat plants, including iguanas and most tortoises, have a more complicated stomach and long intestines. Crocodilians have extremely large stomach muscles that grind flesh into tiny pieces.

Poisonous reptiles produce their venom by means of venom glands on the sides of the head. The venom affects a victim's circulatory system or nervous system.

Many reptiles live in very dry, warm habitats, so conserving water in their bodies is extremely important. Consequently, in the majority of them the liver converts nitrogenous waste into uric acid, which after excretion by the kidneys, passes to the cloaca where water is resorbed and solid uric acid crystals deposited. These then leave the body as a moist paste, using only a fraction of the water that would be needed to excrete urea as urine.

The senses

For most reptiles the senses critical to their survival are: sight, hearing, olfaction (smell) and thermosensitivity (heat detection). The relative importance of each is strongly correlated with the behavior and defense mode of any particular species. *This is to reinforce the idea the book teaches that, the key to the animal remedies is an understanding of the animal's behavior, especially defensive modes.*

Sight

Most reptiles have good vision, apart from the snakes, which have a different mechanism. Species active during the day (diurnal) have eyes with round pupils; e.g., turtles, nonvenomous snakes, and diurnal lizards. Species active at night (nocturnal) have slit-like eye pupils; e.g., alligators, crocodiles. Nocturnal venomous snakes' pupils are vertical slits, which can be closed almost completely in bright light. An anomaly is the coral snake, which although venomous has round pupils. Some reptiles can also differentiate colors.

Although many snakes have poor sight, they usually manage to detect moving objects which are fairly close to them by moving the lenses of their eyes forward; the lenses move backward to see distant objects. In some snakes, the lenses can also change shape. In some burrowing squamates the eyes are reduced or absent. Lizards need acute vision, because many hunt fast-moving prey like insects. They also use brilliant colors to attract mates and even to warn other males from their territories. Especially remarkable are the chameleons' eyes which move independently of each other while they scan for insects. Aquatic reptiles like crocodiles have specially adapted eyes that can spot movements close to them and also help them hunt at night. But they cannot form sharp images and are unable to focus for long on stationary objects. Some lizards and tuataras have a light-sensitive area on top of their skull, known as the third eye (parietal eye), which is thought to control diurnal and seasonal patterns of activity by measuring day length. In reptiles the lower eyelid is also usually movable and at least partly scaly. In many lizards and in all snakes the lower and upper eyelids have become fused and the eye is covered by a large, fixed transparent disk - the spectacle, which protects the eye from damage. The spectacle becomes scratched and dirty over time and is shed with the skin at each sloughing cycle.

Hearing

The ears of reptiles, as in many other animals, perform both sound reception and equilibrium functions. Most reptiles: snakes, earless lizards, turtles, tortoises, and amphisbaenians tend to have poor hearing. The tympanum is absent or covered by skin, and the inner bony structures are often modified to receive ground vibrations through body tissues. The reptiles with the best hearing are those that detect sounds in the high-frequency range, such as the lizards and crocodilians.

Olfaction (smell) and thermosensitivity (heat detection)

Olfaction and heat detection devices in reptiles are primarily used to locate food (or prey) and detect predators (or danger), which is critical to their survival. Olfaction also serves in finding and attracting mates.

Reptiles taste and smell using an organ in the roof of the mouth called the Jacobson's organ, a small cavity lined with "**sense detectors**" that recognize chemical changes in and around the mouth. Although all reptiles of the order

Squamata (snakes, lizards and amphisbaenians) have Jacobson's organ, some rely on it more than others. The snakes especially, and various lizards, continually collect airborne particles by flicking their tongues which they then insert into the Jacobson's organ. The receptors in this small cavity recognize and identify chemical changes and concentrations in their surroundings, helping the animal decide which way food or mates are located. Thus it helps the animal "test" its environment – to locate prey, find mates, and generally obtain information about its surroundings.

The pit vipers of the Viperidae family, and some boas and pythons, have highly sensitive heat detectors made of terminal nerve endings that line the surface openings in the front of the head. In the pit vipers, these 'pit organs' is a large "thermal stimuli sensing opening" between the eye and nostril on each side of the head, whereas in boas and pythons, several smaller openings line the upper lip and sometimes the lower lip as well. (For more information on pit organs refer page 897.) Crocodilians have a similar set of organs in their skin called integumentary sense organs that help them detect pressure waves in the water and tell them how far away their prey is. These are especially useful for animals whose eyesight deteriorates rapidly underwater.

Food habits

Most reptiles are carnivorous and eat other animals, and they prey on almost any creature they can catch. However, some lizards and turtles eat mainly plants and local fruits (herbivorous).

Larger reptiles, such as the big constricting snakes and the crocodilians, will attack and eat much larger prey such as pigs, deer, larger lizards, and even human beings. Snakes in particular can swallow large animals as a whole. By unhinging their lower jaws and stretching their skin they can ingest animals considerably broader and heavier than they are.

Tortoises in the wild are mainly herbivorous (e.g., African spurred tortoise), eating mostly grass, leaves, flowers, and fruit, although some show omnivorous behavior (e.g., Speke's hingeback tortoise), adding insects and small animals to their diet. Turtles can be herbivorous (e.g., yellow-headed temple turtle), omnivorous (e.g., Southeast Asian box turtle), or carnivorous (e.g., Florida softshell turtle). The marine iguana is notable in that it feeds almost solely on algae it finds on underwater rocks. Its terrestrial relative, the common green iguana, is primarily herbivorous, preferring green leafy plants and ripe fruit, although it will occasionally eat a small amount of carrion or invertebrates.

Some reptiles eat only certain animals or animal products (specialized diet). For example, map turtles eat freshwater clams and snails, and African egg-eating snakes feed on birds' eggs, as their names suggest; while the king cobra exists on a diet that consists almost entirely of other snakes. Leatherback turtles, the largest of all sea turtles, feed almost exclusively on jellyfish and other soft-bodied sea creatures.

Smaller lizard species typically have varied diets comprising insects and other invertebrates of many kinds. Meanwhile many snakes eat frogs, small lizards, fish, rodents and other small mammals.

As a result reptiles have developed highly predatory and opportunistic instincts, alongside astonishing reflexes which help them hunt and capture fast-moving prey. Lizards, turtles, crocodiles and many snakes simply grab their food with their mouths and chew or swallow it whole, but some reptiles also have more sophisticated means of subduing prey. Like the venomous snakes bite their victims swiftly and inject powerful toxins, which quickly kill or paralyze them. Constricting snakes, such as pythons and boas, literally squeeze their prey to death before swallowing it.

Life cycle and reproduction

Like most other animals, reptiles compete for territory and access to mates, with both their same species and other animals. Most reptiles reproduce sexually. The male releases sperm (male sex cells) into the female opening that leads to the reproductive organs. In a process called fertilization, the sperm unite with eggs (female sex cells) within the female's body. The fertilized eggs then develop into new offspring. In some lizards and snakes, females can reproduce without mating. This process is called parthenogenesis.

Courtship

Most reptiles mate during the spring, and the young are born in summer. Most reptiles display elaborate courtship rituals specific to a specie. These rituals or signals provide information not only for species identity, but also about the gender and reproductive readiness of an individual.

Various modes of communication come into play in reptile courtship, including:

1. Visual displays, such as the stereotyped movements and changes in coloration that are part of the courtship of iguanid lizards (which includes the iguanas, chameleons, anoles and relatives). Male chameleons puff themselves up and change color when courting females, while pregnant

females display vibrant coloration to indicate that they are no longer receptive to mating. Among male anoles, head bobbing signals readiness to fight, defend territory, or engage in courtship, and inflation of the dewlap impresses females and intimidates rivals.

2. Olfactory cues, such as those given by certain chemicals in the gonadal secretions of reptiles, communicates the status of a female with regard to her previous mating with other males. In the brown tree snake, for example, pheromones indicate sexual attractiveness in females; create a trail that leads males to females. This allows males to find other males so that they can fight to establish territory and mating rights, and allow females to follow other females to optimal egg-laying sites.

3. Vocalization, including crocodilians' bellows and lizards' barks, grunts, squeaks, clicks, and clucks. The lizard best known for its mating-call vocalization is the tokay gecko of Southeast Asia. During the breeding season it reverses its solitary habit and calls loudly and repeatedly, "to-kay, to-kay" in order to attract a mate. When male (bull) American alligators want to attract a mate during the breeding season, they produce a loud, low-frequency roar, or bellow. The bellowing of one alligator will stimulate others to join in, until there is quite a chorus! The slightly quieter crocodiles rumble, cough, or bark to attract a female.

Egg laying

All turtles, crocodilians, and the tuatara, as well as some lizards and snakes, lay eggs (oviparous). A few species of snakes and lizards are viviparous (giving birth to live ones). Some snakes and lizards are ovoviviparous (eggs develop within a female and are hatched either inside or outside her body).

All the egg-laying reptiles lay them on land. Many reptiles lay leathery-shelled eggs which allow air to enter, and at the same time, prevent the loss of vital fluid. Once fertilized, the eggs are fully equipped to feed and protect the embryo until hatching time.

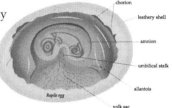

Compared to reptiles, amphibians are characterized by a two-stage life cycle in which the eggs hatch into aquatic, gill-bearing larvae (for example, tadpoles). They eventually metamorphose into air-breathing, mostly terrestrial adults.

Parental care

Parental care is rarely seen in reptiles. They typically deposit their eggs in a burrow and leave them to hatch on their own. **And as soon as they are hatched, the babies are on their own.** Though the crocodilians, especially mothers, often guard their nests (often times quite ferociously). Adult crocodiles will also respond aggressively to hatchlings' distress cries. Crocodilians from the same brood stay together for a period of time, often up to four years in the case of the American alligator. A degree of parental care is also seen in pythons, mud snakes, and some skinks. The female wraps her body around the eggs, incubates them and even protects them. Even in the viviparous species (from which some parental care might reasonably be expected), the live-born young are on their own after emerging.

Behavior

Locomotion

Reptiles are creatures that have unique forms of locomotion and get around in a number of ways. Unlike mammals, which primarily use their legs, reptiles tend to use their bodies and spine as major elements of locomotion. The structure of reptiles' shows developmentally improved methods of locomotion on land, where the primordial water

Lizard's sprawling gait with legs splayed out

is not available to buoy up the body. Some modes of locomotion in reptiles are:

- Walking and crawling
- Clinging and climbing
- Swimming
- Flying

The body design of most extant, (still existing), reptiles' shows quadrupedal sprawl: four limbs extend out laterally from the body. These quadrupedal reptiles, such as lizards and crocodiles, tend to keep their stomachs very close to the ground, with the legs splayed out to the side. With few exceptions, most four-legged reptiles have this same awkward, sprawling leg position, which keeps the center of gravity quite low and makes it more difficult to raise the body off the ground.

In contrast, the erect leg position of the quadrupedal mammals, whose limbs are directly underneath the body, allows more efficient movement and agility.

Despite this awkward motion, some reptiles are capable of moderate speeds. Crocodilians raise their bodies off the ground and make short, fast rushes. Short-bodied lizards also can move fast for short distances. In fact, some lizards can lift their front legs off the ground when running. Longer bodied lizards have greater difficulty in raising their bodies, since they have short legs. This forces their bodies to move more like snakes. In fact, the reptiles with the shortest legs actually have no legs at all. These are the snakes.

Most reptiles do not migrate, except the few that do to reach favorable nesting sites or more favorable feeding sites. For example, loggerhead sea turtles' usual seasonal migration takes them a round-trip distance of 2,000 kilometres (1,240 miles) to reach their nesting sites. Some individuals have even been recorded migrating up to 4,828 km (3000 miles).

Methods of defense and attack

Methods of defense

Reptiles are tempting targets and prey for many types of predators, including large fish, birds, mammals, and other reptiles. Most of the enemies prey on small or young reptiles. Large adult reptiles generally are safe from all attackers except man.

Most reptiles are placid creatures and their first line of defense is usually to hide or flee, but when seriously provoked they will bite. So as a first line of defense, most reptiles try to avoid being seen by their predators. Many are nocturnal and use the cover of darkness to avoid notice. During the day, most reptiles tend to remain hidden, beneath dead leaves, rocks, and logs or in underground burrows. When escape is not possible, many reptiles use elaborate displays to frighten or confuse the predator. For example, the *Chlamydosaurus kingii* (frilled neck lizard) will face its enemy and suddenly spread a wide frill around its neck while gaping its open mouth. The trick of puffing up or enlarging to intimidate predators has been perfected also by members of the dangerous cobra family, which raise their impressive hoods when threatened. Others, such as the thorny devil lizard, are covered in fierce-looking spines, while yet others raise themselves up on their front legs and inflate their bodies to make

85

themselves look bigger. Many other snakes will hiss or gape their mouths when threatened, often striking viciously at would-be intruders. Some reptiles are so big and aggressive that they have little need for defense mechanisms as adults. Big crocodiles and large constricting snakes have few natural predators and simply rely on their intimidating size and impressive armory of teeth or muscles to scare away curious visitors.

But by and large, reptiles are very agile and alert to their surroundings and use a variety of strategies and protective mechanisms.

Below are listed some means of defense adapted by reptiles:

Camouflage (crypsis)

Reptiles avoid confrontation through camouflage. Using a variety of grays, greens, and browns. These animals can blend remarkably well into the background of their natural environment. It is amazing how difficult it is to see a smooth greensnake that is moving through the grass! Several kinds of lizards also change their color to match their surroundings. Some turtles, such as snapping, mud, and musk turtles, are colored and shaped to blend in with their habitat (cryptic coloration and morphology).

A beautifully camouflaged desert horned lizard (Phrynosoma platyrhinos calidiarum)

Countershading is an interesting form of camouflage for reptiles that live in the water. Many turtles have light colors on their bellies and dark colors on their backs. This color pattern makes them less visible to aquatic predators that see them against a light sky. Birds and other predators hunting from above also have a hard time spotting them against the dark water. Even some of the larger predators, such as snapping turtles and alligators, have countershading, perhaps to be less visible when stalking their prey.

A lot of species use spots, stripes, and blotches to break up the outline of their bodies when viewed against leaves or soil. In some lizards camouflage is also a means of surprise mating strategy.

On the contrary, some reptiles, unlike the ones that use camouflage, have colors that do not necessarily blend with the background.

In fact, many times the markings are quite bright and even gaudy. The eyes of the predator, however, are tricked into thinking the shape they are seeing is not an animal, (mimicry of inanimate objects in the environment).

Body form and posturing

Many reptiles scare off potential predators with threatening postures or behaviors. Snapping turtles, when encountered on land, can be very aggressive, snapping their jaws and lunging. Probably the most notorious warning among reptiles is that of the very deadly rattlesnake, whose chilling rattle, (of the tail), is capable of making most animals halt in their tracks. Some snakes will rise up as if poised to strike an attacker. This act also has the advantage of making them appear larger and perhaps more threatening.

Ironically, the great survival success and abundance of reptiles in the natural world makes them attractive prey animals for other predators, especially when they are young. Not only are they very common but they are often fairly easy to catch too. Even the fastest snakes and lizards are at risk when hunting in the open or basking in the sunshine.

Although many reptiles have evolved defense mechanisms to discourage predators (as mentioned above), those predators have in turn developed means for dealing with them. Most snake predators concentrate on tiring their opponent and confusing it with rapid movements, and many are at least partially resistant to the venom of the snakes that share their habitat. Perhaps the most famous of these is the Indian mongoose, which hunts highly venomous snakes such as cobras with great skill and fearlessness.

All sorts of other animals eat reptiles of one kind or another. Birds, especially, are major snake and lizard predators. Some species, such as the secretary bird and roadrunner are specialist snake killers. Even humble hedgehogs are known to enjoy snakes in their diet. One striking example of a reptile-killer is the tiger shark, which regularly attacks and eats large sea turtles, shell and all. Even crocodiles are not immune. While the adult crocodiles are only at threat from humans, other creatures such as monitor lizards may eat their eggs, which they dig up with their well-adapted claws.

Few specific defense mechanisms of reptiles:

Death feigning and mimicry

Amongst snakes, the eastern hognose *(Heterodon platirhinos)* has the most impressive defense behavior. When threatened, it flattens and inflates its neck and raises its head off the ground, hissing loudly, and striking a resemblance to the venomous cobra of southern Asia. It may strike but rarely bites.

Western hognose snake feigning death

87

If all this fails, the snake rolls over, writhes as if in pain, opens its mouth, sticks out its tongue, and plays dead. It is a real actor. You can pick it up and it will remain limp. But if you set it down right side up, it will flop over onto its back again.

Lizard tricks

Some kinds of lizards have tails that will break off when grabbed by an attacker, which they later grow back (autotomy). The lizard escapes, while the attacker is left with just the tail. Spiny lizards have sharp spines that discourage predators, and skinks have smooth overlapping scales that make them hard to hold onto. Horned lizards have special muscles that can burst tiny blood vessels at the edges of the eyes. They can squirt a stream of blood as far as 3 feet at an attacker.

Snake coils (postural warning and aposematic coloration)

The ringneck snake coiling its tail and displaying the warning color

Some reptiles do not avoid or hide from predators, but instead frighten them off by displaying warning signs that use posture, bright coloration, or both. For example, newts have glands in their skin that produce toxins. In order for this toxicity to protect an animal from being eaten, the predators must be reminded that they are about to eat something that will make them sick. The animal assumes a defensive posture that prominently displays the brightly colored parts of its body that either remind of or produce noxious chemicals. The subspecies of the ringneck snake, such as the prairie ringneck, will coil the tail and display the red warning color underneath at the first sign of danger. If picked up, these snakes will secrete a foul-smelling musk. Another common method of alerting a predator is by being very brightly colored. For example the brightly banded, venomous coral snakes provide a display that suggests noxious effect to predators.

Suits of armor

Some reptiles, such as alligators, are protected by their tough skins. Turtles and tortoises carry their defense system around with them, their shells. Box turtles (*Terrapene carolina*) have hinges in the bottom shell that enable them to pull it tightly against the top shell to completely protect their head and limbs from a fox or a raccoon.

Copycats (mimicry)

Interestingly, a reptile may be truly venomous or maybe just bluffing. Some harmless snakes have colors and patterns that are similar to those of venomous species. In this way, they take advantage of markings that bring back unpleasant memories for predators. Any predator that fears the deadly coral snake (*Micrurus tener*, Genus-Micrurus, Family-Elapidae) is unlikely to attack the scarlet kingsnake (*Lampropeltis triangulum elapsoides*, Genus-Lampropeltis, Family-Colubridae), which is not venomous but looks quite similar to the coral snake.

Note the difference in the color pattern between the coral snake (Micrurus tener) (l) and the kingsnake (Lampropeltis triangulum elapsoides) (r)

Spitting

For venomous snakes, a good offense may be the best defense. The African spitting cobra can accurately spray venom at the eyes of a predator, sometimes hitting its target from as far away as 3 m (9.7 ft). This can easily blind an unwary predator.

Methods of attack

From bony shells to sharp teeth, camouflage and warning colors, reptiles protect and defend themselves in a variety of ways.

Some reptiles actively pursue their prey, while others employ a 'sit and wait' strategy until prey comes lose. The ambush hunters attack their prey from a concealed position in such a way that they are neither seen nor heard, i.e., they attack very stealthily. For example the death adder *(Bitis gabonica rhinoceros)* may lie hidden in the leaf-litter with its tail exposed, while a modified terminal caudal scale intermittently waves from side to side. This acts as an insect-like lure to attract prey.

Most reptiles fight by biting and scratching, and some of the larger species inflict deep wounds. Crocodilians and large lizards strike sharp blows with their powerful tails, which they use as a whip. The bite of a venomous reptile can be fatal. Chameleons have long, sticky tongues that they project with remarkable accuracy and speed to zap up unsuspecting insects.

Territoriality

Many reptiles often conflict with members of their own species over control or dominance over a particular territory. Males also fight for breeding access to females. Among several types of lizards, males perform ritualized displays to declare their claim to a territory. For example, in many species of monitor lizards, males contest a territory by engaging in a grappling match that involves standing on their hind legs and trying to push one another over. Some snakes, including many rattlesnakes, also engage in shoving matches. Male tortoises sometimes butt their shells together to determine which is dominant.

An iguana displaying its bright colors asserting dominance

To illustrate classic reptile energy, i.e., the camouflage, the hidden nature and the sudden attack, we can understand the behavior of the *Cerastes cerastes* (desert snake). This snake remains hidden and well concealed underneath the sand, just protruding its eyes above the ground, waiting and watching for its prey. The moment it senses a victim around, it will just leap forward with its killing grasp and devour the unwary prey in no time!

The Cerastes cerastes hidden under the sand waiting to ambush!

Humans with reptile-energy express it on the broadest level via the general pattern of animal-energy expression:

Kingdom - Animal features

- Victim/aggressor
- Me versus you
- Conflict within self
- Survival
- Competition

Subkingdom – Reptile features

An understanding of the nature and manifestation of reptile-energy in patients is best approached by the natural history of reptiles, some concepts of which are outlined below. As an outgrowth of studying reptiles' natural history, there is the recognition of useful alert words, listed below. A patient requiring a reptile remedy may repeat or say these alert words with emphasis or emotion in the course of the interview.

Reptilian characteristics expressed as human behavior

Reptiles, being cold blooded, have to come out in the open to gain warmth. This is important for all their vital functions, yet it leaves them feeling very vulnerable. It is their unique and individual manner of adapting or coping with this function that differentiates them from the other groups of animals. This creates a conflict in them between: *being seen to come out, and being visible versus being hidden, unnoticed, and camouflaged.* In this process of coming out of their retreats, reptiles are extremely careful of their surroundings. This is unlike the cold-blooded insects, and spiders to some extent, which are very impulsive.

Reptiles are very *alert and agile,* as they thoroughly scan their surroundings. With the aid of their keen senses, a person demonstrating reptilian behavior will exhibit symptoms of being careful of their surroundings, by being *watchful, vigilant, and guarded.* It is only when they feel it is conducive for them to come into light, that will they do so. They come out of their hiding only under optimal conditions. The moment conditions become unsuitable for them, or if they sense or perceive the slightest hint of attack, they simply rush back into their retreats.

In order to go unnoticed reptiles have interestingly adopted an array of *deceptive strategies*. They could be right there in front of you, just under your nose, but you still don't see them. You don't even recognize them as they can be so beautifully veiled. One can see them only when they want to be seen.

This *hiding and deceit,* when seen in a human, is referred to as *"two faced"*. A person, who puts up a false façade in front of you, can behind the scene, be a completely different person. This other side is imperceptible to the world, which means that the "real him" will be invisible to others. They live two completely different lives. One side of them is very nice and the other side is violent and destructive. Their opponent is completely unaware and oblivious of the underlying threat or attack. Being deceitful is either observed in the patient's behavior, or it is an issue that they can be particularly sensitive to in people's behavior around them. For example a woman who may need a reptile remedy can say, 'My mother-in-law behaves so different in front of me, but when my husband arrives she completely changes!'

Reptiles have a remarkable ability to *suddenly spring into action from this position of being undercover and inconspicuous.* This sudden outburst of activity is either to: defend themselves from a possible threat when they either run, hide or escape into their retreats, or it's a sudden attack from a hidden position. They *cannot endure prolonged exertion,* unlike mammals, and need to conserve their energy. From an absolutely silent, hidden or camouflaged position, they can suddenly spring into action. In their attempt to defend themselves, reptiles are also capable of *suddenly changing their behavior.* They either change their form, color or shape. An onlooker is left completely aghast in response to the reptile's behavior!

'*Suddenness*' therefore is a crucial feature aiding reptilian survival. Sudden attack from a hidden position, which is completely unexpected, leaves one in a state of astonishment. Many times this gives no time to escape, or even to react. A common example, to illustrate this feature, is the behavior of a wall lizard. We often see them up on the wall, lying in one position, absolutely still. When you go closer, they still appear to remain static. On further approach, they simply dart off, wriggling away, into their retreats. Or they could simply amputate their tail, leaving their attacker stunned, as they simply scurry away. This example illustrates the reptilian ability to spring into a sudden burst of activity from a position of absolute inactivity.

To *escape and hide*, as an avoidance behavior, is another essential means of survival in reptiles. After a detailed study of reptilian behavior, covering the four main orders, along with materia medica, provings and cases, we came to see that reptiles have a feeling of being at a *disadvantage*. The first reaction when being attacked is to escape and hide. Escapism in human behavior can be reflected as incompetence for a face-to-face fight, which is, unlike mammals. Reptiles only attack when repeatedly provoked or cornered.

Interplay of all these expressions in patients, is indicative of a reptilian energy. With this underlying common reptilian feeling, each order will further set itself apart from another with its own individual characteristics and specific features. For example: the snake can suddenly go from a limbless creature that slithers along the ground to a springing up S-shape attack mode, hissing, hood flaring creature that could even bite you. The lizard can leave you completely stunned, by breaking off its tail, suddenly uncoiling a long retractile tongue to zap an unwary victim, or simply changing colors and becoming completely invisible. Or from an absolutely still and motionless lazy-looking position, the crocodile's powerful musculature can generate a sudden, violent lunge of massive destruction. The poky, appealing tortoise or turtle suddenly slips inside its shell in retreat, hiding within protective armor to wait for the danger to move away.[1]

Alert words that reflect the reptilian need to come out:

Appear	Come out
Be noticed	Come to light
Be seen	Emerge
Come into sight	In the open
Come into view	Visible

Few synonyms related to the reptilian need to bask:

Lie around	Absorb
Sprawl	Soak
Spread out	To flatten out
Stretch out	
Warm up	

---

1. The above reptilian understanding is based upon a thorough study of their behavior in nature, coupled with cases which follow in these two volumes and our materia medica.

Alert words that pertain to the reptilian desire for camouflage/remain hidden:

Blend	Keep cover
Blend seamlessly	Keep under wraps
Bury	Not noticeable
Coil	Mask
Conceal	Merge
Countershading	Mimic
Cover-up	Mysterious
Curl	Obscure
Disguise	Playing dead
Hide	Stealthily
Hibernate	Unnoticed
Inconspicuous	Veil

Alert words that indicate the reptilian deception:

Conspiring	Manoeuvring
Conniving	Pretence
Crafty	Secretly
Deceit	Scheming
Devious	Sham
Dishonest	Slippery
Double-crossing	Sly
Duplicitous	Snake in the grass
Fabrication	Sneak
Fallacy	Strategy
Falseness	Stealth
Fraud	Treacherous
Guile	Trickery
Hypocritical	Two-faced
Lying	Two-timing
Plotting	Underhanded
Manipulation	Untrustworthy

Alert words that reflect the reptile tendency to attack suddenly:

Suddenly, suddenness (very important in reptiles)

Sudden attack

Ambush

Completely unexpected

Out of the blue

Completely unprovoked

Sneak attack

Attack from a hidden position

More reptile alert words that pertain to their characteristic sudden attacks/ change of behavior:

Abrupt	Hunt (by stealth or trickery)
All of a sudden	Stalk (inconspicuously)
Astonishing	Bite, grab
Bewildering	Thrust, leap, lunge, spring at
Rushed	Kill
Shocking	Change form (color, shape, etc.)
Startling	
Take you by surprise	
Unanticipated	
Unforeseen	
Unpredicted	

Alert words that reflect reptiles' initial fight or flight response to being attacked:

Bury	Glide
Climb	Go inside
Go undercover	Hide
Dart off	Run away
Enclosed in shell	Shut off
(very specific for the testudines)	Slide away
Escape	Slither
Flee	Take flight

- **Violence**

  In reptiles you don't really see a physical, one on one fight, as you do between the mammals. It's a need to cause extreme harm or injury, or they feel that's happening to them.

  Alert words that reflect the violent streak in reptiles:

  Kill

  Murder

  Destruction (almost complete destruction)

  Shoot

  Stab

  Blood

  Death

- **Bright colors**

  Bright colors are used to attract the opposite sex or to warn an anticipated danger.

- **Very little or minimal parental care** (with very few exceptions)

  This reptilian characteristic can be expressed in humans as *indifference or uncaring behavior exhibited towards ones' children;* an example can be seen in the dreams of the remedy *Dendroaspis polylepis* (the black mamba snake):

  - Dreams, children, neglecting child
  - Dreams, children, caring for debilitated child (the opposite*)

    * *Sensitivity is the most important thing to be understood in a patient, and sensitivity always denotes opposites; thus the opposite of what the patient says with spontaneity or emotion is quite likely to be true as well.* In humans, we can see this as a need to be independent from a very early age.

- Images and words that describe **swallowing things as whole.**

  This relates to the reptilian ability to swallow their prey whole.

  A few alert words descriptive of the action of swallowing:

  Devour

  Engulf

  Gulp down

  Swallow up

  Gobble up

- **Jealousy between males**

  Strong rivalry is observed between males. As also seen from the rubric:
  Mind; JEALOUSY; general; men, between (4): ars., **lach.**, puls., verat.

- **Ability to starve or go fasting for long periods,** from the reptilian ability to go without food for long.

- **Sensitive to extreme heat and cold.**

- Alert words that indicate the nature and function of the characteristic reptilian **dry, scaly skin:**

Function	Characteristic
Barrier	Peeling
Protection	Shedding
Defense	Flaking
Guard	Molting
Armor	Coming off
Shell (specific for testudines)	

- A patient manifesting one of the especially aggressive, powerfully built reptile families often will persistently emphasize a need to be strong, tough, and aggressive. This is in order to "best" others. A patient whose energy is of one of the skittish reptile families, may convey the reverse; a lament of being too weak to ward off bully aggressors. However, a cautionary note: this sense of prowess, (or its converse, vulnerability due to innate weakness), can be difficult to distinguish from the broader animal kingdom theme of aggressor and victim. Words emphasized or repeated by patients whose energy derives from the aggressive, muscular reptiles (or the small, wary ones) include:

Alert words (which describe the reptilian musculature):

Sturdy

Powerful

Muscular

Strong

Robust

Tough

Dangerous

98

Opposite:

Frail

Weak

Feeble

A typical situation depicting reptilian behavior:
(Pertinent words in bold)

One of the situations typical of reptilian behavior, reflected in man, is the world's most security-conscious airport, Ben-Gurion. This is the home of EL AL Israel Airlines. Having lived for decades with bombs and suicide attacks, Israel designed the industry's most impenetrable flight security more than 20 years ago. The extremely lengthy and gruelling preflight probing is sure to make even a regular customer feel like a **suspect. Watching closely** for the slightest contradictions, the screener will dissect a passenger, thoroughly, as though a **lethal conspiracy** were afoot.

Why did you buy your ticket at the last minute? Why are you carrying wrapped boxes? Who chose them in the store? These are a few of those exhausting, inquiring questions which are asked to avert any possible **catastrophe.** They actually plan for the blackest day to such an extent, that they even change the airport's schedule so frequently, just **to foil terrorist planning.** This makes it hard for some agencies to keep up. In fact, EL AL's security kicks in long before the passenger will notice. Call an EL AL office in any city to book a ticket, and your name will be checked against a computer list of terrorist suspects compiled by INTERPOL, the FBI, Shin Bet (or ISA, Israel Security Agency). In fact, the ISA's reptilian attribute of stealth is seen in the motto on its emblem which reads: **The Defender Who Shall Not Be Seen.** And the ISA's official web site assures that, "The ISA and its employees continue, as always, to serve as **the hidden shield** of the people of Israel."

"We don't ask the same questions to everyone; there's **a surprise element** so people can't prepare their answers," said one of EL AL's spokesmen, adding that **they don't reveal** many of their security **secrets** publicly.

As if that's not enough, once you board your EL AL flight, up to five armed **undercover** agents will travel with you in **strategic** aisle seats, **ready for attack.** Furthermore, like many Israelis, cabin crews are former soldiers in the Israeli military who have received combat training. The cockpit door, of reinforced steel, is locked from the inside before passenger's board and is opened only after everyone has disembarked at his or her destination. No matter what's going on in the rest of the plane, it never opens during a flight.

Unexpectedly, for passengers with return tickets, leaving Israel is often even more rigorous than flying into the country. Passengers leaving Israel are hammered with questions by screeners: Whom have you met? Where have you been? Did you travel to Palestinian areas? Did you eat in anyone's home?

Security officers will even **watch over** cleaning crews while they service the aircraft in foreign airports.

Dreams

These are the dreams we got while we were working on the reptiles; these dreams we saw were quite unusual to us. We do believe that these dreams have significant reptile issues. We offer it to the reader as an observation rather than as an absolute fact.

A dream of Rajan Sankaran:

While contemplating human expressions of snake behavior, I dreamt that I was in a car with expensive things in it. I was parked in the street with other cars. A young woman approached me. I suspected that she was trying to steal something from the car. I knew when the woman came along that something was fishy, that she was going to do something—that something was wrong. So before she could come close to the car I got out and took her away at a few steps distance and was talking to her, closely watching her. Suddenly I turned back to where the car was, and I saw that the car was gone. It had been stolen by an accomplice, while the woman kept my attention on her, and I was expecting *her* to steal. But the real attack came from another side. And when I turned around, the woman was gone!

The main issues in this dream are:

- You are weak; the other person is strong

- The attacker is strong

- Get him in the vital spot

- Deceive

- And you escape

Dreams of Meghna Shah:

1. I am on a holiday with my mother. When we reach our destination, we realise that the place is frequently mobbed by a local gangster group. But we still decide to carry on with our trip as the place is extremely beautiful. We sit in a bus with its windows broken (possibly by these gangsters). Suddenly from nowhere this group of men attacks the bus. They all cling to the bus, in a typical Spiderman position, with their feet flexed and glued to the bus top. Somehow we manage to get out and run to a nearby construction site. We are hiding behind some half-built structure. There is a mall next to this site where all the other visitors have hidden. I suggest to my mom that we should also go and hide in that mall. But she says, "The gangsters are very likely to attack the mall, but if we go and hide in the local area (which seems to be very close), they will not come there." We will be camouflaged there. We run to that lane which is inhabited by the locales. It's a narrow lane and we are trying to find someplace to hide. Then a mango shopkeeper allows us to come into his shop and tells us to hide behind a table. But we are still scared that the gangsters could come anytime.

2. I see myself in a house with my brother's wife R and few other unknown people. Right opposite that house is a terrace where I see one of R's male friends sitting over the edge of the terrace with his legs hanging out. He is silent, but I get a strange feeling from him as if he is transmitting some negative energy to me. I am not sure what's playing in his mind, but it's definitely something evil. It's as if he's trying to take control over me. Then suddenly I feel as if the ground below my feet is shaking and then suddenly I collapse. I am so petrified and wake up feeling extremely scared. I've never felt so scared before.

3. I am walking on a green path and suddenly green-colored ghostly creatures rise up from the ground. It is as if they were lying there (camouflaged) and now they want to attack me. I am trying to run from them and hide somewhere. After some time I see some other creatures, also green in color, but they look different. They seem to be more friendly.

To summarise a typical reptilian form of attack:

-   Remain hidden, camouflaged, go unnoticed

-   To be seen, come out in the open, expose one self

-   Feeling at a disadvantage

-   Employ many devious tactics (to remain hidden)

-   Suddenly spring into action—a sudden change in behavior or ambush

-   Violence

Comparing reptile and snake features

Another case, where the qualities of a lower taxon may be confused for those of a higher, is that of snakes (suborder serpentes) and reptiles (class reptilia). The general features of a reptile can be mistaken for snake features; the deception, two-sided nature, duality, camouflage, etc. This can also happen the other way around. To avoid this confusion, we need to understand the difference between reptiles and snakes in general. A snake case will exhibit general reptile themes and the specific snake themes which are as follows:

•   The in and out tongue flicking is a characteristic observable in snake cases (and in a few lizards that comprise the exceptions, particularly the monitor lizard).

•   The characteristic serpentine motion, (seen in patient hand gestures), is the snake's peculiar movement in the absence of functional limbs.

•   A sensitivity of the throat area and the characteristic sensations linked to it such as choked, suffocated, and strangulated.

- Snakes' mode of attack is either poisoning (envenomation) or squeezing (constriction) and then swallowing the victim whole. Exceptions are the two poisonous species of lizard (the Mexican beaded lizard — *Heloderma horridum* and the Gila monster — *Heloderma suspectum*).

- The ability to survive without any limbs.

  The characteristic mode of locomotion is: to crawl, creep, slither, burrow, swim, etc.

- Shedding/molting of the skin as a whole.

- Highly flexible jaw movements. The ability to swallow large objects, almost twice their size.

- Heightened sensitivity of smell and taste.

Testudines

Tortoise, turtles and terrapins

Homoeopathic remedies

- *Chrysemys scripta elegans* or *Trachemys scripta elegans* [red-eared slider]

- *Eretmochelys imbricata* [Hawksbill turtle]

- *Geochelone sulcata* [African spurred tortoise]

- *Lepidochelys olivacea* [Olive Ridley sea turtle]

- Ovum *Chelydra serpentina* [egg of Common snapping turtle]

- *Terrapene carolina* [box turtle]

- *Testudo hermanni* [shell of Hermann's tortoise]

- *Testudo hermanni* [blood of Hermann's tortoise]

Introduction

The shelled reptile

Turtles, tortoises, and terrapins are members of the order Testudines. They are amongst the oldest of all living reptiles. **They are the only reptiles that have a shell built into the skeleton, allowing them to more or less conceal themselves entirely within the shell.**

Although the word 'turtle' is widely used to describe all members of the order Testudines, or Chelonia, it is common to see certain members described as **terrapins**, **tortoises**, or **sea turtles**. Precisely how these alternative names are used depends on the type of English being used.

- British English normally describes these reptiles as turtles if they live in the sea; terrapins if they live in fresh or brackish water; or tortoises if they are entirely land-living.

    (In the book we follow this rule.)

- American English tends to use the word turtle for all species regardless of habitat.

- Australian English uses turtle for both the marine and freshwater species but tortoise for the terrestrial species.

Turtles living on dry land are called tortoises (they go to water only to drink or bathe); those living in the marine environment are called sea turtles; terrapins are small turtles that live either in freshwater marshes (British nomenclature) or in coastal saltwater or brackish regions and rely on nearby freshwater for drinking (American nomenclature).

Turtles are essentially unchanged since their ancient Triassic ancestors. The earliest species appeared around 230 million years ago, making them one of the oldest reptile groups, much more ancient than lizards and snakes. About 313 species are alive today; though some are highly endangered. These animals have evolved so little since they first appeared that even today we see them carrying the **bony cartilaginous shield, the shell** (developed from their ribs).

Tortoises live longer than any other animal on Earth. They are known to have lived longer than 150 years. Because of this, in some cultures like China, tortoises symbolize longevity.

The oldest tortoise ever recorded, in fact the oldest individual animal *ever* recorded, was Tui Malila, who was presented to the Tongan royal family by the British explorer Captain Cook shortly after its birth in 1777. Tui Malila remained in the care of the Tongan royal family until its death by natural causes on May 19, 1965. This means that upon its death, Tui Malila was 188 years old!

Tortoises and turtles are regularly incorporated into human culture by painters, photographers, poets, songwriters, and sculptors. They have an important role in mythologies around the world and are often implicated in myths about the origin of the Earth. Tortoises are frequently depicted in popular culture as wise, easygoing, and patient creatures, with a gentle disposition (snapping turtles aside). Due to their long lifespan, slow movement, sturdiness, determination and wrinkled appearance, they are an emblem of longevity, stability, steadfastness and tranquility in many cultures around the world. As a result of its role as a slow, peaceful creature in culture, the tortoise can be misunderstood as a sedentary animal. However, many types of turtle, especially sea turtles, frequently migrate over large distances in oceans.

In Chinese mythology, the tortoise is one of the 'Four Fabulous Animals'. It represents the water element. The other animals are the unicorn, phoenix, and dragon. These animals govern the four points of the compass, with the turtle the ruler of the north, symbolizing **endurance, strength,** and **longevity**. In Aesop's fable 'The Tortoise and the Hare', a tortoise defeats an overconfident hare in a race.

Habitat

In general, tortoises and turtles have adapted to a wide range of habitats. They can be found on dry land, in the forests, in fresh water, in brackish marshes, on the seashore, and in the open sea. Diverse species of freshwater turtles occur in still waters, such as ponds, and running waters. A few species of freshwater turtles, like the true sea turtles, leave their aquatic habitats only to lay eggs. There are other species that are amphibious, which regularly move about on land.

Classification

Kingdom: Animalia
Phylum: Chordata
Subphylum: Vertebrata
Class: Reptilia
Subclass: Anapsida
Order: Testudines

Suborder:
Pleurodira [Side-necked turtles]

Family:
Chelidae [Snake-necked turtles]

Family:
Pelomedusidae [Helmeted turtles]

Suborder:
Cryptodira [Hidden-necked turtles]

Superfamily:
Chelonioidea
Family:
Dermochelyidae
[Leatherback sea turtles]
Family:
Cheloniidae [sea turtles]

Superfamily: Testudinoidea

Family: Chelydridae
[Snapping turtles and
big-headed turtles]

Family:
Emydidae [box turtles
and pond turtles]

Family:
Testudinidae [Tortoises]

Family:
Bataguridae [Old World pond
turtles]

Superfamily: Trionychoidae

Family:
Kinosternidae
[Mud and musk turtles]

Family:
Dermatemydidae
[Mesoamerican river turtles]

Family:
Carettochelyidea
[pig-nosed turtles]

Family: Trionychidae
[Holartic and Paleotropical
softshell turtles]

Difference between the two main lineages of tortoise:

Cryptodira (Hidden-necked tortoise)	Pleurodira (Side-necked tortoise)
Cryptodirans can, by a vertical cobra-like bending of the vertebral column of the neck, **draw the head directly into the shell** (although in some modern species, only partial withdrawal is possible). Includes the sea turtles and majority of species that live on land or in rivers and lakes.	Pleurodirans merely **fold the head under the front edge of the upper shell by a sideways movement, either to the right or to the left**. Found only in Australia, South America, central in southern Africa and Madagascar.

(In most parts in this chapter, we will discuss the more familiar **slow-moving, stump-footed, and inoffensive tortoises.** They remained on the land even as their relatives, which include most of the turtles, swam away. A separate section on sea turtles is given on page 125.)

Generalized anatomy

Tortoises and turtles are characterized by: a **heavily armored shell, four elephantine limbs,** and a **horny, toothless beak** in their jaw.

Origin of the shell

All reptiles are covered with scales, as were the tortoises' ancestors. As they evolved, the ribs expanded outwards, **enclosing** the hip and shoulder joints. They enlarged and fused with other bones beneath the skin. They widened and eventually joined together to form a **bony box**. The scales enlarged to form a continuous shield of horn (scutes) on the surface of this bony case. Some species like the soft-shelled and leatherback, lack scutes, and instead has soft, leathery shells. The basic **armor** was then complete.

The shell consists of two parts:

- The carapace (upper shell)
- The plastron (under shell)

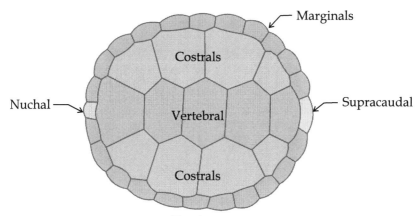

Tortoise carapace

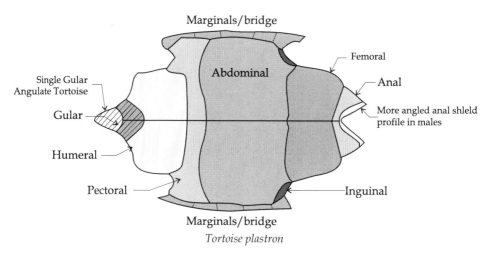

Tortoise plastron

These two parts are connected by bridges between the front and hind legs. These two protective structures consist of 20 to 30 bony plates that are fused with the ribs, the vertebrae, the hip and the shoulder girdle. This means that the tortoise **cannot crawl out of its shell**. The vertebrae are particularly interesting for the modifications that have occurred. The vertebrae of the neck and tail are small, allowing for a high degree of flexibility, while the vertebrae of the central portion of the vertebral column are enormously elongated and inflexible. They are fused with the bony layer of the shell, acting as a support for the carapace.

By developing a shell, tortoises inevitably **sacrificed speed**. So they **can't sprint off when there is danger, but with the protective shell they do not need to**.

The shell contains pigments which give each turtle its distinctive coloration. Shells are commonly colored brown, black, or olive green. In some species, shells may have red, orange, yellow, or grey markings. These markings are often spots, lines, or irregular blotches. One of the most colorful turtles is the eastern painted turtle (*Chrysemys picta picta*) which includes a yellow plastron and a black or olive shell with red markings around the rim.

The most important and primary function of the **shell** is to **enclose** the soft parts of the body, providing **protection** and camouflage. When attacked or threatened the tortoises are able to **safely withdraw or retract their head into the protection of this shell**. Both the tail and the head can be **tucked into their covering** when required. **The shell cannot be 'taken off'** (as cartoons would lead us to believe) any more than you could 'take off' your spine and ribs; hence they are **permanently attached to this protective covering.**

The shape of the shell reflects the lifestyle of the tortoise. The land-based or terrestrial tortoises have rather **heavy shells**, which make it difficult for any predator to **bite** or **crush**. In contrast are the aquatic turtles whose shells are

Terrestrial tortoise – heavy and dome-shaped shell　　*Sea turtle – light and streamlined shell*

streamlined and **light. These traits help them swim or dive faster. With more agility, slipping easily** through the water, they also **avoid sinking in the water**.

The shell can have some variation. For example the terrestrial (or land-based) species, like the Indian tortoise, have a domed shell that is difficult for predators to bite or crush. Whereas the African pancake tortoise has a flat and flexible shell which helps them to hide in rock crevices. Some species have a massive shell, much greater in size then the predator, literally outgrowing them. Some tortoises have developed reduced shell openings, thus outwitting a predator who tries to scoop out the meal within the shell.

In order to be able to enlarge, **the shell is made up of separate plates which can grow independently of each other**. As the turtle grows, new rings of bony tissue form around the edge of each plate, allowing the plates to retain their

A closer view of a tortoise shell showing the fused plates and the rings

shape and increase in size. It is also believed that the number of rings on each plate is a guide to the turtle's age.

Scutes on the shell

The shells are covered with a layer of keratin (the same type of material that makes up our fingernails and horses' hooves). The keratin is arranged in patches called scutes, or shields. The scutes, however, do not precisely overlap the bones. Instead, they are staggered, which helps give the shell more rigidity. Although the scutes form the familiar outer layer of the shell, it is the bony layer underneath which actually provides the shape, support and protective qualities of the shell.

Only three families lack these horny plates on the shell: the soft-shelled turtles, the Papuan soft-shelled turtle, and the leathery turtle. The horny plates are instead replaced by a thick, leathery covering. In the soft-shelled turtles this covering is flexible, at least at the edges.

Tortoises do not have teeth. They have **horny beaks** and **sharp jaws** which help them **grasp, bite, cut, and chew** their food. Carnivorous turtles usually have knife-sharp ridges for **slicing** or **sawing** through their prey. Herbivorous turtles have serrated-edged ridges that help them **cut through** tough plants. Turtles use their tongues to swallow food, but **unlike most reptiles**, they **can't stick out their tongues to catch food**.

Since their ribs are fused to the shell, they cannot move their ribs to draw in and out the air from their lungs. Instead, they use muscles at the openings of the limb pockets, near the tops of their legs, to provide the necessary pumping action.

Tortoise foot

The shape of the limbs differs between terrestrial and aquatic species. In most terrestrial species the fingers and toes have more or less grown together to form solid, club-shaped or elephantine-shaped, sturdy feet. While in aquatic species the individual digits are distinct and clearly recognizable. Some species have webbing between the digits, or else the limbs are flippers.

Tortoises are known for their **slow, lumbering movement** because of their **heavy shell.** The upper portion of the tortoise's legs forms an arc. This results in their curving out from the body rather

115

than extending straight under as in mammals. Their claws are generally quite long, which helps them **dig** and **crawl** onto rocks or wood when they want to bask. Males tend to have especially long front claws that they use to **grab** onto the female while mating. These long claws also appear to be involved in courtship.

Sex determination

In some species, males have a longer, more protruding neck plate than their female counterparts. In other species the claws are longer on the females. In most tortoise species the female tends to be larger than the male. (Some believe that males grow quicker, while the female grows slower but larger.) The male also has a plastron that is curved inwards to aid reproduction. The easiest way to determine the sex of a tortoise is to look at the tail. The females, as a general rule, have a smaller tail which is drooped down. The males have a much longer tail which is usually pulled up and to the side of the rear shell.

Characteristic feature of testudines

Shell, the protective armor enclosing the body parts.

Ability to withdraw or retract inside the bony shell (except the sea turtles which, with their nonretractile neck and limbs, either cannot or can only partially withdraw inside the shell).

Food habits

Tortoises and turtles are selective in their choice of foods. They can be **herbivorous, carnivorous, or omnivorous**, depending on locality and availability of food items. **Tortoises are usually herbivorous**, grazing or browsing on leaves and fruits which they **eat with full energy**, almost **continuously**, with a **singleness of purpose.** The tortoises are also quick to take advantage of fallen fruits and even animal carcasses. Many species also eat animals such as caterpillars that appear incidentally in their food. Most will even eat carrion, given the chance.

The sea and freshwater turtles are usually omnivorous. Freshwater turtles often start life as insectivores, finding enough small aquatic larvae and other small prey to survive. Their diet includes seemingly inedible things such as cacti, deadly poisonous jellyfish (leatherback turtles), fish of many types, and so on. Turtles of several families specialize in eating mollusks, and have broadly expanded jaws for crushing their prey.

The results of the common mistake of feeding a tortoise commercial cat or dog food, often made by amateur pet tortoise owners, illustrates the nutritional needs of these reptiles. Feeding a tortoise cat or dog food for its diet will eventually kill the animal, through metabolic bone disease, caused by the food's high levels of protein and low levels of calcium and other minerals. The high protein content of cat or dog food causes the tortoise to grow too rapidly, resulting in deformity of the shell. **Tortoises require very little protein; hence, meat should not be fed**. Whereas **calcium is extremely important** in a tortoise's diet, to give them the right minerals to enhance shell growth and repair.

One of the tortoise's important roles in the ecosystem is to spread the seeds of many plants in its droppings.

Mating characteristics

Though they appear to be cold and passive, tortoises and turtles are quite passionate. They can become extremely **gregarious.** In most, but not all, social interactions are mainly involved with some aspect of courtship. **When it comes to sex, tortoises are truly driven creatures.** It has been observed in groups of red-footed tortoise in captivity that no male could walk by a female without climbing aboard and taking care of its genetic posterity. Courting and mating rituals of tortoises usually involve a considerable amount of time since their body is **encased in the heavy, cumbersome shell.** Making love in a suit of armor is definitely not an easy task! But the males have a clever solution. The underside of the male is concave and thus fits on the female's dome, which is smaller than the male's. This does not make **clambering** on top of the female an easy job for the male, but once on top, it remains without **slipping off.** The two shells fit together as neatly as two spoons. The male will then cajole and sometimes even **bite and push** the female before the pair copulate. Once started, it goes on for a long time. Turtles in that sense are quite **resilient**, and are known to **reproduce in spite of any external injury or handicap (like loss of a limb), etc.**

Characteristics of courtship (also explains their mode of attack):

- **Male fixation behavior** or **zeroing in behavior,** whereas males extend the head and neck forward and point it directly at the female.

- **Ramming and butting of shells** between potential males fighting to mate. They can also bite each other's legs in tests of strength to establish superiority. Sometimes one tortoise is able to **flip another on its back**. It

117

then gets **stuck** and finds it **difficult to right itself onto its feet**. Then they either die or are beaten up. A male will also do the same things (butting the female's shell repeatedly) to a female. This is his attempt to convince her to mate with him, until she responds by becoming quiescent, enabling him to **mount**. He will also **bob his head** at her and **chase** her. **Sniffing** and **butting** of the shells are two common preludes to copulation among most tortoises. **The sense of smell** seems important in establishing age, sex, and readiness to mate.

-   **Trailing** is frequently employed during courtship where the male follows the female. Often the male will initially move rapidly to close the distance between the two. Trailing continues with the male at a close distance behind the female.

-   **Biting** is sometimes attempted by a male when the female will not stop during trailing or initially stopped and then moved during mounting attempts. Some males often employ biting as part of the courtship ritual.

-   **Attempting to mount**

-   **Vocalization** where the most commonest rhythmic **grunts** or **bellows** associated with **abrupt exhalation** during pelvic thrusting by mating male tortoises. When giant tortoises mate, far from feeling they have to hide or be cautious, the **triumphant roar** of the mounted male is audible from a great distance. It is one of the memorable expressions of reptilian passion, and one of the oldest voices in the world. At this point, they are no longer "blocks . . . stones . . . worse than senseless things (*from William Shakespeare's "Julius Caesar" (I. i. 34)*", but rather animated beings, as well as social and complex. Similarly, in females, there is also courtship vocalization.

All tortoises and turtles lay their eggs on land. The sea turtles present a special case. Though clumsy and vulnerable on land, **they must come ashore to lay their eggs**. Tortoises do not care for their young, with few exceptions like the Burmese brown tortoise and the yellow mud turtles (*Kinosternon flavescens*); these stay at their nests for a few days after laying to protect the eggs from predators.

Aberrant sexual behavior

Instances of **female to female courtship** have also been observed in some species. Typically, the entire male/female courtship routine, (excluding penetration), or major portions are played out. This includes vocalization and mounting.

Behavior

Many tortoises become **inactive in the summer** when the weather is very dry and hot. **Tortoises cannot bear extreme heat.** The tortoise, like other reptiles, lacks sweat glands to diffuse the external heat. Hence, they **seek shade, hide in burrows,** or **soak** in water, (in the case of turtles), and spend the hottest part of the day there. On cooler days they will seek out a warm spot to sunbathe or bask. In this respect turtles are able to maintain their body temperature more effectively than tortoises, as their amphibious behaviour serves as a medium for thermoregulation.

Typically for a tortoise, their low-slung body gives them a singularly low viewpoint on the world. Since they are just a few inches above the ground, a taller animal would literally overlook them. Their viewpoint may be further compromised by viewing their world through a narrow tunnel. Somehow, a more or less correct integration of all factors occurs within that little head, which aids their survival.

Hibernation

Hibernation for a tortoise is a period of inactivity, generally spent below ground in a burrow or den during extreme winters. Similarly they aestivate in summer. They do this by building or finding specialized **retreats**. The heart rate, respiratory rate, body temperature and all the other functions are much slowed down while in the burrows during hibernation. Some species only emerge from their burrow for a very short while, to feed either in the early morning or late afternoon or to mate or lay eggs. **They emerge very cautiously, and at the slightest sign of danger, they race back towards and down their burrow with astonishing speed.**

To find these species that spend most of their lives hibernating in the burrow is a great challenge. They can only be trapped at the mouth of their burrows when they emerge for their daily activities. Summer thundershowers trigger a brief flurry of above-ground activity. This is the time when the tortoises emerge from burrows to drink and travel.

Hibernation is important for a tortoise's survival because it assists the following functions:

(a) Thermoregulation

(b) Protection from predators

Burrowing, digging

The tortoise is aptly called 'the master of the underworld', as it digs burrows which vary considerably in length (upto 30 feet) and type. The style of burrow is dependent upon the region, soil type, and vegetation in which they are found. The tortoises have also developed many adaptations for digging. Studies have shown that when a telescope is passed through these burrows it has to pass through many twists and turns in order to reach the rear end of the burrow.

Some species become miniaturized and flattened, living under rocks or in rocky crevices from which they emerge only when it thunders. The open sandy area in front of the burrow, called the apron, is often used by the female tortoises for a nest site.

Each tortoise will dig several burrows within its home range or territory. Some borrows are visited by several different tortoises at different times. Sometimes more than one tortoise can stay in one burrow.

Burrows provide protection or shelter from: predators, fire, and weather changes like extremes of heat, cold, lack of moisture, and excess moisture. The tunnels are an invaluable refuge. Other animals, called commensals, often take advantage of the tortoise's burrow but neither help nor harm the tortoise. There are about 100 species reported to take shelter in a tortoise burrow. Tortoises are often called "wildlife landlords" because their burrows are essential; they protect them as well as the lives and well-being of many other species.

Home range

Each tortoise has a home range, or activity area. A home range is the area in which a tortoise travels, feeds, sleeps, courts, and has its burrows. This is the area with which the tortoise is familiar. Large tortoises have large home ranges and small tortoises have small home ranges. Females are more sedentary than males and do not move about as much, so they probably have smaller home ranges. Tortoises appear to have a good sense of compass direction. They also are very familiar with local landmarks. They can travel in a straight line to find burrows. They also know locations of other tortoises (e.g., males know the location of females), drinking sites, mineral licks, and particular food sources.

Skin and molting

Turtles and tortoises do not molt their skins in one event, as snakes do, but they do it continuously in small pieces. A lot of dead skin is also accumulated as thick knobs and plates which provide further protection outside the shell.

Auditory communication

This behavior is observed in tortoises, in addition to the mating process, (as described above). They also **chirp**, have a nighttime **calling chorus** (in some species), and **moan low** during egg laying.

Methods of attack and defense

It's interesting to study the survival strategy of a tortoise, **with its compromised locomotion, poor attacking ability, massive body, and awkward stance of the limbs. All this makes it easy for a predator to capture it, without even giving a chase.** The life of a tortoise is quite dominated by the paucity of available responses when danger does threaten.

Method of defense

Withdraw or enclose inside the shell

The most important component of the tortoise survival strategy and a major means of protection, is **pulling its head completely inside the shell and covering the openings with the limbs.** This kind of survival strategy leaves very few predators that can actually harm them, other than humans.

Geochelone pardalis with head withdrawn into the shell

The legendary **tough** shell of the tortoise acts like a **suit of invulnerability**. Due to which tortoise's have also been known to **survive fires by withdrawing into its shell, secure in its portable fortress**.

The **armored** shells of tortoises may seem impregnable, but tortoises have their predators. Even the **heavily armored** terrestrial tortoises occasionally fall prey to cunning predators who find their weaknesses, like the enterprising lions that are known to **crack open** tortoises and the killer whales that can crack open the turtles and **mince** them like meat. There are egg predators, such as the Gila monster, kit fox, coyote, and badger. Predators of juveniles include ravens, roadrunners, some snakes, kit foxes, bobcats, badgers, coyotes, and probably the spotted skunk. Coyotes and kit foxes may **dig tortoises out of their burrows and eat them up**. These predators can eat the tortoise without breaking open the shell. They are capable of **swallowing** the tortoise **whole, or even smashing them against rocks and then eating them**. The large and powerful bearded vulture has the ability to overcome the tortoise's **defensive shield**. To **extract** the marrow from the shell, the bird picks it up in its talons. It then **flies to a great height, and drops it, often on a stone** that it regularly uses as an anvil. Any bone may need dropping several times before it finally **splits** and **yields its contents**. The birds use the same method for **cracking open** tortoise shells.

When the tortoise is enclosed in the shell, it becomes difficult to make out if the attacker has left or not. So to **safely emerge**, a tortoise will stick its head out to check its surroundings before coming out fully.

Hibernation and burrowing

(Explained earlier.)

Cryptic behavior

The characteristic pattern of their shell makes them very cryptic. Possessing a coloration and/or pattern serves to conceal them.

Tortoises have the distinct disadvantage of being non-swimmers. They cannot, therefore, take advantage of other thermoregulation or "flight from predator" facilitation that going into the water affords (like seen in the aquatic turtles).

Man is the key question for tortoise survival today. Tortoises are generally hunted for their flesh and shell. In tropical South America, a tortoise seen is a tortoise doomed. Sadly, it will be taken to a village or market, probably **trussed** up, so it cannot extend its head and limbs, and ultimately **chopped open alive.** Tortoises are mainly **slaughtered** for their meat. Habitat destruction is another threat to their survival. They cannot live if they do not have undeveloped land with plenty of food and room to dig their burrows.

Environmental threats

Many tortoises die in forest **fires**.

Method of attack

Tortoises are **too slow moving to pursue active prey**. They are capable only of **butting** or **ramming** rival males with their shells.

Although aquatic turtles that live in murky, clouded water, **hunt by ambush, remaining motionless** in the hope that a fish or crustacean will accidently come along. Some of the aquatic turtles, like the snapping turtles, living in shallow lakes, rivers and swamps, will **prey on almost anything that comes within range of their sharp jaws and cavernous mouths** (if small enough to be swallowed).

An interesting piece of news extracted from the internet gives a glimpse of a tortoise's life:
(Important words are highlighted.)

A man who police believe tortured an endangered tortoise by trying to **cut him out of his shell** and **throwing him against a wall** was arrested.

The tortoise was **slashed** and **stabbed** after being stolen from the home of an autistic boy. After he was **brutalized**, the tortoise was **dumped** in the bush behind an apartment complex and an anonymous caller told the family where to find him.

The tortoise was later reported to recover at a rehabilitation center. He remained in guarded condition and was being fed through a tube in his neck.

"He's getting more relaxed and coming out of his shell more often", said the center's owner. Following that, he gave the owners some hope when he reached a key milestone in his recovery: **bringing his head out of his shell and taking his first steps**. The tortoise collapsed but then managed to take eight steps.

"When he finished, he had a tear in his eye ... as did the rest of us", the owner said. "It was an excellent, great sign."

The owner also said that she and her son danced with happiness when they heard of the arrest. Her son has not been sleeping well since the attack, she said.

"His **security fell apart**", she said. "He was afraid that somebody was going to come and steal him and take him away and hurt him."

"Now he feels **safe**. Now he can go out and play", she said.

Sea/marine turtles

Introduction

(Here the reader should keep in mind that the sea/marine turtles have a different lifestyle and behavior as compared to the semiaquatic turtles and the land tortoises.)

Sea turtles have lived for a remarkably long time! Compare their period on earth (150 million years) with that of humankind (5 million years)! Sea turtles have also **survived through tough odds**. They managed to survive the event that caused the dinosaurs to become extinct 65 million years ago. They even survived the intense cold of the ice ages that gripped the planet for much of the past 3 million years.

With the exception of females that come ashore to nest, sea turtles spend their entire lives at sea and are well adapted to an aquatic existence

So far two families of sea turtles are known:

1. Family Cheloniidae includes all sea turtles with scutes (horny plates) covering their shells.

2. Family Dermochelyidae are scuteless turtles with only one modern specie, the leatherback turtle. A leatherback turtle is covered with leathery skin (instead of the hard shell). It is the only marine turtle whose backbone is not attached to the inside of its shell.

Sea turtle mating

Generalized anatomy

Adult male and female sea turtles are almost equal in size.

Depending on the species, sea turtles range in color from olive green, yellow, greenish-brown, reddish-brown, or black.

Sea turtles exhibit the most **extreme foot adaptations to water** of all the turtles that moved to the sea. They are so at home in the sea that they even mate while **swimming**. They primarily depend on the sea for their survival. They only **travel to the land to lay their eggs**. In fact, they are part of the only group whose members have to **drag their bodies across the ground**.

The digits have fused to form **paddle-shaped** limbs or **flippers**, with which they **propel** themselves through water. (Compare this feature to the terrestrial tortoises, who have strong legs with claws for scrambling on the ground.) **The forelimbs in turtles are more strongly developed than the hind limbs.** Occasionally one or two claws are present on each front flipper. With the **powerful wing-like strokes** of their long, front flippers, they **glide swiftly in water.** This makes them very efficient **swimmers.** Sea turtles can **swim long distances over a short time.**

The sea turtle's shell helps it swim fast, too. Its shell is large, more streamlined, less box like and flatter than most other turtle shells. The bony shell is less substantial. It's the perfect shape and **light** weight helps them **cut through the water with the least amount of effort** (compared to the heavy, dome-shaped shell of the terrestrial tortoise). Most sea turtles have **hard shells** that are like suits of armor (except the leatherback sea turtle which has a soft shell). A hard shell is made up of several plates. These plates fit together like pieces in a jigsaw puzzle. They make the shell **firm and tough.** Even a shark's **razor-sharp** teeth can't bite through it. On most turtles, hard scales cover the parts of the body that are not protected by the shell.

Another difference in sea turtles is that they have salt glands in their eye orbits. This allows them to live in a saltwater marine environment.

They have large upper eyelids to protect their eyes.

Like other turtles, sea turtles **lack teeth**. Jaw shape varies among species. Each specie has a jaw shape adapted for its diet.

Reproduction

All female sea turtles travel to the land to lay eggs. Females of most species usually come ashore at night, alone, most often during high tide. While emerging on the beach, turtles have to be **cautious**. They need to go **unseen and unnoticed** by predators. Turtles go in an **'egg laying trance'** which can be sometimes exploited by predators.

A female sea turtle **crawls** above the high tide line, and using her front flippers, **digs** out a "body pit". Then, using her hind flippers, she digs an egg cavity. Sea turtle eggs are soft-shelled and papery to leathery in texture. A female may deposit as many as 50 to 200 (depending upon species) "ping-pong-ball" shaped eggs into the egg cavity that she digs in the sand. Amazingly, they do not break when they fall into the egg cavity, as the eggs are surrounded by thick, clear mucus. The female covers the nest with sand using her hind flippers.

Burying the eggs serves three purposes:

1. It helps protect the eggs from surface predators.

2. It helps keep the soft, porous shells moist, thus protecting them from drying out.

3. It helps the eggs maintain proper temperature.

Female green sea turtles (Chelonia mydas) dragging on the beach

Females may spend two or more hours out of the water during the entire nesting process.

Most females return to the same beach where they hatched to nest each year. Recent studies suggest that some females of some species will visit more than one nesting beach (other than the original beach) in a season.

Turtles go through a lot of **exhausting efforts to lay their eggs**. Hence, during the time before and after, they are more likely to be attacked.

Hatchlings use a 'carbuncle' (temporary egg tooth) to help **break open the shell**. After hatching, the young turtles may take three to seven days to dig their way to the surface. They usually wait for the night to head towards the sea, as it reduces risk of predation. They travel in groups, something that is important to their survival, because they have no parental care to provide assistance.

There are several theories as to how hatchlings find the sea.

1. Hatchlings may distinguish light intensities and head for the greater light intensity of the open horizon.
2. During the **crawl to the sea**, the hatchling may set an internal magnetic compass, which it uses for navigation away from the beach.

When a hatchling reaches the surf, it **dives** into a wave and rides the undertow out to sea. A **"swim frenzy"** of continuous swimming takes place for about 24 to 48 hours after the hatchling enters the water. This **frantic activity** gets the young turtle into deeper water, where it is less vulnerable to predators. There have been reports of swimming hatchlings **diving** straight down when birds and even airplanes appear overhead. This diving behavior may be a behavioral adaptation for avoiding **predation by birds**.

Common behavior of the sea/marine turtles

Freshwater turtles are able to withdraw their heads inside their shell. But the sea turtles, because of the presence of flippers instead of the sharp claws, cannot withdraw their head and legs inside their shell, (they are nonretractile).

Some of them, like the loggerhead, don't even need to, because their large size, hard shell, and rough and scaly skin on their neck protect them from predators. These defenses are usually sufficient for adults and larger juveniles, but these turtles are sometimes preyed on by sharks and killed by humans.

Since they are cold-blooded, sea turtles have a slow metabolic rate. This slowed metabolism allows them to stay **submerged for long periods of time**. They can **hold their breath for extended periods of time and dive to incredible depths**. However, as they evolved from land-based ancestors, **they do need to breathe air**. They can wait for long periods underwater, but from time to time they need to make a **dash to the surface and take a deep breath right away.** They have to physically open their lungs to breathe. Turtles don't drown as they are conscious breathers. But they will die if they cannot get to the surface or if they run out of air. A possible cause of running out of air is getting **trapped** while hiding from a predator. The sea turtle that finds itself in such a predicament must choose between being attacked by the predator, or dying hidden under a crevice while holding its breath. **Out of the water, turtles are almost deaf and can hardly see.**

On land the sea turtles move very slowly when they come to lay eggs. They are quite awkward and vulnerable on land, but they are fast swimmers, compared to the terrestrial tortoises or other turtles. They are even much faster than the fastest Olympic swimmer. Sea turtles are able to **move with extreme quickness in water**. In their environment, they are capable of **tremendous bursts of speed** that human swimmers envy. Green sea turtles (*Chelonia mydas*) are said to swim at a rate of 30 feet a second!

They are excellent **divers** too. They can simply **glide** through the water as gracefully as birds fly through the air, using their flippers as if they were wings.

Through swimming sea turtles reduce some of the problems that a heavy, cumbersome shell brings to a land-dwelling tortoise. Weight is much less of a handicap to an animal that spends its life supported by water. Even getting rid of parasites is much easier for turtles because the sea is full of fish, eager and willing to make a meal of the worms, lice, algae, and other organisms that attach themselves to a turtle's shell. So there are **cleaning stations** on coral reefs where turtle make regular calls to be tended by fish that station themselves there to provide a cleaning service. **The turtles rest in a peculiar position with their flippers bent and dropped down which means 'please clean me'.**

Sea turtle's senses are very sharp. **This reptile's sense of smell is its strongest sense.** Some scientists believe that a sea turtle has a stronger sense of smell than a dog has. A sea turtle uses its keen nose to find prey even in murky water and to smell a nearby enemy. A sea turtle opens its mouth slightly and draws in water through the nose. It then immediately empties the water out again through the mouth. A sea turtle can also hear well. Sea turtles don't have ears but they have eardrums that are covered by skin. With these eardrums, sea turtles can hear low-pitched sounds about as well as humans. The eardrums also help sea turtles **detect vibrations** along the ground or in the water.

Sea turtles have good eyesight. They can see clearly when they are swimming through the water. Their eyes help them **spot small prey in the open seas.** Though they have keen eyesight in water, they are short-sighted in air.

A sea turtle is **sensitive to touch** on the soft parts of its flippers and on its shell.

Sea turtles are not generally considered social animals; however, some species do congregate offshore. Some sea turtles gather together to mate or travel together to nesting grounds. Usually the hatchlings, after reaching water, remain solitary until they mate.

Hibernation

The turtles that are found in freshwater lakes are known to bury themselves in the mud and hibernate. Sea turtles don't hibernate, except for one group found near Baja Mexico, that is thought to bury themselves in the mud at the opening of the Gulf of California. **Sea turtles don't hibernate** because they just go to warmer water, and stay in the tropics during the winter. Generally they go in to a semi-hibernation state, usually at the bottom of the pool, where they may remain for long periods according to the external climate.

Migration

Sea turtles are not only powerful swimmers, they are also able to **migrate long distances**. They can migrate 2,000 kilometres (1,240 miles) to reach their nesting sites. They are able to determine which direction to travel irrespective of ocean currents. No matter how far they have wandered during their juvenile years, the **adults migrate back to the beaches where they were hatched**. How this is done is still not understood clearly. They probably use a combination of the earth's magnetic field, the directions of ocean currents, water chemistry and memory. Migration habits differ not only among species but also among different populations of the same species. The greatest distances are travelled by the leatherback turtle, which ranges from tropical seas to almost Arctic waters in pursuit of jellyfish, its preferred food.

Method of attack and defense

Method of attack

Carnivorous turtles are able to move their heads quickly to **snap** and to **ambush** prey.

Method of defense

The sea turtles especially have to deal with killer whales, sharks, and similar threats, while aquatic turtles have to face large fish, predatory birds, and some mammals. **Crocodiles are the turtle's oldest predators.**

Spear-like wounds have often been observed on dead bodies of turtles. Fishing nets are the biggest cause of sea turtle deaths. This is evident from the **rips** and **cuts** on the skin of turtles that died in the nets as they **struggled to reach the surface to breathe**. Powerful killer whales leave greater injuries on the turtles like **teeth marks, holes,** etc.

Many times, due to severe injuries, a turtle can also **bleed profusely**. If not attended to, they can die following a state of **shock**.

The turtle's hold on life is so deep and abiding that it is even possible to rip turtles from their shells and remove their intestines while they are still alive! Therefore, it is not surprising that they are symbols of longevity and wisdom in many cultures. Even decapitation fails to produce rapid death in a turtle. This is testimony to the animal's **exceptional ability to withstand extreme anoxia and assault, as compared to other animals where it would prove lethal immediately**. The turtle's **tight grip on life** can be seen in the extremity of the recommended veterinary procedure to cause rapid and painless death: an overdose of lethal drugs followed by "**pithing**", **or destruction of the brain.** In Tesco stores in China the turtles are in essence **chopped up alive** using a large machette-like tool. **Turtles remain conscious and aware throughout this procedure.**

Swimming, diving

They are **ever alert to danger**, and at the slightest sign of trouble, they **slip into the water and remain submerged** for many minutes.

For defense, the turtle also relies on its **tremendously strong jaws.**

Animal kingdom

At Sensation level A, one can see that the main issues are:

- Survival – the need or instinct to survive
- A process and a life story
- Struggle with self or situation, a conflict
- Me vs. you, competition
- Hierarchy
- Comparison
- Sexuality

Subkingdom – Reptile

At the Sensation level B, one will commonly observe the following reptile features:

- Feeling defenseless, at a disadvantage, weak
- Wanting to hide and escape
- Thermal sensitivity
- Lack of parental care
- Camouflage
- Hibernation

Manifestations of testudines expressions in human

These features are specifically indicative of a tortoise. (Specific expressions of the semiaquatic and sea turtles are covered later.)

Body parts and its functions:

- **The Shell**

  The most characteristic feature of tortoises is a feeling of extreme defencelessness. Hence their primary mode of defense and survival is withdrawal to safety inside their shell, to pull back into their protective shield. The need to have the shell, their protective shield around them, is very vital; **the shell provides them safety and protection, as well as camouflage from all external threats**. At the same time, being shelled and encased within this armor restricts their view of life, movement, speed, and ability to progress in life.

Expressions of the shell and its function

Protection from outside threats/danger and camouflage — the main function of the shell is to protect from the outside threat. The main feeling in seeking this protection is a need to disappear, to remain hidden and to camouflage. This is the main point of difference between the shelled mollusc and testudines.

Comparing Testudines and Mollusc

Referring to the case of *Testudo hermanni* from Susanne Sieben, there are certain expressions of the patient like:

- *I switch off and am busy with my inner being. So that I am not there anymore.*

- *This shell that I don't tell anybody what is going on. That is the protection, that I don't let anyone in... I am naked and he can see everything of me. Like a shell... I am internally naked and he can see everything of me.*

- *I am totally absent – I did not get anything.*

- *At this moment you live somewhere in your fantasy.*

- *At this moment you are not there in reality.*

- *I can come out and show myself like the turtle, and stick my head out, and the legs and I can walk around and don't have to go.*

- *Zack... I am in.*

- *I am really not there anymore as I was before.*

From this we understood: that in testudines, the shell and their ability to withdraw into the shell, is primarily to disappear, to remain hidden and to camouflage (an important reptile theme). To hibernate is another important testudines feature. Deceptiveness of the tortoises is also a part of the other reptilian features, for example: high sexuality, violence, attacking, biting, snapping, and tearing. In the mollusc the idea of withdrawing into the shell, is a specific defensive action, to protect their *soft and delicate* parts. The shell is seen as a barrier, as a wall, or as a protective sheath, that protects their delicate and vulnerable inner parts. In molluscs the main feeling is not hiding, but a feeling of softness and vulnerability. Since they are soft and tender, they need a hard shell outside.

Testudines	Mollusc
Shell: provides camouflage, helps them to remain hidden, not to be seen, to withdraw and disappear	Shell is the hard barrier that protects the soft and vulnerable inside
The opposite: is to be visible, naked, be seen, to show, reveal	To close, to wall off, to put on a sheath, put on an armor
Protection against a sharp, unexpected attack	
Hibernation	
In tortoises: it is coming out and withdrawing	In bivalve: the movement is opening and shutting

Here are listed various synonyms of the source words and expressions of the testudines experience with the shell.

Synonyms of the shell (also common to the Mollusc):

Armor	Guard
Barrier	Make things rebuff, bounce off
Casing	My house, my home
Cocoon	Portable fortress
Confine	Protect
Cosset	Safety
Cover, covering	Security
Defensive shield	Shelter
Encase	Shield
Envelope	Suit of invulnerability
Fortify	To insulate
	Tough
	Wall

Qualities of the shell, can be seen as possible source words in testudines case

–   Dome shaped, arched, vaulted

–   Heavy, bony box

–   Spikes, knobs, plates

Threat to the shell

Possible synonyms (also common to the Mollusc):

Shots	Crunch into	Knock against	Smash into
Assaulted	Crush	Mince	Spear-like injuries
Attacked	Cut or cut up	Mutilated	Split
Battered	Dig	Rupture	Stab
Beaten	Fall apart	Scoop out	Thrashed
Bore inwards	Fall on a stone	Security falls apart	Thrust
Break or break open	Fracture	Sharp	Tortured
Chop open alive	Hit	Shatter	Trussed up
Chop up	Holes	Slam into	Yields open
Crack or crack open	Invaded	Slash	
		Slice	

These sensations can also be expressed with a hand gesture showing an action of being hit, struck, or stabbed.

At a more human level, the testudines sense of threat and fear is expressed as:

- To shy away, introvert, timid, bashful, reserved, withdrawn.
- To cringe, or move backward defensively, in fear.
- The world outside is too harsh, scary, cruel, dangerous.
- Fear of being exposed, coming out, emerging, putting oneself forward.
- Thrown from height (birds pick up tortoises and throw them from high places on solid rocks to break open their shell).
- Themes of fire, being burnt (habitat fires present one of the major threats to desert tortoise's survival).
- Patients who need a remedy from the Testudines order can exhibit fears that come from being slow and vulnerable outside the shell. This is compounded with the feeling of being tremulously withdrawn inside the shell, with words such as *trembling, shaking, coldness*, etc.
- A "testudines" patient is usually initially hesitant to enter a new or stressful situation, but once they become comfortable they are fine.

Defensive action—to withdraw inside the shell

This action, of withdrawing in the shell, is absent in the sea turtles. They will possibly exhibit the other features related to the shell. They are able to counterattack (unlike the defenceless tortoises), and they snap at predators.

More words used by the human "testudines" patient that suggest or name parts of the turtle experience:

Box in	Safe inside
Close off	Shut it off
Close up	Shy away
Draw back	Slip in
Go inside	To repel outside negativity
Move back	Tuck in
Pull back	Tucked into
Pull inside	Withdraw or enclose in their shell
Retreat or retract into their shell/covering	

This feeling, of retreating or retracting, can be expressed with hand gestures. Either both hands closing up to depict the closing of the shell, or showing the withdrawing action to depict the pulling in of the head inside the shell.

Compromised and restricted movement due to the shell

This protective shield restricts the testudines's movement and compromises their speed (except the fast-moving sea turtles). They cannot sprint off, jump, or run like the other reptiles.

Possible synonyms:

Blocked	Limited
Clenched inside	Recoil
Constrained	Restrained
Constrict	Restricted
Contract	Shrink
Cower	Slowed down
Cramped	Stuck
Cringe	Unable to move
Curbed	Unable to move forward and progress
Grounded, unable to get off ground	Wrapped up inside

To emerge out of the shell (opposite of restricted mobility)

Patients whose illness has a testudines energy pattern can also demonstrate the opposite of this feeling of being inside the shell, i.e., the desire to go out, emerge, expose oneself, move ahead and make progress. This is also what they fantasize or see in other people.

Possible synonyms:

Break through	Move on
Burst through	Movement
Come out	Open up
Emerge from	Progress
Free	Propel
Get through	Reveal
Go ahead	To be exposed
Go forwards	To be out there
Move ahead	Uncoil
Move forwards	Unravel

Defenceless

Tortoises simply back off, by retreating inside their shell, and never attack (except the aggressive sea turtles).

Few synonyms:

Exposed

Helpless

Insecure

Open to attack

Powerless

Unarmed

Undefended

Unguarded

Unprotected

Unshielded

Vulnerable

Weak

Still, like a stone/play dead or sit and wait

Once they retreat into their shell, they are still, motionless, like a stone.

They become hard, stonelike, like a dead thing, after they retract inside their protective shell. This feature was noted in Staria Manos's case of Ovum *Chelydra serpentina* (Common snapping turtle). They will remain withdrawn and hidden, waiting for the danger to pass (to sit and wait).

Carry their home along

The shell is indeed a protective armor, but it also requires the testudines to carry this heavy dome — this weight — along with them all the time. Like carrying one's home on their back. They cannot crawl out of their shell or take it off. They are permanently attached to the shell.

Few synonyms:

A heavy burden

A weight pressing on me

Dragging this weight around

Like a backpack

Like a rock

Feeling heavy — like a weight or burden as seen in the proving of Ovum *Chelydra serpentina*. This possibly reflects the burden of the shell they carry on their back).

Mating characteristics:

The following features, or source words, can be expressed by patients in different situations in their lives. They need not be present all together or as one process.

– Very high sexuality, extremely driven, passionate, gregarious, homosexuality (especially in women)

– Butt, ram, smash into, slam into, collide, knock against, push

– Flip, turn over onto the back, toss over, difficult to right itself onto its feet, be knocked off balance

   (When a tortoise flips for any reason it becomes extremely difficult to come onto its feet. It is more or less the end of it. So the biggest challenge for them is to be able to be on their feet and not get tossed over.)

– Clamber, climb, mount, go up, stack

– Clamber without slipping off or falling, latch on, cling on, hang on

- Bite, grasp, cut
- Making sounds- grunt, bellow, abrupt exhalation
- Resilient

Resilient –They are firm and persistent. To 'pursue till death' was expressed by Staria Manos's patient who received the remedy *Testudo hermanni* (Hermann's tortoise).

More words:

Determined

Firm

Obstinate

Persistent

Resistant

Steadfast

Strong

Stubborn

Tough

The experience of testudines, with the shell and the characteristic expressions of their mating behavior, calls to mind a situation like being *brutally raped*. This particular situation would well explain these typical testudines' descriptions of behavior:

- High sexuality
- Feeling defenseless, weak, vulnerable
- No protection
- Butt, ram, knock, hit, push, bite
- Brutal attack

Possible human expressions related to the testudines behaviour:
- Hibernation (except in sea turtles)
- Locomotion
    - Awkward, lumbering, slumbering, clumsy, gawky
    - Slow, idle, lazy, indolent
    - Hide, burrow, dig, retreat (land-based and semiaquatic turtles)
    - Sink, soak, submerge (in semiaquatic and freshwater turtles)

- Vocal expressions: grunts, bellows, abrupt exhalations, chirping, or low moaning
- Thermal sensitivity: sensitivity to or aggravation from extreme heat
- Good sense of direction, familiarity with local landmarks
- High calcium requirement (only observed in testudines behavior)
- Aggravation from meat (again, only observed in testudines behavior)
- Home range; to come back to one's home, homesickness (this feature is particularly enhanced in some species)

Specific indications of semiaquatic or freshwater turtles

- *Shell: ability to withdraw head into the shell (in some cases only partially)*
- Locomotion

  On land

  - *Dig, burrow, grasp*

  In water

  - *Swim, dive, submerge*
  - *Float, sink, soak, paddle, wade*
  - Do not migrate or swim for long distances like the sea turtles
- Hibernate

Specific indications of sea/marine turtles

Behavior:
- Inability to withdraw head into the shell
  - Nonretractile
- Sea turtles can glide effortlessly in the water, but move with great difficulty on land. It is possible that the patient might express this feature as experiencing two types of movement:
  1. Laborious and strenuous (like the one sea turtle experiences on land)
  2. Gliding and effortless (as it experiences in the water)
- Locomotion: fast moving (as turtles are supported by the flippers and flat, streamlined shell)

<u>In water</u>

- Swim; swim long distance over short time, migrate
- Dive, glide, quick movements in water
- Powerful, wing-like strokes, propelled by flippers
- Tremendous burst of speed

<u>On land</u>

- Emerge cautiously
- Dragging, laborious movements

- Submerged in water for long time, while holding breath
  - Dash to the surface to breathe air
  - Fear of getting out of air, gasping and suffocation
- Sharp senses: sensitivity to smell, sound, vibrations, touch
- Characteristics of reproduction
  - Digging, burrowing
  - Ability to survive tough odds
- Characteristic behavior of a hatchling
  - Crawling
  - Swim frenzy
- Sharp vision under water
- Can withstand severe injuries and extreme degree of anoxia
- Solitary

Characteristics of attack and defense:

- Ambush attack
- To hide, get trapped
- Severe injuries described in such terms as: slice, saw, cut through, snap, crush, spear-like, speared, hacked, holes, sharp wounds, piercing, stabbing, knife-like, razor-sharp, ripped, or chopped open alive (these key words, that describe severe injuries, arise from the turtle's feeling of being exposed to attacks by the larger predatory animals such as killer whales and sharks)
- Bleed profusely.

Comparison between sea/marine turtles, tortoises and semiaquatic/freshwater turtles

	Sea/marine turtles	Terrestrial/ land-based tortoises	Semiaquatic/ freshwater turtles
Ability to withdraw inside the shell	Unable to withdraw head and limbs into the shell.	Able to withdraw into their shell.	Present (sometimes even partially).
Habitat	Primarily in the sea. Go to land only to lay eggs. Will dig and burrow on land only to lay eggs.	On land.	Can be equally on land and water. Some of them are primarily land based and go to the water only to cool off during extreme heat. Able to dig and burrow on land to lay eggs as well as to hibernate.
Locomotion	Pertaining to their aquatic habitat: Fast moving, swimming, diving, paddling, gliding, slipping, propelling through water. Turtles show tremendous bursts of speed. They migrate and travel long distances.	Pertaining to their land-based habitat. Slow-moving, sprawling, awkward, lumbering gait.	On land: Walk, or come to land to lay eggs. Dig, burrow, grasp. In water: Swim, dive, submerge. Float, sink, soak, paddle, wade.
Feet	Webbed or flipper-like feet.	Short, club-shaped, sturdy feet.	Sharp-clawed feet.
Shell qualities	Flat, streamlined shells which aid swimming and prevent sinking.	Heavy, dome-shaped shells which are difficult for predators to bite or crush.	
Hibernation	Do not hibernate.	Practices.	Practices.
Migration	Migrate over long distances in a short time. Move with tremendous bursts of speed.	Do not migrate.	Do not migrate over long distances like the sea turtles.

	Sea/marine turtles	Terrestrial/ land-based tortoises	Semiaquatic/ freshwater turtles
Behavioral characteristics & Type of attack/ attacked feeling	Hunt by ambush. Sea turtles are more prone to severe injuries and wounds from larger predatory animals, like killer whales and sharks. This is in comparison to the other turtles who are attacked by fishes, mammals, and birds. The degree of violence and aggression perceived (and even inflicted on others) is much greater in a sea turtle.	Generally calm, peaceful and docile. Tortoises have a gentler disposition. The degree and intensity of violence in tortoise is much less than that in turtles.	Feeling of being attacked on their exposed parts.

Comparing testudines with snakes and lizards

Differentiating features	Tortoises/turtles	Snakes	Lizards
Characteristic body morphology	Presence of shell	Limbless squamates with long, elongated and slender body	Limbed squamates with various body adaptations
Characteristics of the mouth parts: jaw and tongue	Horny beak and sharp jaws	Tongue that flicks to detect prey	Tongue that flicks to detect prey (only seen in few species)
Skin molting	In small pieces	All at once	Absent (except few species)
Locomotion	Slow, lumbering gait in tortoise Swim, glide, paddle, dive, propel in turtles	Crawl, creep, slither, climb, swim	Fast, agile, short burst of quick activity, scurry away, jumpy, jerky, cling and climb on smooth surfaces, runs
Other behavioral characteristics and specific methods of attack or defense	The shell and its functions Ability to withdraw or retreat into the shell Heightened sexuality Bite, cut, chew, grasp, slice, saw Hunt by ambush (in sea turtles) Migration (in sea turtles)	Poison, venom Ability to constrict Swallow whole Threatening postures: S- curve, hood, etc. Serpentine movement Sensitivity at throat level Clairvoyance	Characteristic way of communication via various signal instincts like enlarging, puffing, use of bright coloration, ornamentations, etc. Autotomy: self-amputation of a limb or body part, in order to escape predation Ability to change colors Bite, stun, shake vigorously, chew, swallow whole

Difference with Row 2

In the elements of Row 2, the main feeling is: "I am not developed enough to exist without the protection/shell. That shell is not part of me. It is somebody else from outside, giving me that protective cover." This is why they show extreme dependence on somebody else. "It is a process by which I live inside of someone, and now it is time to come out. Once I come out, there is no going back; no withdrawing." Therefore in Row 2, it is only "in to out". There are no animal themes: survival, me vs. you, hierarchy, etc. There are no reptile themes: hiding, sudden attack, camouflage, etc.

In the following section we will be studying remedies from the following families:

Sea/marine turtles	Semiaquatic turtles	Tortoises (land tortoises)
Family: Cheloniidae [Sea turtles] Remedies: *Eretmochelys imbricata* [hawksbill turtle] *Lepidochelys olivacea* [olive ridley sea turtle]	**Family:** Chelydridae [Snapping turtles and big-headed turtles] Remedies: Ovum *Chelydra serpentina* [egg of Common snapping turtle] **Family:** Emydidae [box turtles and pond turtles] Remedies: *Chrysemys scripta elegans* or *Trachemys scripta elegans* [red-eared slider] *Terrapene carolina* [box turtle]	**Family:** Testudinidae [Tortoises] Remedies: *Geochelone sulcata* [African spurred tortoise] *Testudo hermanni* [Hermann's tortoise]

Family:
Cheloniidae
hard-shelled sea turtles

Homoeopathic remedies
- *Eretmochelys imbricata* [hawksbill turtle]
- *Lepidochelys olivacea* [olive ridley sea turtle]

Eretmochelys imbricata [hawksbill turtle]

Superfamily: Chelonioidea

Family: Cheloniidae (hard-shelled sea turtles)

Genus: Eretmochelys (hawksbill sea turtles)

Species: Eretmochelys imbricata

Common name: hawksbill sea turtle

General information on the family Cheloniidae: read Sea/marine turtles on page 126.

Habitat

Adult hawksbill turtles are usually seen: resting in caves and on ledges, in and around the coral reefs, shoals, oceanic island lagoons, or continental shelves. These are habitats containing SPONGES. As a HIGHLY MIGRATORY species, they have also been encountered in a wide range of habitats.

Anatomical characteristics

The hawksbill turtle has several characteristics that distinguish it from other, closely-related species. Its elongated, tapered head ends in a BEAKLIKE mouth (from which its common name is derived). The taper of ITS BEAK IS

Hawksbill sea turtle (Eretmochelys imbricata)

MORE SHARPLY PRONOUNCED AND HOOKED than that of other sea turtles. Each of the hawksbill's flipper like forearms has two visible claws. The scutes overlap in such a way as to give the rear margin of its carapace a SERRATED look, similar to the edge of a saw or a steak knife. The scutes of the hawksbill's carapace have an irregular radiating pattern of brown/black on amber. The plastron is usually clear yellow, but it may have a small amount of dark pigmentation.

Food habits

While they are known to be omnivorous and feed on surface drifting organisms when young, adult hawksbill sea turtles feed chiefly on a few select species of SPONGES from the order Demospongia. Many of these sponges have GLASSLIKE SILICA SPICULES which prove prohibitive to other animals. Hawksbills are also resilient to lethal species of sponges. A small percentage of the hawksbill's diet may also consist of sea jellies, fish, crustaceans, sea plants, and the algae that grow in shoals.

Characteristic behavior

They are most comfortable in water less than 18 m deep. Young hawksbills cannot dive deeply and live on masses of floating plant material until they are older.

Specific method of attack and defense

Because of their tough carapaces, hawksbill turtles have no major predators, as there are few creatures that are capable of biting through their protective shell. Sharks and estuarine crocodiles are a few of their natural predators. Octopuses and some species of pelagic fish have also been known to prey on the adult turtles. Gulls and crabs prey on the hatchlings, while dogs, raccoons, rats, and humans pose a threat to the eggs.

Possible expressions of the hawksbill sea turtle in patients

The hawksbill turtle will express all the features of the sea turtle along with some specific source words:

- Beaklike, hooked, sharp (probably crushing is more pronounced)
- Sponges, silica

Lepidochelys olivacea [olive ridley sea turtle]

Suborder: Cryptodira (Hidden-necked turtles)

Superfamily: Chelonioidea

Family: Cheloniidae (sea turtles)

Genus: Lepidochelys (ridley sea turtles)

Species: Lepidochelys olivacea

Common name: olive ridley sea turtle

General information on the family Cheloniidae: read Sea/marine turtles on page 126.

Habitat

The olive ridley turtle has a large range within the tropical and subtropical regions in the Pacific and Indian Oceans as well as the Southern Atlantic Ocean.

Anatomical characteristics

The olive ridley turtle is a LARGE SEA TURTLE that can weigh as much as 45 kg (100 lbs) and have a length of up to 75 cm (30 in). The skin of the turtle is OLIVE GRAY. The distinguishing feature between male and female turtles is the male's long, prehensile tail which extends past the carapace (the female's does not). The relatively THIN SHELL (compared to other turtles') is somewhat heart-shaped and olive in color. Each of the forelimbs has two claws.

Food habits

The olive ridley is chiefly carnivorous, feeding on invertebrates and protochordates such as jellyfish, snails, shrimp and crabs. They particularly CRUSH AND GRIND the prey. The olive ridley turtle has a tendency to eat a wide variety of foods, and this has led olive ridleys to attempt to ingest trash such as plastic bags and styrofoam. Surprisingly, in captivity, this species has been observed to be cannibalistic. Most feeding takes place in SHALLOW, SOFT-BOTTOMED WATERS.

Mating characteristics

The ridleys' solution to **threats awaiting them on the shore where they come to lay their eggs** is quite dramatic. Forming MASSES called 'arribadas' (Spanish for *arrival*), THEY OVERWHELM THE EGGEATERS BY THEIR SHEER NUMBERS. It is not unusual to see THOUSANDS OF RIDLEYS CLAMBER OUT OF THE LAPPING WAVES, and the beach becomes black with them as they start digging holes to deposit eggs. This procession of MASS NESTING continues until evening, when the ridleys suddenly vanish.

Characteristic behavior

The olive ridley sea turtle spends most of its time within 15 km of shore, preferring SHALLOW SEAS for its feeding and sunbathing. Not much is known about the behavior of this turtle besides that it makes regular **migrations** to and from the nesting beaches during each year. They typically sunbathe **at the surface of the ocean, usually in** LARGE GROUPS **so as to escape the cold temperature of the water beneath them.** In mild climates, when the water is warm, they do not sunbathe.

Specific method of attack or defense

The olive ridley turtle will normally **swim away or dive to deeper water,** rather than confront a predator, which is often human. While on land, mature females will defend themselves by **flapping** their front limbs.

Lepidochelys olivacea - Mass nesting

Lepidochelys olivacea case, taken and presented by Jacques Echard

Case of a French male, 52-year-old, first seen on 13 November 2007.

The patient has a cerebral injury, manifested by vertigo. This is the result of a stroke, caused by atrial arrhythmia. His need to take anticoagulants prevents him from **continuing his job as a joiner and carpenter**. Such work involves physical labor that exposes the patient to a risk of injury, and thus contraindicates the use of anticoagulants. Injury in patients on anticoagulants can result in internal bleeding, which may go unnoticed by the patient himself. He is a divorcé of many years and has been depressed since his divorce.

D: Tell me about your state?

P: Tiredness. No general strength. No desire to do anything. If I don't do it today, I will do it tomorrow. I do postpone. If I don't do it either day, there's no matter. Physical problems; the neck and cervical vertebrae are blocked. Painful; it is **grinding and cracking**.

Mechanical problems. I am worrying about selling my house or not.

After having lived for 30 years in France, if I come back to Germany to the source, I would go back with a small bag, with what I had left with thirty years ago. If I go back, it's like a failure to me, because I have not achieved my aim to get a house. And if I go back I will have to go to my sister's building ... I am afraid of that... **I will be a little too much under the family's thumb,** a little bit under cover. (HG: with significant energy, he puts his hands out in front of him, flat, palms down, and pushes them down as if pressing toward an imaginary bottom).

"I will be a little too much under my family's thumb"

They would like to take care of me, as they are like that, but it would be too much. I've seen it during the boat cruise that we all took with my brother some time back. My brother and sister are unmarried and they are used to living alone. They both have some habits, and they cannot be conscious of it.

(The patient means that during a cruise, he became aware of how his family's entrenched behavior still takes over and controls him.)

You are a little bit **crushed**. They don't even care about it. With my brother we were in a 12 sq m/14 sq yd. cabin, it was short with space, but also reduced as to the spirit. (HG: shows a narrow space with hands.)

"You are a little bit crushed"
"Short space but also reduced as spirit"

(By reduced as to the spirit, the patient is suggesting that his identity, personality, and liveliness were confined or diminished in the tight, close environment of the cabin that he shared with his usually overbearing family.)

I need to make my own way, and I have to talk with them if I have to move back to Germany. If I don't do that, she will take me under her control: *Do this! Do that!* I need to tell her to sometimes just give me a break, I want to be alone. To go back to Germany would mean I **lose my independence and freedom**.

I am very tired. I begin something but don't finish, I move to something else; never organized (HG: shows movement from one point to another).

D: Beyond facts, what's your feeling?

P: I have lost pleasure while working, pleasure of coming to an end in my activity; instead of finishing some work, I am changing activity. Always asking the question of going back to Germany or not; if I do it, I will do it with my mind, my reason, but not my heart.

D: Feeling?

P: No way, no clear path in my life. My life is a failure, because when I left Germany to come to France everybody told me not to leave. You are crazy! And now, it's like taking a step back and telling them, 'okay you were right, as you said, it didn't work'.

D: Your feelings about this failure?

P: To begin with, we were neither poor nor rich, so I have no regret from the material point of view when I come back to Germany. But I can see I have been less successful than my friends. But what is it to achieve one's life? Is it to get a big car and large house and a lot of money? In my opinion it is more to feel good in one's spirit; my life has been corresponding to my taste and own wish, which was to get freedom of spirit. I have never been attached to material things.

D: Talking about freedom and making this hand gesture? What do you mean?

P: It has been the same way in my life. A long time ago I quit Germany because I was afraid to be **crushed** by my father (HG: same as before: hands out, palms down, hands pressing downward).

D: Feeling of being crushed?

P: To live and do things as I wanted and wished to do.

Not being watched over. My father kept an eye on me.

And also fear of responsibilities and entering in this chain of professional life, of being watched over, being given orders, and give orders myself. That's when I came to France, to push all of this aside, **not to have a chief above me, being my own boss, not being in a hierarchy scale**.

D: What is it to have somebody above you?

P: Actually not pleasurable. The feeling of somebody watching over you, I don't like it; I prefer not to have much material things; **I need myself to be free**, making my own decisions.

D: Feeling?

P: If I have somebody watching over me, it means **he is stronger than me and he has got the power on me**: I must do what he says — but if he is not there, then the decision is mine.

D: Stronger, has the power?

P: Actually, it's as if you sell yourself to the boss: you give your knowledge, your physical force, in exchange of getting food and to be able to live, but you are not free in your decision. How can I do this?

It comes back to the same point: the simple fact of somebody telling me how to do this — if somebody tells me how to do simple thing, I don't like it. When my brother told me not to smoke, I started to smoke even more.

D: Feeling?

P: Give me a break; you don't get to decide for me.

D: What is the feeling inside?

P: This is a forbidding. This is something I don't want to listen to, that I refuse to do and obey because somebody has told me.

D: What's your feeling inside? Not intellectual.

P: It's difficult to explain, because I come back to the superior level.

Actually, **I close myself**; I don't speak much, no pain, not physical or mechanical.

D: Go ahead?

P: It's just like the **tortoise** (**HG: shows both hands, one top, one bottom**, like a container): **somebody touches my head and I am closing myself in** my **carapace** — my **shell** — and I **withdraw** my **head and** my **legs**, and I just **shut myself** in (HG: shows the withdrawal with hands and head).

D: Meaning?

P: **Actually, I desire to shut myself.** But you don't get to do this at your workplace, since you can't refuse your job. But now I have left my job and I don't work anymore. So, maybe it's because of that, when I get to work for myself, I am not obliged to do things, so I postpone.

D: But how is it physically?

P: Tiredness in the morning when I am leaving; I have no feeling of rest, not the feeling of force.

D: What do you feel?

P: I feel I have to do something, but I don't like it; I need to . . . I have to . . . . You need to do things to be normal in life (HG: makes quotation marks in the air with fingers). Doing nothing bad, doing something — I don't like it: no desire, no aim.

D: Describe I don't desire, no force. What's your feeling?

P: When I was working, I thought, *I will get time when I retire*, and now that I don't work, I don't even do anything.

D: What was so difficult at that time that you were thinking to retire when young?

P: Most difficult was that my boss would hold me for 8 hours every day. I was living more for my boss than according to myself. I wanted to live for myself. I cannot stand having someone above myself. If ever somebody tells me to do something, just because it comes from somebody else, I block myself against it (HG: fingers clenched together).

155

D: Tell about block myself? What are you doing when you clench your fingers?

P: I am complaining *poor me* — sometimes I get to say, *I am fed up, let me be quiet*, but actually I am not happy, so don't keep quiet. I do something here and there. I am quiet on one side, and on the other side, I am so nervous. I change channels on TV . . . . I am so unstable.

D: Describe?

P: I feel more acknowledgements when I work at his home.

NB: He has been working at a homoeopathic doctor's home.

It's much more quiet, although it is difficult, as I have to start in the morning.

D: What's the feeling when you have to start working?

P: I am thinking, *I've got to go, I promised* . . . . Just the fact that I tell myself *I've got to do it*; it makes me think, *I don't feel like doing it*.

D: Then what's the feeling?

NB: Patient stays stuck a long time in the facts – cannot reach next level – and then feels a pain in his right arm as he begins to speak.

P: It's difficult to tell.

D: What is happening with your arm?

P: When I press on my arm it gets painful. Maybe it's a reaction to what we are talking about.

Tiredness, no desire to move, to get up, to walk, to talk — if you don't do it you think, you have to do it; I never feel good, neither if I do it nor if I don't, like a circle (HG).

D: Feeling at that moment?

P: Always an excuse not to do it. I feel . . . no desire to — don't feel like doing — **I feel like going into my carapace like a tortoise which shuts into it ... (same HG: shows withdrawal with hands)**. Don't feel like talking, happy that nobody calls up, **I don't have to see other people.** The more you talk the more you have to justify yourself, to explain why and how, why you made this decision…to come back to Germany. No need to justify: *I want this!* and *stop it! that's enough! release me!*

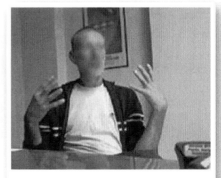

"I feel like going into my carapace as a turtle (tortoise)"

156

D: Tell me about both your gestures, blocked and shut in?

P: I feel like going for a nap, to sleep. You are tired, you are sick; don't feel fine sometimes, because I get dreams. **Desire to retire under covers**, just not to explain myself (HG same: with significant energy). I tell myself, "Tomorrow I will do it," and then in the morning I find any excuse not to do it, "always the same circle" (HG: hand moves down and again down).

D: What is this HG?

P: It means that I come back to the same circle, I begin something and don't finish it. I feel like finishing, and at the same time I feel "I am fed up".

D: Feeling?

P: Disgust, like towards life, it pisses me off, (HG: puts hands in front of him, raising them up and up). It's a point now where I feel blocked. I want to say, "Let's stop, it doesn't work, let's leave it."

NB: Here he meant that he wanted to stop the consultation.

D: Tell me about your dreams?

P: Right now it's a melting of German souvenirs and France. I mix people up. Dreams of reliving things from the past, bad experiences, and other things I don't remember. Sometimes dreams are pleasant, quiet and sunny, while some are of bad experiences. Things you don't have to do anymore, things which didn't work out. Things you don't have to do or say again and again.

D: Feeling?

P: Anguish, half awake, you need to wake up as you stop it.

Like you are in the sea, you can't breathe — I need to come up to the surface of the sea to get oxygen. To be within the sea and you are afraid not to have enough oxygen, and you tell yourself you need to come up to the surface to take some oxygen.

(This is very specific for a sea turtle.)

D: The experience is that you have been a long time under sea and you have to come up in a short time?

P: Yes, right, correct!

D: So it's when you have to do something, it is when …

P: (Interrupts) Yes, it is when **I get blocked!** Actually I could think that I will do things just for myself, but I don't even do them, it is stupid, but I don't feel like doing them. Then comes the block. I feel blocked just because I have to do it.

D: What is blocked?

P: It is the arm, just as if muscles would **contract** and being too short, a bit like soreness, as well as if I had been working in force for three days (HG: opens hands and then closes them into fists in front of him).

D: What do you show with your hand?

P: It pulls me, as if I am pumping, as if I attract something.

I try to catch something, try to move my muscles although it is painful.

"As if I had been working in force for three days"

D: Go on with what is coming up to you?

P: My right hand is mine, but my left hand is not mine. It's no more really mine. I feel it, and it is hot (HG: showing with hands).

NB: He is actually talking about the after-effects of the cerebrovascular accident on his left arm, which remained for a while.

P: This . . . I can't do it; **I can't pull my arms back**—it pulls me there . . . too short.

D: Means?

P: **I get the feeling my muscles are too short, as if painful, as if I have to pull or to stretch it in order to move it (HG); as if it is too short, then you have to pull and stretch it to make it longer; I never got this before. Too short and I have to pull back to stretch them.**

D: What do you feel in your shoulder?

P: It's too short, it doesn't work, doesn't stretch, painful and lack of force, both sides. It's hard if I touch it (shows different parts as I ask). It is stiff and hard.

Not like concrete but like … how can I say? … (escapes) … painful!

D: Like what??

P: **Normally a muscle is not contracted too much, just as it fits, but here... Just as if you have always to make an effort to hold or pinch something, I try to do it in order to explain and transmit it to you...It is embarrassing, you don't feel like...Muscles are contracted, too short, muscular tension doesn't fit to contraction, something wrong in the mechanism. As if you constantly make an effort to do something.**

D: Tell more?

P: Just if I undress my jacket it pains; hurts me. **It's too short, too small, limited for motion, too small, too short , too contracted which prevents me to move (HG: moves shoulder up and down) as I did before.**

D: Tell about your spine and shoulders?

P: As if some defect (HG: shows neck) — it goes to spine . . . I feel like its **grinding**. Something that doesn't fit, not in proper place, something **contracted** (HG: puts hands down), hurts me (HG: moves shoulder to explain as if some embarrassment[1] in neck).

D: More?

P: **Something packed, tight, hard (HG: hits right fist into left hand). It's like concrete covered by hard rubber.** Concrete would mean it doesn't move at all. There, it is in between hard rubber to hard moss (means it is in between hard and soft, concrete and rubber), it still moves but with difficulty.

D: Tell about crushed again with HG?

P: It is related with my father and my sister.

If you get back to the picture of water, you take it and you crush it in the water (HG: again shows the hands moving downwards, palms down). You take it under your command and you crush it and put it underwater.

D: Means?

P: **You prevent it to get oxygen or to do movements, take under command — you crush it, you force it, you put it under water (same HG).**

(To crush it under water, prevent it to get oxygen — another indication of the sea turtle.)

D: Describe crushed?

P: *NB: tells the story of his wife, who wanted him to do what she wanted and not what he enjoyed doing.*

There is somebody or something, and I have to do it. At this very moment I feel **blocked**, I don't feel like doing it.

---

1   Note meaning of *embarrassment* as it is used here, from its French origin, *embarrasser*, meaning *to block or obstruct.*

D: So tell about blocked?

P: Blocked is the same; if you crush somebody you block him, you prevent him to go on moving to do things.

"*My sister will crush me*"
"*Press me in the form she desires*"

Doesn't mean destroy, but impeachment, preventing, stopping to do, enclosing you within, e.g., my sister—she doesn't want to crush me, reducing me to nothing, but to press me in the form she desires... Dominating, giving order and being given (HG: palm facing down and moving downwards).

Yes ... somebody tries to be superior. Somebody who tries to influence, to give me order, who wants me to do as he wants.

D: Feeling that time?

P: Wants to go back home, to close my door, lie under covers and say, "You piss me off; I better be alone".

D: In the body?

P: Tiredness, **heaviness, no action, hard disk on pause, not dead, not very lively, retired . . . .** fatigue.Muscular pain, **difficult to move**, arms and legs heavy, inactive like a computer on pause, doesn't work out, like asleep. **Makes much efforts to do motion**, soreness, not feel like moving because it drains you out too much force. You need force to move.

D: Why so?

P: You need force to move; and I need to command to my arm to move; as I force myself to do things, force myself to do the movements ; I tell my legs "let you walk" because I have to walk ahead, to push the engine, the lawn mower for instance . You do things not because you enjoy it but just because it has to be done. (Moves shoulders up and down as if embarrassed[2].)

D: What is this movement?

P: It is to find my way to the right or left (makes a new HG going round, snakelike, in front of him). Motion doesn't come automatic; it is difficult,

---

2   Used here to mean *blocked* or *obstructed*, from the French *embarrasser*.

embarrassing. I have to give command from my brain. Effort, means use much energy and then you are even more tired and you have to rest and you don't want to rest because you have to do something, but you – you don't feel like doing effort: it's like a circle (HG: describes a circle).

D: But what do you feel within? How is motion?

P: It is **hard**, embarrassed (moves shoulders), you have to give order...**Less supple, heavier, not so easy than before, more effort, more energy.**

D: What is it that you have to do— more efforts and give commands?

P: **Like a heavy ...Before it was made by itself, alone.**

D: Main sensation?

P: **I get less force than before, less supple.**

D: What happened when you quit Germany?

P: I didn't feel like doing a job after what I studied. **Maybe also the idea of staying in a fixed spot (HG: hands extended flat, palms down, going down);** to settle, to fix oneself, is to follow a path already well established (HG: hands held out in front of him, parallel to each other, move ahead). Not to follow the path you want to follow. My liberty is to be on point A, stay there three days, decide on the spot to go to B, doing what I want, as myself and others feel good. Liberty is not following what has been planned, allowed to go right, left, back, anywhere, anytime.

D: What is liberty?

P: **It is to be allowed to do things without somebody above me. Without being restricted in between two walls (HG – with significant energy – hands parallel, palms down, one above the other and moving back and forth several times). In between two walls, predestined, pre-programmed. It is also being crushed: you cannot go right, you cannot go left, you have to follow the established path, a bit like on the highway.**

Case analysis by Jacques:

The main themes running through the case:

- When I have to start something, I have to make a conscious effort, to force myself.

- When somebody tells me what to do and how to do it, I need freedom not to have somebody above me who tells me what I have to do .

- And so I block myself: *block* means you are crushed by somebody ("if you block him you crush him, and when you block him, you prevent him to go on moving to do things"). I refuse to execute what I am being pressurised to, and I retire into my carapace, head and legs, to be quiet.

- And you don't feel like moving because it drains out too much force from you.

The patient's main, repeating modes of thought and action can be summarized:

- Don't bother me; if you do so, I will block and retire into my carapace.

- I can't stand to have somebody above me who gives me orders, who can crush me.

- This carapace protects me from being crushed and dominated, but at the same time, this carapace is like a prison and limits my freedom.

Following the case along:

Turtle is first expressed as an image: when the patient says, "It's just like the tortoise: somebody touches my head and I am closing myself in my carapace, my shell, and I withdraw my head and my legs and I just shut myself in". It could be only an image, if it did not tie into everything at the depth of the patient's case. But we can see that it comes directly from the source of his illness, because it remains, and continues to pop up as the case taking moves toward the energy of his case, the source of his discomfort. I made sure of the remedy not only with the image (that struck me), but more. The image became the source, through the hand gestures and corresponding non-human specific words and an understanding of the sensation and the case itself.

This is very important to understand about the source, and by extension, about my prescription. If you watch a sea turtle on the ground dragging itself along, the energy you catch from it is that of laborious, difficult movement. On land, all is so difficult for the sea turtle to do: locomotion (limbs are stiff and hard, quite jerky-like) looks as if it asks much energy, as if this heavy thing is on the shoulders. This idea, almost a palpable feeling, of burdensome weight, runs all along the case with many hand gestures, and with the patient's own naming of this carapace thing, into which he can escape when something or somebody bothers him too much. So I prescribed Sea turtle.

162

Kingdom: animal

- Dominating / dominated.
- Submissive.
- Someone who is stronger than I.
- Someone who has power over me.
- It's a process of seeing the patient's multiple situations that have to do with competition and dominance emerge (rather than identifying sensation or motto), especially by watching the many hand gestures.
- Someone who controls me by ordering or forbidding.
- I have someone above me, stronger than me.

Subkingdom: reptile

It is not difficult to establish in this case, because of the patient's comfort in pulling himself into a shell. The desire for concealment that is a characteristic of the reptiles, is also a direct hallmark of his remedy's source, the turtle.

The patient says:

- To thread his way right or left, through people and things (HG: arm slides right and left, like a snake).

Turtle is the remedy for sure, as the patient experiences much of his life's definition and parameters in terms of turtle characteristics; including even a sense of a carapace and a withdrawal coping mechanism analogous to the action of a turtle pulling into its shell. Some of his sentience, such as that of having been in the water a long time and needing to come up for air, is more specifically characteristic of marine turtles than all turtles.

Source: sea turtle

- Blocked: if you crush somebody, you block him, you prevent his going on, his moving to do things, (the difficulty of movement, repeatedly described by the patient, is reminiscent of the sea turtle's awkward land locomotion).
- Desire to withdraw into a carapace, withdraw my head and arms (HG).
- Something outside of me reduces my space or spirit (HG), *(sense of turtle carapace weighing upon, surrounding him).*
- Fear of being crushed (HG).
- Sensitivity to, and awareness of, limitations on movement, living space, and physical performance can be seen when the patient talks of too short, too small, limited motion, too contracted, prevention of motion, (HG : shoulder moves up and down to show blocked movement).

- As if you constantly make an effort to do something, *(sense of sea turtle's laborious effort to move on land)*.

Patient declares that force is needed to move, and then he speaks of not feeling like moving, because movement drains too much force, *(again, sense of sea turtle's laborious effort to move on land)*.

(NB: Can just imagine how uncomfortable the patient's illness must feel, since one of the attitudes it imposes on him is that of living with a carapace on the shoulders!)

Source words that indicate the carapace:
- Hard to touch (patient refers to different parts of his body during the consultation).

- Stiff and hard (HG: patient indicates upper arms).

- Something packed tightly, hard (HG: patient hits right fist into left hand); like concrete or something hard covered by hard rubber (apt description of a carapace).

- Heavy on shoulders, it's too short, it doesn't work, doesn't stretch, painful and lack of force, both sides (conveys how uncomfortable a human patient's illness must be if it makes him feel as though he is inside a carapace).

- (Without being) restricted between two walls (HG).

- Follow the established path, a bit like a highway.

- Muscles feel too short and unable to be stretched. When the patient begins to move, he gets a feeling like pain, that his muscles are too short (HG). (This sensation of *something too short* in the arms and shoulders is maddening to the human patient but perfectly natural in the sea turtle.)

- The word *crushed*, which appears throughout the patient's case, can be seen in turtle terms as a description of that which the carapace is designed to protect against.

- The patient's illness causes him to feel blocked, prevented from doing things, inside a carapace.

Source words indicative of a sea turtle's life in the water:
- Try to breathe, come up to the surface to get oxygen.

- Patient feels as though he is being crushed, pushed down in water, and blocked or prevented from moving and doing things.

164

- Patient discusses the concept of *crushed* that he feels as taking over someone, commanding him, forcing him in such a way that pushes him underwater and prevents his getting oxygen (HG same).

Turtle psychology: issue of independence

The patient speaks of and is concerned with these ideas, which reflect a theme of independence in sea turtles:

- I want things according to my will.
- I don't want to lose my independence and freedom.
- I become aggravated when my way of life is dictated by another.
- I prefer a state of not being given orders and not giving orders myself.
- If I am pressed upon, I withdraw into my carapace.
- Wants to get its own rhythm and will.

Author's comments:

Very early in the case the patient say's 'I close myself in my carapace. I withdraw my head and legs like a tortoise.' When a patient says these words we often jump to tortoise. Here we warn the reader that more than 90% of patients who say such things may not even need a tortoise or reptile nor an animal remedy. Any image of the source at the beginning of the case must be treated with great caution. But in this case later on, the patient in different situations confirms not only the withdrawal but several other features of the turtle including cracking, crushing, coming to the surface for oxygen, etc. We can see that the characteristic animal and turtle expressions are not only found in his imagery but also in his physical symptoms like the cracking, pulling of the muscles, etc. So we find not only in mental, but also physical and several features of the case, along with the feeling of being dominated and dominating, feeling blocked and unable to move.

Remedy: *Lepidochelys olivacea* LM5

Jacques: The patient was suffering from a very chronic and deep pathology which in my understanding required a daily stimulus of the remedy. So to avert any aggravation that might result from a C potency, I chose the LM scale.

Follow-up 1 on 2 January 2008:

P: **Much better!!** I feel better in my spirits. I feel like doing things quite easily now, very quickly — on the very moment. Rising up in morning with more energy. Making plans for the day after — instead of waiting what will happen, I decide myself what will happen; much more active. I make projects — even things I never had found, time to do before — I do carry them out. Now, I do it because I feel like I enjoy doing it. Before I wasn't doing anything: I was rising and just waiting for evening. Before, to do or not to do was same, equal: no difference.

I retook the same rhythm than before, to feel like doing, to enjoy. It gives me a more regular and structured, normal life.

It's a whole another way to consider life and things. You want to do things, you want to make fun of it. When shopping, I look what I enjoy — what I like — in departments. Before, I had standards: always same thing.

D: Dreams?

P: Yesterday, mixing of time and places, Germany and France. No nightmares like before, but dreams where I feel good. I am dreaming early in the morning. They changed a bit.

Before: I dreamt but I felt bad, I got night perspiration; when I woke up in the morning I didn't feel as if I got rest; I was also awakened every hour. I felt bad a bit like nightmares, bad position or whatever, fear or whatever, I don't know — I felt bad.

Now: I feel better — my nights are nice, no wake up. In morning I feel rest; I feel like getting up with joy.

D: How is your physical health?

P: I feel less tired. I got more force and more endurance. I begin things, and I finish them; it changed a lot. My physical force is not completely like before, not so intense: more than 50% improvement on force. It's easier to make motions, less painful. I have more flexibility, I have more freedom to do it.

Before I was stiff, now I feel more mobile freedom and supple. I was, like, blocked (HG — with significant energy — moves arms and turns head right and left). I felt like something too short in arms and shoulders. Before, I was blocked in the spirit and in the body. It's easier to do things — now I feel more freedom, more movements.

You feel like doing things and you do it even if it is painful. Less feeling of being enclosed, blocked, in between two walls. It is that you do things from your own will, and you are happy after, even if you perspired a lot.

So, the patient is ameliorated at the sensation level and at the general, physical (symptoms) level as well. The amelioration is also at the image/dream level (where the sensation can become articulated via probing questioning of the practitioner).

P: I actually do things and I finish them.

Remedy: *Lepidochelys olivacea* LM7

Follow-up 2 in November'08 (scribed by the homoeopath):

I had to call him, because he didn't feel it necessary to come back. He is perfectly fine: he is doing some work again, but cautiously, because he has not yet discontinued the anticoagulants. He has written to a matchmaking agency in order to meet a girlfriend; taking such a step and being in such a relationship would have been unbearable for him previously. He has met a girlfriend, and they are establishing a relationship. He is perfectly happy.

No remedy given.

Follow-up 3 - Phone follow-up on 6 March 2009:

He continues to remain fine. That's the reason he didn't follow up. He is very busy in his new relationship. He is very amazed that those little pills might have changed him so much.

No remedy given.

Possible expressions of the olive ridley in patients

All the characteristics of sea turtles can be expressed along with specific expressions of the olive ridley sea turtle:

- Specific color — olive gray
- Thin shell
- Shallow, soft bottomed waters
- Large groups, mass
- Clamber, climb, scramble, mount
- *Lack of free movement (refers to the olive ridley's stiffened limbs and difficulty in moving on land)*
- *Being boxed in or similar descriptions of being restrained within a small area (refers to the shell)*
- *In some cases, the 'shell boxing in' may be described as a wall*

Family:
Chelydridae

Homoeopathic remedy

Ovum of *Chelydra serpentina* [Common snapping turtle]

Introduction

The Chelydridae comprise a family within the taxonomic suborder Cryptodira (the hidden-neck tortoise and turtles which draw their heads directly into their shells).

Chelydridae is composed of three species:

* *Macrochelys temminckii* (alligator snapping turtle)
* *Chelydra serpentina* (common snapping turtle)
* *Platysternon megacephalum* (big-headed turtle)

Generalised anatomy

Members of this family have: VERY LARGE HEADS, STRONG CLAWS, and STRONG JAWS. The upper jaw is hooked and capable of delivering a POWERFUL BITE. It is also capable of SLICING THE PREY APART. As their name suggests, they are LIKELY TO SNAP AT ANYONE, WHEN THREATENED OR ATTACKED.

Their HEAD AND LIMBS CANNOT BE RETRACTED FULLY INSIDE THEIR SHELL, because their head is so large and their SHELL IS REDUCED IN SIZE. This offers LESS PROTECTION but GREATER MOBILITY than do the shells of other turtles. The lower shell, or plastron, is quite small. This facilitates FREE ACTION OF THEIR LEGS AND HEAD, and allows them to RAISE THEIR BODIES UP OFF THE GROUND WHEN WALKING ON LAND, SO THAT ONLY THEIR TAIL DRAGS.

They have LONG STRONG TAILS WITH ROWS OF RIDGES/TUBERCLES. In the species *Platysternon megacephalum,* its tail equals the length of the carapace.

A bit of folklore has sprung up that suggests the best way to lift a snapping turtle is by the tail. This can injure or kill the turtle, since the tail is part of the vertebral column. If a snapping turtle must be moved, it is best to lift it with a shovel. Gripping the back of the shell on both sides is safer for the turtle. However, this can cause injury to the human doing the lifting; from either the snapping jaws' swinging around on the long neck or from the flailing claws.

The turtle, with it's LONG NECK, CAN QUICKLY SWING ITS LARGE HEAD FAR FORWARD, AS WELL AS SIDEWAYS AND BACK OVER THE UPPER SHELL.

The snapping turtle's have a SAW-TOOTHED crest, dull and rough carapace with HEAVY KEELS and MARGINAL SERRATIONS. The legs are large with WEBBED toes.

The snapping turtle: note the rough skin and shell, and the sharp, hooked jaw

Chelydra serpentina: the incomplete shell and the long ridged tail

Food habits

Approximately one third of the diet of these turtles is aquatic vegetation. The rest consists of fish, insects, crawdads, snakes, small mammals, birds, snails, earthworms, and frogs.

They have also been known to eat waterfowl and carrion. In fact, stories are told of the snapping turtle's carrion detection ability being called into service, to locate victims of drowning or homicide. Snapping turtles have been the object of 'finger-pointing' regarding their role in waterfowl predation, particularly duck. They tend to attack sick ducklings, and are thought to play an important role in controlling the spread of bird flu viruses.

Behavior

Snapping turtles RARELY SUNBATHE OR BASK ON LAND, as other turtles do. Instead they FLOAT just below the surface of the water and SOAK up the warmth there. Snapping turtles WALK or BOUNCE along the bottoms of the shallow, muddy waterways that they inhabit.

Dwelling

These turtles mainly live in permanent water bodies, ones that are filled with water all year long. While they are able to survive in somewhat salty waters, they typically PREFER FRESHWATER, because they have to return to freshwater to rehydrate. They are **sedentary** creatures, preferring to live in SLOW-MOVING WATER BODIES, where the BOTTOM IS COVERED WITH SOFT MUD, and the DEPTH IS SHALLOW enough that they can reach the surface with their heads while WADING.

They spend the majority of their time SUBMERGED IN THE MUDDY BOTTOMS within which they can hibernate and concealment is possible. They will

TRAVEL QUITE A DISTANCE OVERLAND TO NEST in sandy, sunny nesting sites. This demonstrates their semiaquatic nature. Large male snapping turtles have ESTABLISHED TERRITORIES, where they may remain for many years. The females are a bit more peripatetic, or wandering about. They travel from their home territories in order to nest and may locate in a new place after they have nested. Snapping turtles show FIDELITY FOR THEIR HOME TERRITORY. Snappers that have been carried from their home territories can find their way back, as long as it is within a reasonable distance.

Snapping turtles, in climates with seasonal cold, survive the winter by hibernating. It is now known that the blood of hibernating turtles changes, in order to function like antifreeze in car radiators. As a result, the turtle's body temperature can drop to only a few degrees above freezing, which is much lower than that of most animals that hibernate. Snapping turtles may hibernate in groups. Even though hibernating snapping turtles have been observed moving under the winter ice, they are very vulnerable to predators, since they cannot move quickly enough to defend themselves.

Specific method of attack and defense

The snapping turtles are known for their unfriendly personality. This is because they QUICKLY STRIKE OUT with their long necks and powerful jaws, and SNAP at any passing animal, be it a fish or other prey that they want to eat. They will even snap at a person who comes too close. With their compromised shell size, which offers them less protection than other turtles have, their best way of defense is a strong offense. Snapping turtles are BOLD AND AGGRESSIVE FIGHTERS. Their massive, sharp-edged jaws cause them to be the TERROR OF MOST AQUATIC AND SEMIAQUATIC CREATURES. Interestingly enough, they BEHAVE MUCH MORE THREATENINGLY AND AGGRESSIVELY ON LAND THAN THEY DO IN THE WATER. Snapping turtles in the water would rather swim away from a threat than confront it. There is some debate as to whether the snapping turtle's attack is motivated by a grumpy bad temper, or fear and self defense.

The snapping turtle LIES BURIED, or camouflaged, in the mud with its EYES AND NOSTRILS EXPOSED, in water shallow enough to allow it to raise its long neck up to break the surface with its nostrils. It is then able to AMBUSH AN UNSUSPECTING PREY. This position also helps them to breathe without moving out of the mud. They can LASH OUT THEIR DECEPTIVELY LONG NECK WITH AMAZING SPEED, PROPELLING THE STRONG, and SNAPPING MOUTH WITH GREAT ACCURACY. Adults will DRAG LIVE PREY, such as water fowl, INTO

THE WATER TO DROWN their catch. This is a practice which can sometimes be hazardous to the snapper, due to the clawing and biting of the prey. With their hooked jaws, they GRASP the prey and then TEAR IT APART with their strong claws.

Macrochelys temminckii (alligator snapping turtle):

Besides being the biggest member of the snapping turtle family, the alligator snapping turtle has another interesting feature. It uses a bit of flesh on its tongue to draw in hungry fishes. This "lure" not only looks like a pink worm, but also wiggles like a worm. When a fish approaches to nab an easy lunch, the turtle quickly lashes out and clamps its strong jaws around the unsuspecting fish.

Chelydra serpentina [Common snapping turtle]

Order: Testudines (tortoise and turtles)

Infraorder: Cryptodira (hidden-neck tortoise and turtles)

Superfamily: Testudinoidea (tortoise and freshwater turtles)

Family: Chelydridae (snapping turtles and big-headed turtles)

Genus: Chelydra (snapping turtles)

Species: Chelydra serpentina (common snapping turtle)

Common name: Common snapping turtle

The egg is the source of the snapping turtle remedy used, because that is what was proved and was most readily available. Any part of the creature carries the energy and could have been used to make the remedy.

Introduction

Chelydra is from the Greek chelona, meaning tortoise or turtle. Cognate (from a similar origin) with the Latin *chelydrus*, meaning an amphibious snake or water serpent. This is referring to the HIGHLY AQUATIC NATURE and PRIMITIVE APPEARANCE OF THIS SPECIES.

Serpentina is from the Latin *serpens*, meaning snake. Cognate with the late Latin *serpentinus*, meaning snake-like. This is referring to its LONG NECK.

Mating characteristics

During the breeding season male snapping turtles engage in territorial battles with rivals in shallow water. The competitors face each other and then LUNGE FORWARD; SCRATCHING, KICKING and sometimes BITING each other for up to an hour. This follows the general aquatic turtle behaviour of male competition, which includes gaping, biting, shoving, and clawing.

Snapping turtle mating involves:

- GAZING, or facing each other in the water.

- EMITTING BUBBLES from the snout.

- BITING THE NECK or shell of the other.

- The male's **mounting** the carapace of the female from behind, HOLDING ON WITH THE LONG CLAWS of the front and rear legs, and sometimes biting the female on the top of her head.

Characteristic behavior

Dwelling

Snapping turtles are NOT SOCIAL creatures. Social interactions are limited to aggression between individuals, usually males. Snapping turtles can be very vicious when removed from the water, but they become docile when placed back into the water.

Snapping turtles communicate to mates with leg movements while the turtles face each other. Snapping turtles also use their sense of smell, vision, and touch to detect prey. They may SENSE VIBRATIONS IN THE WATER.

Like most turtles, snappers can go for days or even weeks without eating. When food is available they will eat all they can, and may become quite fat. Snapping turtles become more sedentary as they age. They can live to be 60 years old.

Specific method of attack and defense

The eggs and hatchlings of snapping turtles are preyed upon by: other large turtles, great blue herons, crows, raccoons, skunks, foxes, bullfrogs, water snakes, and large predatory fish, such as largemouth bass. Once snapping turtles become larger, there are few animals that prey on them.

Excerpts from the proving of Ovum of *Chelydra serpentina* **(NHA proving):**

Master prover: Eric Sommermann, PhD, RSHom (NA) led the proving of *Chelydra serpentina* for the Northwestern Academy of Homeopathy in 2004.

Source: 10-15 snapping turtle eggs from Northern Minnesota; provided by Alex Lanning.

(Note: The proving symptoms are sorted according to general testudines's features and the specific indications of semiaquatic and snapping turtles.)

Proving symptoms related to general Testudines features:

- Strange sensation when driving through a tunnel at night…felt like I was a cell or something very small passing through a blood vessel (akin to being in the shell).
- Dreamy feeling. Feeling altered, like I wasn't quite all there. Not really connected to what I am doing. I felt drunk when I got up this morning. My speech seems slurred, my body heavy, my head feels heavy, and I feel like I can't think clearly. A fuzzy feeling in [my] head, as if I couldn't quite make sense of the moment. Mental cloudiness, confusion, dazed, difficulty concentrating and focusing on tasks, distracted easily, and feeling spacey. Shake my head to get rid of the feeling and get back to the present.

- I am actually thinking quite clearly. Everything [seems] clear, more color, sharper. [I] caught myself looking at flowers on bead cover, noticing them. I felt upbeat and positive, like surrounded by possibilities and potential that I will succeed, like a window or opening portal of opportunity – I can almost see it, as if something opened up in the cosmos. I am very blessed, very aware. I want to be still and see what I can feel and experience. I have a deep desire to go inwards. I desire to meditate.

- I craned my neck trying to make out what I was seeing and almost stopped the car to look. I was noticing details I have never seen and being curious about it.

- I feel like if I don't accomplish something each day I am losing time, getting behind. If I get behind I feel like I will never catch up. Sensation that time is running out.

- [While traveling] at one point [I suddenly realized] we were on the wrong road. I just had this sense we were on the wrong track. I went to the map and I was right. It was dark and in the middle of the night and the road just didn't feel right (feeling of being within the home range).

- I am packing up to go home. I am really looking forward to getting home.

- It's windy and I do not like it. I am restless and I want to stay home inside my house. (In this and the above feature we can see the testudines nature of wanting to come back home, homesickness.)

- Dream: I was at some place where there were many places to hide. I was there with several people, and someone was the object of much scorn and being made fun of. At some point, a companion and I had to crawl on the ground to avoid being noticed by anyone. Later in the dream, I took part in poking fun at the targeted person and was told by the others in the group, "We didn't know you had it in you!" The place where things occurred was a log structure with many steps that I had to hide and crawl around on. After waking up, I felt terribly sad and upset that I had made fun of someone and had disappointed my companions. (The feeling of disappointment stayed with me for most of the rest of the day.)

Specific features of the semiaquatic turtles:

- Dream: I am with my daughter in a car, in a town with steep hills. There is ice and snow. I try to get up a hill so I can get out of town. I can't get up the hill, so I back down. I find another hill that looks clearer. I get to the top. At the bottom on the other side is a pool of water. A man drives in so he can get out of there. He goes down deep and the pool seems to get larger. It looks like he won't be able to come up. Finally he swims to the top. All of us watching let out a sigh of relief. I wonder how I will get out of this place. I think I need to call my husband to see if our car can go through the pool unscathed. (I have a feeling of discouragement, that there is no way to get out of this place.)

- Dream: Not well remembered. I was going to a classmate's house. It was in a remote place. I had a little snowmobile to get there. She was on it with me. I was concerned because the area we were going into was a

177

wetland. I wasn't sure if it would be frozen solid and we might go into the water. Sure enough, it started to get quite slushy and the machine wouldn't dig in. I was afraid we were going to sink in and get stuck. I really gunned it, and we got out and went up an incline where it was more solid. When we got to the top, I picked up the snowmobile and looked at something like a large 'toy rabbit' with little feet on it, for the tracks. No wonder it wasn't doing the job. (In these two dreams we see images of water, swimming, dig, sink.)

Specific features of the snapping turtle:

- I was very **easily and quickly offended** by a conversation at work. I took it personally and felt like I was being insulted. I immediately felt as though I had to defend … I didn't strike out at them, but it was a bit of an internal struggle to make the choice to leave the room. I got very shaky inside and my face was very hot and flushed. Extreme irritability and annoyed with everything.

- Irritability accompanying hemorrhoid. I feel it is disgusting to have this tail thing hanging out of my butt.

- I am revealing way more than I am comfortable with at times…I feel vulnerable.

- I have **very little desire to socialize** and the mindless chatter of people is aggravating me more than usual. I want to be left alone. Aversion to company. Desire to hide and rest.

Characteristic physical symptoms noted from the proving:

- Sensations: pressure as if squeezed during vertigo, pulling down back of head.

- Eye: Pain, as from a nail; sand, sensation of; vision foggy.

- Ear: Pain, acute, sharp

- Hearing: Acute. The sound was echo-like…it was like whale sounds underwater.

- Smell: Acute.

- Sensation in throat: It is as if someone were putting pressure there with their finger.

Case of Ovum *Chelydra serpentina*
By: Staria Manos

Originally this case was taken, of a middle-aged woman diagnosed with bipolar disorder accompanied by schizophrenic ideation, in 2003. I prescribed two bird remedies, because the patient felt blocked in, trapped or caged, which did nothing. Then Phosphorus, because she feared attack, acted impulsively, and felt forsaken, which helped some, but was not the simillimum.

In September 2005, I attended a seminar by Dr. Jayesh Shah, in San Diego California, in which he presented themes of mollusc and gastropod remedies. Dr. Shah presented a case of a young boy with autism in which the patient's mother kept talking about a wall. Dr. Shah asked her to draw it, and her sketch of 'a wall' looked like a turtle. I found this case of turtle to have similarities to the case I was struggling with. As soon as I arrived back at my office I scheduled an appointment and retook the case.

She has been on medication for her illness since she was 17 years old. When her illness flares up she sees people who are not there. Her symptoms are reminiscent of those experienced by the main character of the movie *A Beautiful Mind*. She smells things that do not exist. She always hears voices. When she feels better, the voices are lower and she can distinguish them from real voices. When her illness flares up, 'they' scream frightening and horrible things that 'they' will do to her. The level of fear this woman lived in is incomprehensible. She was not able to work for more than a few months at a time, because the stress of work and dealing with people would cause a flare-up of her illness. There were times that she could not leave her home for months. She has been hospitalized for this illness during flare-ups.

Excerpts from the portion of her case taken in 2003:

D: Main complaint?

P: Just to help me get better balanced, to help me enjoy things again. **To give me more of a sense of security.** I don't feel like I really have it.

I am always aware of my surroundings. Whenever I am out, I check out everybody. In the restaurant, the parking lot, and all the cars that went by, I want to be ready to hit the pavement, before the bullet. No security in my marriage, either. Like I say, I want to see it coming, so I can prepare myself to be **safe. Fear makes me feel unsafe or insecure. I** would like to be in an environment where I don't have to worry about being safe. **I am always looking around. I am always aware of my**

179

surroundings, growing up in the city and because **nobody was ever around,** I had to be aware of my surroundings. **Fear of some one attacking me, being brutally raped.** Rape is a big thing, ever since I was a kid. I would never want to be in that position. Rape... just being defenceless. **I think it would be somebody bigger than me. It makes me feel unprepared or having no power over the situation.** Fear if H (husband's name) and I ever break up I would have to face the world again and start all over. Facing the world, getting a job, making money, in traffic, getting a place to live. My health would put me in a bad situation. Devastation, I will get sad, depressed (sighs).

D: Tell me more about your illness?

P: Fear, scared; the things that I feel and the voices that I hear are scary. They are lewd, mean voices. I still have a hard time taking showers when I am naked in the bathroom. It is one or more male voices. I have a fear of voices in the bathroom; I think they have cameras. The only time I don't feel afraid is, if it is a house I am familiar with. It is only until I know for sure there are no cameras that I feel safe. **I just find ways to hide so they don't see me.** It is hard to explain. It has been since I was 17 or 18 years old. The shower is a very vulnerable position to be in. It is a very vulnerable place to be. Like *Psycho* and the shower scene. I listen to my intuition when walking the dogs. If it says 'don't go', I don't go. When I was getting ready to graduate, **I wasn't ready to go out into the big, bad world.** I didn't know what I wanted to do. I dropped out, and I had a nervous breakdown.

Follow-up, case retaken October 2005:

D: Main complaint?

P: **Vulnerability**, 'cause that branches into my fears, and that branches into my paranoia. Vulnerability, I think is the core of it all.

D: Vulnerability is like what?

P: **I thought about the little kid on the freeway, or a storm, and it is just chaos all around, and it is unprotected. Exposed to whatever, to danger.** You just stop and wait to see what happens. I don't really react or respond until I am **touched, attacked,** or **held**; then I respond. **Just wait and see.** Scared, **exposed,** afraid (HG palm of hand upward, fingers touching the desk) kind of like, "Okay, what is going to happen next?"
This is a key point of this remedy. Normally in the animal kingdom you expect prey to run or a predator to attack or fight. In danger she stops and waits. She speaks in 3rd person many times.

D: Exposed?

P: Not a good feeling, it is bad. It is like a little, bitsy baby **on its back; you are vulnerable**. There's so much going on, like too much going on, and it is chaotic and you cannot do anything about it, so you **just sit and wait**. When you are not involved in a storm, **you have removed yourself from the chaos**. Your senses are so overwhelmed. When I get overwhelmed, **I just shut down (HG) I go flat line**, so I just have to stop. I have to step out of the situation.

D: Chaos?

P: Like being in the middle of a tornado (HG flailing in a circle) you see the funnel and the cloud, dirt and paper, and there is that little baby in the bottom of the funnel with his little white diaper. What does a baby know about all that? It is like in the *Wizard of Oz*, in the window you can see all the stuff going by, but instead of the house, it is the baby. **I just don't understand it all and I cannot do anything about it**, so I am just there. Just waiting to see what is going to happen. Am I going to get hurt? Where are you going to land? Whatever happens...

D: Tell me more about vulnerable?

P: To me, it is **like sneaky or crafty or smart, sort of, because you don't really see it coming. It is just there; like it comes out of nowhere (HG claw like)**, like a dream, you fall asleep; you don't hear it or see it until it is too late. Either you are **harmed or hurt or killed**. Or, like all the time, you wake up panicked, and nothing is there.

I ask her to tell me about the hand gesture, which is claw-like (she has used this hand gesture repeatedly, with her fingers pointing in different directions or touching the desk).

P: Somebody is already there. **They are too close**; you are a goner. (Same hand gesture, fingers outward.) **Makes me want to breathe hard. It must be like the epitome of vulnerable, an attack on innocents. It is an attack from the bigger animal.** There is no real competition. It is a done deal. It is the bigger animal. It is too late, you're a goner. It is like being struck down. It is like a dog in submission over you, and your **stomach is exposed** and **you have no defenses whatsoever**. He is going to do… he is going to do… It is a male that is bigger than me who's going to harm me or rape me or kill me, or all those things. It must be because when she (a girl in her school) **attacked me**. I started **kicking and thrashing and screaming**; I was only 6, in a small crowded room.

D: Tell me more about 'your stomach is exposed'?

P: It's 'You got me'. There is no, 'give up' (HG hands up) **your underside is showing, you are off balance, like a turtle on its back, you cannot defend yourself. You're stuck, you are at their mercy. You're trapped, because here is this other (HG) attacker and you are trapped. You can't move. You could scream and cry, but you're trapped. I am like, shaking.**

D: Off balance?

P: Totally reminds me of a turtle on its back, **wobbling** there. **There is nothing you can do until someone comes and kicks you over**; you're teetering (body gesture, wobbling). You're stuck. **Look how high that shell is, and look how short his legs are. He will just sit there and starve to death in the midday sun, he is a goner.**

D: Opposite of vulnerable?

P: Powerful, in control. Not a bad powerful. You are confident, you don't have to worry. It is like a 16 year old. You know everything. Powerful in the sense that you have your youth back. All the things I was before I got sick; **strong physically, beautiful, attractive** like every 16 year old. (HG fingers downward). You haven't been destroyed. You have your youthful strength. All that disappeared when I met H (her husband), **everything just flipped** (HG flipping).

(The patient's emphasis on favorable physical attributes (strength, beauty, etc.) suggests the animal kingdom, with its emphasis on survival through besting others, as the source of her remedy.)

D: Stuck/trapped?

P: Like a predator, like an attacker; **they can see you, but you cannot see them** (HG two fingers pointing outward). When I am alone, I spend time in my bedroom because it is all about 'them' seeing me. I don't know if it is because I have been **beaten down** in some kind of way.

D: Seeing me?

P: It is another powerful thing, someone who has the upper hand. It brings to mind the movie *A Beautiful Mind*. It is like, "What are you going to do? **Why are you sneaking around looking at me?" Exposed; they could see me but I can't see them.** Scared; it is kind of like an 'alert panic', it is complex. It doesn't make sense. There are so many emotions all at once, because you have to be calm to protect yourself. It is a sense of your surroundings. I don't understand that sensation when I am sleeping. **It is the sensation of**

something getting really close to me and it freaks me out (HG outward coming in toward her face and she turns her head). As soon as I get that feeling, I open my eyes and it is gone. It is like a dark black. I am in a black room, but it is also black, like a cloak, not a cloak, it is a … I never see it. It feels like… not heavy… but a presence, it has some kind of presence. If your back was turned and I was there, you could feel my presence. It is fast, and I can sense it coming. I am scared. I get scared and panicky, and I wake up! My windows are closed and my doors locked. The window over my head, it is high (HG) upward.

D: In your room and everything is closed?

P: It is safe, but I am not relaxed. **I am always aware.** I never feel safe, because I can't see anyone, and they cannot see me. You can't see me. **If you can't see me, you can't harm me, but that is not true, either.** You can't see me. You are in the dark, your eyes wide open, and you are quiet and your breathing is quiet and you are just alert. **Waiting to see if you are going to do anything.** Waiting to see if someone is going to see you, or if they won't know that you are there. You are just waiting and planning. It always comes down to protect your self, watch out.

D: Darkness?

P: **I used to like darkness,** not because I couldn't see anything trying to attack me. I used to like it. There was a change of environment… just been in fear of someone attacking me in the middle of the night. The dark has become a vulnerable place.

D: Environment, tell me about your perfect environment — what would it look like?

P: Calm… where I plan, calm, peace. **It is in the pond or the river in the mountains. It is cool.** It is safe. It is nothing harming me. **I am swimming, floating.** I can't hear anything. You see rocks and trees. You just see beauty, and beauty is calm to me, nature is beauty. **It is like a shield, like a guard. It is a protection from getting hurt.**

D: Shield, guard?

P: That **brick wall** (the woman in Jayesh Shah's case talked about a brick wall) that has a light shining on one part of it. It is a tall wall. It is so tall that the light cannot illuminate the whole wall. The top part is black. (I ask her to draw it, she takes a long time. She just draws a brick wall. It is just an image, I think.) It is like a warrior, always at war, **always on guard**, it is a **protection from harm**. It could be anything.

D: Rape?

P: The worst violation of a woman's body. To be brutally raped has got to be … Plan your defense there, either before, during or after. **It just takes my breath away. You just fall over,** "Oh my God!" **You just go limp, play possum** (means: to pretend to be sleeping or dead). I never process. Rape is the most frightening thing I could ever imagine. I hear about it happening to babies, by young boys and men. To be brutally forced by someone you don't know, who is **cruel** and **putrid**. I would fight and kick and scream. If they liked it, I would stop and do the opposite. I don't know what kind of attacker it would be. If I am alert and aware and don't leave my doors and windows open. If they want you bad enough, they will **break in and get you.**

(In the initial case in 2003 she spoke of being afraid of being naked in the shower several times. She believed there are cameras in the drain.)

D: Taking a shower, naked in the bathroom is like what?

P: Vulnerable. It is like a silent rape. It is like you can't stop it. It is not me; it is voices in my head.

D: Vulnerable and watched in nature?

P: Everything. First, like monkeys and lemurs, then, like alligators and crocodile. When he is on top of the water and you just see his eyes. It is kind of spooky. **When is he going to strike?** Just watching him, being alert, being aware, you've got to figure out what to do, how far away he is. **You know he can kill you** (HG fingers waving, they go out and in).

D: HG?

P: **Going into, out of harm, into protection, retracting into their protection or shell or barrier. (HG fingers are out) You're vulnerable. Now, (HG fingers are together) retracted, you are inside, away from danger or harm.**

D: Inside what?

P: Safe, can't get you, everything is okay. **You're safe, you're alone and no one else is there to harm you.** You're safe, you are away from harm. Nothing can get you. Now you can relax, you don't have to worry. It is a good place to be. **Encapsulated in water is the feeling, especially in the pond.**

184

Remedy given: Ovum *Chelydra serpentina* 12C

Now you might think a 12C is a ridiculously low potency, but with the 'Sensation Method', finding the true simillimum is so much easier. The true simillimum has such deep resonance within the overall experience and illness of the patient that any potency will have an effect, so it is possible to begin with a low potency in order to avoid aggravation, without worry that it may be insufficient to produce a reaction. I have had clients experience terrible aggravations using only a 30C. So now I start low and gradually move up in potency. This slow, steady way of healing has proven very positive for me in my practice. Most of my clients report that after three years of treatment, using the same remedy and gradually moving up in potency as needed, they are 80-90% better on all levels.

(The homoeopath in this case uses a method, (favored by some homoeopaths) of beginning the case with a low potency of the selected remedy, and increasing as needed. New systems are being used which select an optimum potency based on how the patient experiences his illness.)

Follow-up on March 20, 2006:

(5 months later she is going through a divorce and does not have the money to come in more often.)

SHE IS WEARING A PIN ON HER SHIRT; IT IS A TORTOISE!!!!

(She has no idea of the substance of her remedy.)

(She is going through a divorce and has gotten a part-time job.)

D: What have you noticed?

P: **Well, I just feel this millstone has been cut off. I have been able to stand erect. I feel stronger. I still fear everyday that someone is going to kill me. I have to be alert. I have to do a lot by myself. I live alone. I almost feel completely comfortable with that.**

D: Fear/ paranoia?

P: I don't know where it was before, but now it is a subtle, though still a constant reminder that keeps me alert. **I don't have the fear like I had before, like someone is watching me.**

D: Unprotected, vulnerable?

P: I think of that more when I take a shower. It still bugs me. Last week, it was the first time in years, I relaxed in the shower. I usually take it as fast as I can, but I took more time.

185

D: Voices?

P: No, the voices have been pretty good, and I am glad. That has been fine. (She still hears them but they are low, not screaming at her.)

D: How long has it been since you remember that overwhelming feeling coming up?

P: Since court and divorce, probably before the holidays... probably November. I know and feel that there has been a difference. I feel stronger emotionally. I am eating better. I am sleeping better. My fears are a little less, I will always have my fears, but it is to a lesser degree. I don't have that dreadful feeling. I have lost some weight.
(Information from written paperwork: Constipation and chills are better.)

Recommendation: She is doing noticeably better.

Order Ovum *Chelydra serpentina* 30C.

Follow-up on June 5, 2006 (9 months after retake):

This follow up wasn't as good. She had not been taking her remedy and everything had gotten worse, especially her fears. She is under a lot of stress with her divorce. The 30C was not strong enough. I moved her to a 200C.

There was good news in the case, however. She had gone to her psychiatrist to get her prescriptions filled and told him about going through her divorce. Her doctor asked her what else she was doing. She said she did not understand. He explained that people with her diagnosis would not be able to handle the stress of a divorce as well as she was handling it, and he asked her if she were doing something else. She told him she was seeing a homoeopath and was on a homoeopathic remedy. His response was, "I have no idea what that is, but keep doing it, because it is working for you!"

Follow-up on August 7, 2006 (11 months after retake):

P: I take the remedy every two weeks on Mondays (Ovum *Chelydra serpentina* 200C). I have been having dreams; before I used to never dream. I just remember they were just scary. The last one, there was this big, swollen, festering face. **A demon was holding me down. I was petrified, it was holding me down. I could not speak and I could not say anything. It was really scary.**

186

D: Overall, how are you?

P: Better. I am getting more adventurous. I am still very fearful. I do wake up once or twice, but I am sleeping a little more sound, not being as jumpy. I know I am not as stressed out. I don't feel as pressured. I keep hearing the voice. I look toward the direction I think it is coming from. I tell myself *Nobody is watching you; they don't care that much to watch every freakin' move I make.* I feel like I am ignoring it more and able to reason. It is just my disease.

D: Anything else?

P: I have to find more balance in going out of the house now. I am slowing down a little bit when driving. I have been enjoying it. I am helping a woman with cancer.

Notice the balance: She is no longer the upside-down turtle.

She complains about her feet hurting and still not being comfortable in the shower, but these symptoms are getting better.

Recommendation: Move to 1M.

Follow-up on September 13, 2007 (almost 2 years later):

She came in, closed the windows, and said **"I just want to hide!"**

(She has not been taking the remedy or her prescription medicines. She is having serious financial problems, and her ex-husband no longer sends money.)

D: What's happening?

P: The sky fell in and I died. I am tired. I am wearing out right now. I can't think any more. Just last week and this week, it is getting difficult to maintain, and too overwhelming. I am just focusing on getting this job (she is looking for a second part-time job).

D: Later that night, I got a phone call from the patient's friend who said that she (the patient) had disappeared. We found her at midnight, walking on a road near the beach. Her disease was out of control. She thought that all her friends and family were dead, killed by 'them'. The police allowed her to come with me and not go to the hospital. I brought her home with me and gave her a 1M every one to two hours, for the next 24 hours, and she pulled out of the manic state. The next day she stayed with friends and took the remedy 3-4 times a day.

I ordered Ovum *Chelydra serpentina* 10M from Helios. As soon as it arrived, she took it.

Follow-up on January 27, 2008 (2 years 3 months after starting this remedy):

Now taking the 10M.

D: Smells?

P: Well, I did smell something a few weeks ago. Not like before, when I smelled it a lot more.

D: Naked and drain in shower?

P: I got over the drain thing. I went on my knees and convinced myself nothing is in there, no cameras. I don't lock the bathroom door.

D: Rape?

P: I feel a lot more confident. I don't have all those fears right now.

D: Voices?

P: I thought the voices would never be gone. I just thought they would be something I had to suppress, but I don't hear the voices at all right now. I also noticed I am not so self-conscience.

For the FIRST TIME SINCE SHE WAS 17, SHE IS NOT HEARING THE VOICES!!!

(She says she feels 70% better.)

D: Work?

P: At work, work is good.

(She has held a part-time job for 3 years now!)

Follow-up on July 4, 2008 (2 years 9 months):

P: I am taking charge and doing what I can, **to break through those walls and barriers. I am standing my ground, instead of falling apart or giving up.** I'm doing what I am supposed to do. For 25 years I was on medicines but it is like a Band-Aid, but it does not help you do anything about it. I've gone a year and a half without any medication, now.

(She has known for some time that her remedy comes from the snapping turtle. She seems to be expressing her delight in and connection to her remedy as she says, "I was thinking...**My happy place is water. That is my happy place. I love the coolness of water, I dream about it. I painted my room in the color of water. I love drinking water. It is so good! It is like a wash. I have bubbles for my home page on my computer, with all these little bubbles coming up and a wave on top.**")

This is the last follow-up to date. She is taking the 10M about every 10 days now. She has not taken her prescription medication in a long time. I have a 50M on order from Helios. If she does not keep up on the remedy, the symptoms will come up again, with less severity. She can sleep. She is not afraid to live alone. Besides working, she has started taking college classes to improve her education. She is helping so many people and has taken in a few stray animals. Stress now affects her more physically than mentally.

I have other patients on this remedy. These are the common features that I have observed in all the turtle cases. They have informed and shaped my understanding of the remedy.

Case analysis

Important tortoise/turtle themes:

- EXPOSED

- HIDING, especially when in danger

- CHAOS, like a storm or tornado

- DARKNESS, fear in the darkness

- VIOLENCE /TURBULENT /SUFFERING

- SHEILD/BARRIER/WALL (one woman talked about being an empty shell)

- WATER, and sometimes rocks or sand

- HELPLESS/DEFENSELESS

- SUDDEN

- SEXUAL: rape, highly sexual, or sexual energy

The main reason I chose Ovum *Chelydra serpentina* over other turtles is the water element in the case. I have found in this and two other cases that they do talk about water, the beach, sand, or rocks.

Authors' comments:

Issues of animal kingdom are very clear:

- Being attacked by someone bigger, stronger, and powerful

- Vulnerable, unprotected, exposed to danger, attacked

- Feeling defenseless

- She speaks more from a victimized side

189

Reptile issues:

- Sudden ambush attack
- Comes out of nowhere
- To be hidden, not seen; sneaky, crafty

From here we need to understand further characteristics of the attack which is indicative of the subkingdom

Important testudines expressions:

Then we see the specific features of the attack or aggression (these features help to differentiate the order):

- Turtle on its back
- Off balance, wobbling, flipped
- Nothing you can do until someone kicks you over
- Darkness (to hibernate, buried)
- Shield, guard, protection from getting hurt
- Break in and get you
- Fall over, limp, play possum (pretend dead)
- Retract into your protection, shell or barrier, away from danger and harm
- Safe, alone, no one to harm you

All the time she says she is: defenseless, vulnerable, unprotected, exposed to danger and being attacked. These themes are indicative of the testudines.

In this particular patient, we see turtle expressions:

- Want to breathe hard
- To be in the pond, river
- Floating, swimming
- Encapsulated in water, in the pond

Specific expressions of *Chelydra serpentina*:

- Sneaky, crafty. It is just there, like it comes out of nowhere. You don't really see it coming. You don't see them, but they can see you (HG this particular patient even demonstrates this theme of sudden attack through her hand gesture that suggests a claw). This indicates the ambush attack of the snapping turtle, to attack from a hiding position.

Here we will again emphasize that any hand gesture is always an expression of the source. It never reflects the source's primary predator or aggressor. For example, if a patient whose remedy is 'white-tailed deer', cups his hand to form a claw and makes a gesture of pawing, it cannot refer to the black bear, a primary predator of the white-tailed deer. Any energy that is demonstrated at any point, is always subjective to the energy of the source.

- Concern about the underside showing (the plastron of the common snapping turtle is proportionally smaller than that of other turtles, covering less than half of the snapper's underside area. It exposes them more, and gives them more vulnerability in this area).

Possible expressions of the common snapping turtle in patients

In a snapping turtle we will observe:

- General features of reptiles: camouflage, bury, submerged, conceal, and hunt by ambush.
- General features of tortoises: the experience of the shell, but the shell fails to provide them adequate security and protection. They become bold and aggressive and defend themselves ferociously. This is as opposed to the other docile tortoises, which retract inside the shell when attacked or threatened. There are also indications of home-sickness and being within the home range.
- The specific features of a semiaquatic turtle: to swim, float, soak, wade, submerge, hibernate, dig, and burrow; also images of water/sea.

Snapping turtle mind-set

Especially attack and defense mode as seen in human patients

The most characteristic feature of the snapping turtle which can be expressed in patients is their snapping disposition.

Snap means:

1. Lose control over emotions. To lose control or erupt in anger suddenly.
2. Speak angrily. To say something or reply in anger or irritation.
3. Bite somebody or something with a quick movement or movements.

191

This is exactly how the snapping turtle attacks:

- Suddenly from ambush position
- Lunging forwards with amazing speed and accuracy
- Powerful bite, slice, tear
- Drag underwater, drown

Alert words that reflect this behavior:

Buried	Snap	Lunge forwards	Speed and accuracy	Aggression
Submerged	Bite into	Spring at	Fast	Violence
Partially exposed	Bite off	Leap	Lightening-fast	Anger
	Chomp into	Pounce	Quick	Hostility
	Crunch into	Grab	Rapidly	Irritable
		Swipe	Swift	Fighting
		Thrust		Ferocious
		Quick thrust		Aggravation from slightest provocation
		Raise their bodies		Scratch, kick
		Lash out		
		Propel		
		Swinging		

Body parts and functions:

- *Shell (partially developed)*
    - Inability to retract completely
    - Remain partially exposed
    - Vulnerability of exposed parts

Behavior:

- *Not social*
- Extreme tolerance to cold (as opposed to reptiles in general)
- Sensitive to vibrations
- Gaze, emit bubbles, biting the neck, hold on tightly

Family:
Emydidae

Homoeopathic remedies

Terrapene carolina [box turtle]

Chrysemys scripta elegans or *Trachemys scripta elegans*
[red-eared slider]

The **Emydidae** family, which includes the box turtles, is the largest and most diverse of all the turtle families. These turtles' sizes range from 11-60 cm/ 4-24 in. Their color is varying, and there are no outstanding physical attributes. Emydids are the principle turtle type sold in the pet trade.

Terrapene carolina [box turtle]

Order: Testudines (tortoise and turtles)

Infraorder: Cryptodira (hidden-neck tortoise and turtles)

Family: Emydidae (box turtles and pond turtles)

Genus: Terrapene (box turtles)

Species: Terrapene carolina (box turtle)

Common name: Box turtle

Introduction

The English name of the box turtle is derived from its HIGH VAULTED (DOMED OR ARCHED) SHELL.

Terrapene carolina consists of six subspecies, which are found throughout the eastern United States and Mexico. The longevity of the box turtle can be seen in its typical lifespan of 80 to 100 years in the wild, and 30 to 50 years, in captivity. Box turtles continue to grow in size for about 20 years.

Anatomical characteristics

Box turtles are most famous for their HINGED SHELL, which allows them to RETRACT ALMOST COMPLETELY INTO THEIR BONY ARMOR TO HIDE FROM DANGER. This retraction effectively SHUTS THE ANIMAL INTO A PROTECTIVE 'BOX'. This LEAVES NO SPACE TO CRACK OPEN, AND NO FLESH EXPOSED.

This SHELL HAS GREAT REGENERATIVE POWERS. There is a reported case of the carapace of a badly burned box turtle that underwent complete regeneration.

They have a steep-margined, keeled, olive-colored, high-domed, rounded carapace with variable markings. They are typically marked with YELLOW TO ORANGE streaks and blotches that often form a 'PALMATE' PATTERN on a dark background. The plastron can be yellow, brown or black, or a combination of the same. The rest of the turtle's body may also have colorful markings.

Food habits

Box turtles hunt for food on land. When young, for approximately their first five years, they are omnivorous, eating a diet of berries, fruits, worms, slugs, insects, mushrooms, and carrion. Adults tend to be herbivorous. All box turtles REQUIRE PLENTY OF FRESH SHALLOW WATER (a depth of one quarter to one third their shell height) to paddle around in, to rehydrate, and to void wastes.

Mating characteristics

In order to mate, the male box turtle hooks his rear claws behind the female's lower shell to keep from falling over. In some instances the female may assist him, by CLAMPING the rear lobe of her lower shell shut on his hind feet. This behavior PINIONS, BINDS OR SHACKLES the male. This extra effort seems to be necessary because the high-domed shells of these turtles tend to make mating a bit awkward. A male turtle that falls over onto his back while mating will die, if he cannot right himself.

Characteristic behavior

Box turtles are often mistaken for tortoises, but they are more closely related to turtles. Despite its name, box turtle, (not box tortoise), this species is PRIMARILY TERRESTRIAL. It also VISITS THE WATER DURING THE SUMMER (SEMIAQUATIC). Box turtles are NOT AS ADEPT AT SWIMMING OR DIVING as the more aquatic turtles. They do **paddle** around in the water and seem to enjoy **soaking** in it. The slight **webbing** on their feet is indicative of their partial relationship with the watery portion of their world.

In order to avoid overheating during the summer, they restrict their activities and **retreat**: **hidden** under logs, **dug** into burrows, or **wedged** under fallen trees or rocks. It is there they remain until disturbed or the sun's path reaches them. **In extreme heat they will seek out the shady pools and puddles to cool off.** Box turtles enjoy **wading** and **soaking** in water.

By nature, **box turtles want to stay within the same area where they are born (home range).** If a turtle is moved even half a mile away from its home range, it may never find its way back and will spend years searching. Box turtles have an EXTREMELY STRONG HOMING INSTINCT that **drives them to return to the place where they were born.** Unfortunately, attempting to do so exposes the **travelling animal to danger** and also **removes it from the breeding cycle** in which it would have otherwise taken part. **Home ranges of different individuals frequently overlap, regardless of age or sex.**

Box turtles are OFTEN FOUND TOGETHER and SHOW NO AGGRESSION towards each other. It is their GENTLE NATURE that, unfortunately, makes them one of the darlings of the pet turtle trade.

Some species of box turtle hibernate, when dwelling in climates that experience seasonal cold weather. They may return to the same place to hibernate in successive years. Sometimes more than one turtle hibernates in the same hibernacula.

A recent study has revealed that a box turtle, while SNAPPING ITS JAW SHUT, CAN PRODUCE LOUD SOUNDS (as loud as 75 dB). It is theorized that this sound could be used to scare away predators or possibly as some sort of mating call.

Specific method of attack and defense

When threatened or startled, box turtles will QUICKLY WITHDRAW THEIR HEAD, LIMBS AND TAIL INTO THEIR SHELL AND CLAMP IT SHUT. BY PULLING THE HINGED PORTION OF THE PLASTRON UP AGAINST THE CARAPACE, A BOX TURTLE CAN COMPLETELY CLOSE ITS SHELL UNTIL THE THREAT IS GONE. There are other types of turtle with hinged plastrons, but ONLY THE BOX TURTLE CAN CLOSE ITS SHELL COMPLETELY.

Predators of this turtle include: raccoons, skunks, coyotes, dogs, ants, crows, snakes, and hogs. Eggs are especially vulnerable to predation. The young turtles are also vulnerable, as their unhardened shells afford little protection.

Case of *Terrapene carolina* presented by Jeff Baker

Case of a 61-year-old female, complaining of allergy to cold.

Over the last ten years the patient has, with the exception of several time gaps, consulted my office for homoeopathic treatment. She has tried yoga, physical therapy, various herbal products, a little bit of acupuncture and meditation, but whenever I see her it's basically the same old story and that's been the problem all along...too much story.

Case retaken on 30 December 2004

P: I don't think I'm doing that great. I seem to have this...the winter...been really stuffy in the morning. Stuffy, coughing. Seems like in the night I'm all right, but that early morning chill...I have to get up and face that early morning chill. And I have this cold sore, which usually goes away really fast, but this one seems like it's gotten infected.

The other thing that's happened is some kind of itch down here (groin) and I used to think of it as a kind of heat.

Since the middle of September I think I had this congestion. I was preparing a proposal for a show for myself in 2008. There was a deadline for it. I was not getting exercise, staying up late, sitting there and getting chilled. **I think it knocked me off balance.** The day I had all that sneezing stuff and blowing my nose a lot, all day long I was running around. I realized that I was starting to take on a feeling that I was taking on responsibility for everyone's happiness. I realized that I can't do that; that I have to not worry about them so much. In some ways that helped the symptoms go away too. The next day was a more relaxing day.

It's fear of the cold or just this whole thing about, do I have pants that are really warm enough, but not too hot? **But then those pants are not going to cover from here to here and I'll be chilled. I don't want to go swimming because I'll be cold.** It seems that all the symptoms come from the feeling of cold.

The idea somehow that it's kind of **constricting**, makes me **cringe**, brace myself against it (hg various gestures). At a movie theater when I get cold and then bring out my shawl to put it on, all of a sudden I feel so comfortable and relaxed.

There's a certain tension with the cold. I'm trying to, with my mind, fight it off.

D: Describe tension.
P: It's kind of like **holding your breath... contracting your muscles**. It just feels like it takes a lot of energy... over a day. And then I think it's also, in the background, kind of irritating or annoying.

This is the time when it's important to move beyond the fact level and attempt to disconnect the sensations from the local level. If you ask the question in a very general way, often times you can bring the patient right to the level of sensation.

D: Say more about tension and contraction. What is tension and contraction?
P: Actually they're opposites. One is like **stretching** and creating a **tightness** by stretching, and the other one is **compression** and being **squeezed**. If I contract, I feel tense. So maybe that's what it's related to; the idea of being tense (hg tightens fists).

197

D: Describe this.

P: Squeezing. Kind of **trying to protect yourself, like some little animal that kind of folds up,** like a snail or a turtle...**might go into its shell.** A pill bug would just **curl up.** If I'm relaxed, my legs are like this; but in tension I'm holding them into a different pattern than the relaxed pattern. I'm putting this energy into **holding them.** And I get this feeling that happy cells would be expansive and floating around, and the ones that are tense are smaller and tighter. **So it feels like it's not just my muscles; it's happening at all levels.**

What a wonderful thing for her to say. Now she's speaking to us as if she's read the book.

D: How is it for the happy cells?

P: They just kind of can enjoy life...just **fluid**, just **floating** around in fluid, don't have to do anything and everything just falls into place (hg fingers lightly moving about). The other ones are kind of huddled together trying to keep warm and they're so preoccupied trying to keep warm that that's their main concern that they don't have time for anything else.

D: How is it to be in that state?

P: Something like fearful comes to mind.
Worry, not going to be able to be warm. Sometimes I think...don't know if I was watching something on TV; sometimes when I feel pretty **introverted**, writing this proposal and then I'm in the company of these people who are just **extroverted** and enjoying life, it would take me a long time to **unravel**. I couldn't just jump in, to be with them. It would take me a while to adjust.

D: What is to unravel?

P: It's the same thing, of coming out of that tightness, that contraction. So unravelling is more like a ball of string, just becoming string again instead of a ball of string.

(She connects unraveling to tightness and contraction. These are important sensation words which describe the process and the survival mechanism. So far we see the need to protect oneself, to go inside the shell, hold on, tightness, contraction, constriction, squeezing, introvert, and then to unravel, like the extrovert people around, like a ball of string becoming string again. We see the two sides.)

198

D: More about the experience in that tightness, in that contraction?

P: Probably an underlying feeling of frustration, anger, *not this again*. It's like I almost want to give up on it. **Maybe it's my particular weakness; that my body always finds that particular groove...to go into.**

D: What's the feeling in that particular groove?

P: Like that feeling of being **restricted**. Trying to control things so that I'll be able to decrease my — **I'm vulnerable, so I'm trying to create these defenses (hg hands cupped, coming together).**

D: What is that?

P: **The shell, the defense.** Can't stay in my wet suit too long, I adjust the windows in the car so I don't feel the air on the back of my head.

D: *Snail, turtle, pill bug, shell*: tell me about that.

P: **I guess this shell is more like a skin than a hard shell...say like those bags. You might carry water in a bag, something that had a little flexibility to it. Feels to me that it's kind of tough, like a turtle's skin. It might sort of move in and out (hg). When I get cold, I get wrinkly; and then when I'm feeling a little less vulnerable, it gets smooth. When I'm warm, I start to open up. I suppose if I ever creep out of this protection, I want it close by so I can get back into it if I need it.** I actually have a shawl that I take with me; that works good, but sometimes I need two.

(This is a very good depiction of the turtle. She tells her need for having her shell – for protection, the process – to move in and out, to open out, to creep out of the protection and the fear – want it close by so that I can get back into it if I need. And the shell is not hard; it is flexible which indicates the softer shelled turtle rather than the hard shelled tortoise.)

D: Say more about this creature.

P: This kind of like creature that's living in this bag or whatever it is. So this creature, without this...I don't want to call it a shell because a shell is kind of hard. I want to call it a bag. What were those things...like those canteens, canvas canteens or a leather...like a leather flask? So I'm inside it and I'm kind of like...if you can imagine, **I'm really tender. I get this protection from this flask.** So if I go outside this flask the conditions have to be pretty good, like green house. **I can't just go out in any kind of conditions, because I need my protection. I'll call it a shell.** So it's kind of like I have a thin skin, I guess. And even though it might feel good to go outside, I don't ever seem to develop a thick skin….cause I always end up getting sick. **So I spend a lot of time between being in the shell and trying to get out of it, and getting out of it and having to go back into it.**

I guess I keep thinking that when I get out, I've finally developed this skin and I'm going to be okay. Then I get **flattened** again.

D: What is *getting flattened*?
P: Kind of like a bug that gets **squashed**. I get sick and then I have to go back in or maybe I don't even get sick…**I just come down with all kinds of symptoms…so I retreat.**

(Her fear is of getting squashed, so she retreats.)

D: Tell me a bit more about the extroverts?
P: They have a sort of **expansiveness**. These are people who you might sort of come across. I don't associate with those people very much. It's sort of a shock that there are people who are **big** and joking around…just in another totally different world.

D: What is that world like?
P: **There isn't any shell at all.**

Here she spontaneously gives us the opposite.

P: **It's like… they're just out there and somehow they seem really strong, like nothing can hurt them.**

So by inference she's telling us that her state, her sensitivity-directly from her other song, the source of her remedy – has to do with being in, not out; weak, not strong; and vulnerable as opposed to impervious.

P: It doesn't matter. They're going around with their shorts, nothing on their feet… nothing at all. **I could be wrapped up in my shell**, but nothing bothers *them*; they're comfortable, loud, joking around and **very spontaneous**. And they seem to be **very open and warmhearted people**. It's like they aren't doing anything: *eh, if you want to go to the store, go to the store.* And **they can do anything**. They can interrupt whatever they're doing to do something else. They don't care what happens… where I'm trying to get my painting done. Always have something I want to do… such as read. **I'm just sitting by myself, that's what I want to do.**

(This is the conflict: to be inside (shelled, wrapped, and restricted) or to be out in the open (spontaneous, to be able to do anything).)

D: Describe the experience of being in their presence?

P: It feels good, but **it's like if you're looking through binoculars in the wrong way. I can see them, but I'm way in the distance**....so it's another way of saying unravelling in a way. I would somehow have to get closer to them.

By unravelling, by being with them for a long time, so I could **come out of my cocoon**. Maybe that's a good word instead of a shell. Feels more cocoon like than shell like.

So now she says <u>cocoon</u>. *In the beginning she spoke of a snail, then a turtle, then a pill bug, then a shell, but now she says it's more like a cocoon than a shell. So you have to be careful. We can't just jump on the image she gives and believe that's the remedy. If you get lured in by the image then you'll go wrong the vast majority of the time. The only way to be sure is to follow every trail she gives us. Images only become highly significant <u>if they are matched by the energy and the sensation. For the image to have real significance, it has to hold!!</u>*

D: Tell me about a cocoon.

P: I remember as a kid there were a couple of kinds...there were these furry kinds and then there were some that were more leathery. If you picked a cocoon you could feel it wiggle; you knew it was full of life because it would wiggle. It was usually pretty full of...the larva, not like the larva was some small thing in the cocoon; it filled it up. My cocoon doesn't have these kind of like spikes on it. This one had ridges or spikes on it. **So my cocoon is this overall leathery or flexible cover.**

Something about what she's saying is out of tune. We're quite all right with nonsense. In fact nonsense is really what we're striving for...because in the nonsense will be the exact language of the source. But cocoons full of larva that have spikes and ridges somehow don't match.

D: Can you tell me more about it?

P: The other kind?

D: Yes.

P: It would feel like a **flexible material**. It seemed like it was covered with plastic, but it had some differentiation about it, not the same all over, but it had some **pointy ridges** on it...I don't know why.

D: What happens with them?

P: They either became butterflies or moths. I can't remember which was which. It's more kind of like the material that it reminds me of. **The thing about the shell is it comes in and out. But with a cocoon there's a metamorphosis.**

When you come out, you don't go back in. It's a cocoon-like shell.

You see how the cocoon didn't sit quite right with her. The more she explored the idea, the less it fit. So what she's saying is that it's about the material, the texture, not becoming something, not metamorphosis, not butterfly or moth!

P: There are other sorts of analogies, like trapdoor spiders or hermit crabs or even something like a chipmunk, which might live in a hole of a tree...has protection. **But I guess the thing about a shell is this sense that you can carry it with you.**

What a potpourri of possibilities: trapdoor spider, hermit crab, chipmunk. Now she's given us a veritable zoological compendium of species requiring protection; that's what they all have in common. But in the end she clears up any possible confusion that might have arisen by coming full circle right back to the shell.

D: So which is it most like?

P: A shell, a soft shell.

D: Tell me more about the critter.

P: I thought I did. A sense of a thin skin. I think sometimes it may get so far into its shell, **be there too long.**

That's probably what happens when it feels like it's at the other end of the telescope. **Feels like it's kind of lost touch with the world. Takes a while to even want to be there again...to remember how to even...live outside of the shell.** I do kind of feel that I'm in there right now, even though I have these guests...and I'm enjoying them...not like those expansive people. And I do feel that even though I'm talking, that I'm just not completely there. And the other day I was feeling it really strongly and I decided to have a cup of coffee, which did kind of **draw me out.**

D: How is it outside the shell?

P: I'd say that there's a lot more variety, more colorful and in a sense brighter; might take a while to adjust your eyes to it. Just a total sense of being more present. When you have a cold, you feel sometimes that there's **this cloud, even over your brain, like fog, something like that (hg same shell gesture).** The cloud sometimes lifts, but when you're in it **you can hardly think straight and you might not want to be bothered by other people.** I know last summer I was ecstatic. I haven't felt this way for years....**just so freeing... to be dry.**

D: Describe dry?

P: Clear sinuses, not mucous **(hg open [opposite gesture])**. And to have all that energy, not to have to be coping with all this stuff.

D: Tell me all about the world of this creature in the shell.

P: **It's quiet and peaceful....very, <u>not much detail</u> in it. Kind of <u>nondescript</u> in a way. Feeling like it's suspended in some haze, so you really don't see the boundaries. BOUNDARIES ARE BLURRED...but it's comfortable and kind of cozy or familiar. It doesn't really need outside stimulation, feels like it's actually very satisfied.**

D: So why does it want to come out?

P: **I think once in a while it wants the stimulation. WHICH MEANS COMFORTABLE, COZY, SAFE, <u>BUT NO LIFE</u>.** I think it just wants to be able to choose. If it feels like going out, then it goes out; and if not, it doesn't--it just stays in. It's not that it wants to be in there all the time. It's not a bad place to be, probably that sense of not being able to go in and out with free will and then all that time it spends contracted to protect itself.

D: What is it protecting against?

P: The cold. And maybe there's other things...it's still sneezing and it's warm.

I don't know. It actually would be fine if there was this shell and it was in its relaxed state and I could go in and out of the shell. That would be fine; that would be perfect.

D: How is the outside world? Is it dry or wet or what?

P: Just like real life, all those things.

Remedy given: *Terrapene carolina* 200 (common box turtle) sent on 3/01/05.

Follow-up on 3 February 2005:

D: Is the cool bothering you as much?

P: I would say yes, because as soon as I let myself get cool I have just as much of a problem as I used to. But I do feel there's a difference. There's some kind of quality of change that's different, subtle.

The other thing that I like to do, if possible, is to take a walk in the morning. I walk, kind of get my blood circulating and it feels like I have a better day, like it clears a lot of stuff out.

I should tell you...a couple of things came to mind. Years ago I was sleeping with my arm over my head and I stopped doing it. But I started doing it again, on this remedy.

D: Feel?

P: **It somehow felt GOOD, that feeling of opening up my chest, stretching, not like I was protecting my head.**

D: Tell me about opening up?

P: I guess I can feel like **I can breathe easier**.

D: Just speak about opening up...whatever you can say.

P: Well I'm opening up and I'm stretching.

D: How does that feel, opening up?

P: Well, fresh.

D: Describe fresh.

P: Little bit cool. Somehow it's some kind of a nice sensation. I keep thinking it's so different, if you open up in here (chest) it's vulnerable, but somehow it protects this area even more. It opens up the side (showing with her arm over her head in that position). It's diminishing, but I'm really noticing it. I kind of peaked out on that...during this month.

D: Say a bit more about opening up...just in general.

P: Well I feel like opening up is a good thing, a positive thing. I feel like I'm still kind of too introverted now. It feels good...that's not a good description.

D: Describe that good feeling.

P: **It's stimulating. It puts me in contact with people and I enjoy that. And it kind of stimulates you, kind of shakes you out of your patterns (hg), lets more come in, more information come in.** So the idea of seeing how you kind of got stuck, habituated to certain things.

D: So are you any more opened up?

P: I took a workshop...I felt **like I finally needed a broader world, not so good to just continue in this reclusive world, as much as I have been (all the while making gesturing, (hg) two arms wide apart, with cupped hands, moving closer and further)**.

Jeff: The remedy would seem to have had some good effect, but it's way too soon to say anything definitive.

No remedy.

Follow-up on 27 June 2005:

P: In April I got my acceptance of my proposal to have my show at the MAC. So I've been painting quite a lot.

Five or six days ago while in Kula[1], I got some bug bites. I was sleeping in a tent visiting a friend. Five days ago I take this nap and usually I feel great after a nap. I woke and just sat inside and **feeling kind of like lead. I don't want to move very fast; I don't want to move really. I don't want to put out very much energy.** I wouldn't mind watching a video or doing nothing.

We do our protocols, rituals, and after my nap **I cannot move...zombie** is another word. So this goes on day after day. Day before yesterday I just stayed in one of the rooms, just **hibernated...didn't want to meet anybody.** I was okay in the morning.

D: More about this hibernation, not wanting to meet anybody.

P: Part of it is these guests coming, didn't know who they were. I just couldn't be much of a social person. Didn't have much energy, just in this state of half sleep, half awake. On that day I was just lying down...like lead, really hard to get up. Then when I finally managed to wake up, it was in really **slow motion.** I would kind of just stare at things in the room, figure out what to do next, finally make it over to the divan[2]...then just stare. Two days ago it finally occurred to me that all this behavior was due to a bug bite. On Friday it was about this big (showing). So I finally got around to thinking it was a bite. Now it's sensitive, but there was a point where the whole thing was just throbbing.

Hot...sensitive like a burn would be, superficially. Bruised feeling. Tender, very tender.

D: What has bothered you the most?

P: The lethargy and the lack of ambition and the need to sleep.

Just this feeling of lead...of weight...the bed is just pulling me down. Little bit more about that. It feels like my metabolism is going really, really slow. Everything; my legs, head, and shoulders feel really heavy. It feels like a weight, just pulling me.

Feels like some state of mind... a dreamlike state, but it's not full of images... not like I'm lying in bed thinking of a lot of stuff. **It's kind of dead. Just very lacking of energy, just very still and kind of like a vacuum... a lead vacuum.** A vacuum is really light, it should be. Emptiness is more like what I mean. Yeah, it's kind of half awake, half asleep.

---

1   **Kula** is a district of East Maui, Hawaii.

2   **Divan** is a piece of couch-like sitting furniture.

You could say drugged, but again it's not full of images... but like a cloud or being in a fog. But there definitely is this heaviness... you just feel pulled against it.

Jeff: Lead like, weight, heavy, vice, tension, compression, locked, closed (with energy patterns, first of grasping or a veil and then later on of withdrawn). She also described the opposite, which is open. Although she did not come back to the source (turtle), the energy, the sensations were all the same.

So what makes this very interesting is that this was a follow-up for an acute problem, ostensibly a spider bite or a bug bite. She even mentioned Lyme disease on the phone. But it was not the bite that was bothering her very much, but the state of lethargy, exhaustion, and the need to sleep long periods of time. It shows how one goes about getting to the remedy, even in a so-called acute situation by the same methodology and it comes right back to the same state of the remedy which has done her so much good. Furthermore, (and this must also have to do with the substance and the source), she described her state as being drug-like, no images. She said it was like hibernation. This must be very similar to how it is for the turtle itself; that when they retract inside their shells for protection, they are in a very inert place, without feelings or images.

Remedy given: *Terrapene carolina* 200.

Follow-up on 3 November 2005:
P: I'm great. I've been feeling like...ever since....getting over the Lyme disease, which kind of **buried me down in this reclusive place**. I want to be proactive, not that I don't know people. Why not call them, instead of waiting for them to call you?

I just feel like I'm being catapulted into some kind of a new person. It's not only...but that was only one experience like that. I went to San Francisco, had a ball, and it was very stimulating. I've been reading the New York Times, and that's something new. I started getting this art appetite. So there was one of those moments I was having, and I just went to New York City to meet a friend.

I bought art, and it was opening up this whole thing. I can spend my kitty money. I don't have to be like that (hg).

D: What's that?
P: We've been talking about that constriction, restriction. Going to New York was fantastic...**liberating**.

D: Liberating?

P: Like **propelled**, like a rocket that's taking off, going into space.

It's kind of **like jumping into a stream**. These opportunities all came along. I could have told them that the painting is not for sale, I could have not gone to NY. So by allowing the painting to be for sale, **a whole lot of things opened up for me**.

It feels expansive, joyful, enlivening, exciting.

D: Opposite?

P: Shut down, lifeless, dull, constricted, all those.

Jeff: Extraordinary follow-up on all levels.

Follow-up on 13 March 2006:

I'm on the verge of maybe having a boyfriend. I met him over the internet. Feels great, like having some spice in your life. I was feeling that I was getting more and more like a nun. The writer I was reading was speaking about solitude and that you can't be really creative if you have other things going on in your life. I see myself being myself.

D: Meaning?

P: There's a lot more spark there; I say what I think and I enjoy stimulating people. The thing that actually interests me about this man the most is that he's interested in poetry.

Jeff: VERY BEAUTIFUL AND SIGNIFICANT FOLLOW-UP.

Remedy given: *Terrapene carolina* 200.

Authors' comments:

The remedy given, *Terrapene carolina*, the box turtle, a hard-shelled turtle, affected a cure, even though the patient's words seemed to describe a soft-shelled one. This shows the power and flexibility of the remedies. The remedy used worked, no doubt, because it was from the same order (here Testudines). This is the point where the particular type of animal can be distinguished by common characteristics as the animal of the case.

Specific features of testudines:

Sensation words that express the idea of survival inside a shell:

- Protect yourself, go into the shell, want to be covered, defense
- Carry the shell with you
- Curl up, holding them, groove …to go into it, wrapped, retreat, be there too long
- Constrict, cringe, stretch, tight, compress, squeeze, contract, unravel
- Squashed, vulnerable, tender, restricted, introvert
- Shut down

The opposite:

- Expansive, out there, strong, nothing can hurt them
- Live outside the shell, to open out, creep out, to draw out, come out of (what surrounds or encases) the cocoon
- Freeing, extrovert, need to be in the broader world, liberating
- Knocked me off balance
- Pointy ridges

Words specific to semiaquatic turtle: Fluid, floating

The box turtle is semiaquatic, and will sit in water if given the opportunity. Hence, it is possible to get images related to water in the case of the patient whose remedy is box turtle.

Possible expressions of the box turtle in patients

In a box turtle we will observe:

- General features of tortoise: high-domed or vaulted shell, ability to withdraw inside the shell, hibernate
- General features of semiaquatic turtles: ability to move on land and water, paddle, wade, soak, hide, dig, burrow, floating

Behavior

- To shut off completely, leaving no space and no part exposed

208

Alert words that reflect this 'boxing in':

Box up	Clamp	Grasped
Clamp it shut	Cling to	Hold down
Closed inside a box	Compress	Immobilize
Pulled in tight	Fasten	Pin down
Retract completely	Fix	Pinion
Sealed up	Grab on	Restrain
Shut inside completely	Hold tightly	Trap
Tightly close the shell	Press together	

Additional features:

- Snapping sound

- Stay within group

- Not very aggressive, gentle by nature, very mild

- Extremely strong home instinct, home sickness, desire to return to the place of birth

- Specific color and pattern: yellow, orange, palmate pattern

Chrysemys scripta elegans or *Trachemys scripta elegans*
[red-eared slider]

Order: Testudines (tortoise and turtles)

Infraorder: Cryptodira (hidden-neck tortoise and turtles)

Family: Emydidae (box turtles and pond turtles)

Genus: Trachemys (sliders) or Chrysemys

Species: Trachemys scripta (common slider or pond slider)

Subspecies: Trachemys scripta elegans (red-eared slider)

Common name: red-eared slider

It should be noted that slider turtles are used in homoeopathy under the names both 'Trachemys' and 'Chrysemys'. At one time in the history of nomenclature the slider turtle, now known as Trachemys scripta elegans, was called Chrysemys scripta elegans. It should also be noted that the Trachemys scripta elegans (sliders), are very similar to the Chrysemys picta picta (Eastern painted turtle).

Introduction

'Trachemys' is derived from the Greek words 'trachys', which means *rough*, and 'emys', the Greek name for a freshwater turtle. 'Scripta' is derived from the Latin word 'scriptum', the past participle of 'scribo', which means *to draw lines* or *to write*. 'Elegans' is a Latin word meaning *fine* or *elegant*.

Anatomical characteristics

The red-eared slider is a medium-sized aquatic turtle with OCELLATE, or 'EYE-LIKE' marking patterning, on the carapace and plastron. Due to this it is often called 'the peacock-eyed turtle'. This information occurs in Wikipedia and was also published in 1908 and 1912, referred to a "peacock-eyed turtle", and cited the taxonomic name as *Clemmys irrigata.* Today, the Burmese eyed turtle, *Morenia ocellata*, appears to be the only turtle whose shell patterns are said to resemble peacock eyes.

The red-eared slider has a yellow and green head with a characteristic REDDISH-ORANGE STRIPE (more reddish) behind its eye. This stripe is exposed when the neck is extended.

The turtle's LOW, STREAMLINED OR FLATTENED CARAPACE helps it SLIP and SLIDE EASILY through water. Males are mature at 3 to 5 years of age, while females mature a bit later, at 5 to 7 years.

Food habits

Red-eared sliders are omnivorous turtles and feed on a variety of small animals and plant materials in the wild. Their diet includes: crayfish, carrion, tadpoles, snails, crickets, wax worms, and aquatic insects. It also includes numerous aquatic plant species: duckweed, water lilies, and hyacinths. Young turtles of this species are more carnivorous than the adults. When young, sliders get about 70% of their diet from animal sources and 30% from plants. By the time that they reach adulthood, they are eating 90% plants, and 10% of their food is from animal sources.

Chrysemys scripta elegans or
Trachemys scripta elegans [red-eared slider]

Chrysemys picta picta [Eastern painted turtle]
Note the similarity between the two species.

Red-eared sliders do not produce saliva, but like most aquatic turtles, they have **fixed tongues**. They must **eat their food in water** in order to handle their food, as their tongues do not protrude from their mouths.

Mating characteristics

Courtship and mating occur underwater. The **male swims backwards in front of the female** and will FLUTTER or VIBRATE the back side of his long claws, stroking on and around her face and head. The female will swim towards the male, and if she is receptive, will **sink** to the bottom for mating. If the female is not receptive, she may become aggressive towards the male. Sometimes a male will appear to be courting another male. This is actually a sign of dominance, and the males may begin to fight.

Characteristic behavior

Pond sliders are **freshwater turtles that live in quiet, softly flowing, muddy bottomed waters,** with suitable basking spots. They prefer quieter areas with basking sites. It is common for the sliders to BASK IN GROUPS. They sometimes form STACKS, basking on top of one another. This is when basking sites are in short supply. As its name implies, the red-eared slider, QUICKLY DIVES into water when threatened. They are **semiaquatic**, usually leaving the water only to bask in the sun and lay eggs. The red-eared slider enjoys large areas, where they are free to **swim.**

The name "slider" refers to the **quick retreat from their basking site into the water,** when they feel even the slightest bit threatened. A startled red-eared slider, which is confronted by a predator away from the water, will try to **scratch and bite.** Red-eared sliders are DIURNAL or **active during the day.** Sliders will sleep underwater at night. They are usually resting on the bottom or **floating** on the surface, while using their inflated throat as a floatation aid.

Sliders become inactive at temperatures below 10°C/50F. They will often hibernate underwater, or under banks and hollow stumps. Red-eared sliders **remain in their familiar territory** unless they go beyond their watery home and venture inland to find a nesting site for egg laying.

Sliders are generally CALM. They have POOR HEARING but are VERY SENSITIVE TO VIBRATIONS. This makes it hard to sneak up on them. They are DECEPTIVELY FAST and **excellent swimmers.**

Specific method of attack and defense

They hunt for prey and will attempt to capture it when the opportunity presents itself.

Their sensitivity to vibration allows them to be quite aware of predators and people. They generally shy away from a threat as their first-line defense. When approached or startled, as the name of the red-eared slider suggests, they FRANTICALLY SLIDE OFF rocks and logs and SLIP INTO the water. Here they find SAFETY UNDER THE COVER OF MURKINESS, AND ARE ABLE TO HUNKER UNSEEN IN THE MUDDY STREAM BOTTOM, OR HIDE AMONG TREE ROOTS and AQUATIC VEGETATION. The young turtles are preyed upon by a variety of predators including: birds, raccoons, alligators and large fish. Baby turtles that have been swallowed by fish have been known to nip at the fish's stomach lining, until the fish regurgitates its testudinate meal.

"They can pull in their head"

Case of *Chrysemys scripta elegans*
By: Uta Santos-König
(Earlier published in "Homoeopathic Links", 1-2/08, Volume 21.)

Introduction:

Mary, a sweet girl born in 1996, came to see me in September 2004. Her mother's concerns were mainly Mary's severe head-aches, intense shyness, her slowness, and her difficulties in falling asleep at night.

Sometimes she even wakes up from the headaches with nausea and vomiting and afterwards a strange feeling in her belly will remain. Sometimes it is helpful for her to drink something very cold, (she always has desire for cold water), or have a cold bath. The pain is located along the temples and the sensation is as if something was pressing inwards.

The pains appear mainly in the afternoon and in the evening, together with tiredness and a lack of energy. After vomiting she feels better.

Heat can also trigger the headaches. Strangely enough she NEVER sweats, however hot she may feel. The frequency of the headaches is three to four times a week. At school she seems dreamy and slow. She needs a lot of tranquillity, in the sense that if it is too noisy she will get headaches and bellyaches.

She is an intense observer, with the result that she never gets the necessary things done in time.

At the age of three she started at kindergarten, where she never spoke a word with any adult person.

She refuses to answer the telephone, never calls anyone, doesn't even want to talk to her friends on the phone. Whenever it rings, she covers her ears. The reason she doesn't want to talk on the phone is because people's voices should sound different.

She is afraid of the dark because of ghosts that may come. She tells me about her secret land, where she has a husky dog and a guardian angel. What is special about this secret land is that the rain there is of fire instead of water. While talking to me she takes long pauses.

Her mother explains that Mary always wants to say things right. That's why she doesn't talk much at school, even if she knows the answers. At home she can talk continually. She is very precise. When talking about a tree, she will not say "a tree", but "a gingko tree", describing the leaves.

She is very social, likes to help others and seems to be liked. She is always invited to birthday parties. Her favorite fairy-tale is "Rotkappchen" (Little Red Riding Hood); the girl with the red cap that meets the wolf in the wood.

Mary is very sensitive to odors. She smells all food before eating. She loves lemons, peppermint, and salads, and dislikes fish and milk. In general, food has never been a great issue.

Pregnancy was normal, and the delivery was very long. There were no problems in the first three years. She likes to move, ride her bike, and swim. Water is her element. She loves the sea and jumps into the water even if it is icy-cold. As a baby she always used to scream if she felt too warm.

She likes to draw and to cook but she dislikes playing with dolls.

Treatment:

I prescribed *Astacus fluviatilis,* (European crayfish, noble crayfish or broad-fingered crayfish) for the following reasons:

Massimo Mangialavori considers *Astacus fluviatilis* a remedy that shares the main themes of the sea remedies which include:

- Immaturity.
- The importance of a safe environment and therefore difficulties and shyness when outside the house.
- They keep their distance (in Mary's case mainly by refusing to communicate).
- HEAD: Pressing and throbbing on small spots, especially on right temple (Vermeulen on *Astacus fluviatilis*).
- Mary dislikes fish and milk – an issue for many sea remedies.
- The Mangialavori theme of SUPERHUMAN PROTECTION in *Astacus fluviatilis* I found this evident in Mary's "secret land" with the guardian angel.
- And of course WATER is a big theme for Mary, although, contrary to what is known for *Astacus fluviatilis* until now, she loves ice-cold water, and her condition is even ameliorated by it.

Follow-up after *Astacus fluviatilis*:

After *Astacus fluviatilis* C30 the headaches are reduced to once a week. This seemed to be acceptable for the mother and Mary, so I saw them again in January 2006.

She complains about more headaches lately, but they have never again been as strong as before, and she has never had to vomit again. The modalities are in general as they had been, except that her face suddenly turns white. She also seems completely exhausted, and there is a very cold sensation in her neck.

Her teacher causes her trouble, as she always criticizes Mary for not participating actively enough at school.

Homework can still take her ages to finish. She likes to learn about animals, of which her favorites are turtles.

I ask her to tell me about turtles, and her whole physiognomy changes as she describes them in a very tender and sympathetic way. What she especially loves is that they can pull in their heads and are therefore better protected.

In December her father had a bad accident and Mary got a shock after seeing him. In this situation the repetition of *Astacus fluviatilis* seemed to have greatly helped her. Nevertheless I decided, after studying on the Internet about turtles, to change the remedy. I gave her *Chrysemys scripta elegans* C200.

Chrysemys scripta elegans:

(Also Trachemys scripta elegans) (Redeared slider)

(From various internet sources)

- A sub-species of pond slider, close to water.
- Turtles are curious animals. They know their surroundings very well and don't like any change. They are loners, who like to be left in peace and tranquility.
- Their sense of smell in particular is very well developed. When you see the throat of a water turtle "pump", it doesn't mean it is out of breath, but that it is smelling.
- By smell they find food and adequate earth to bury their eggs, they also find each other by smell for the purpose of mating.
- Sea turtles don't have a highly developed brain, but their visual, olfactory and acoustic perception is excellent. Inside their nose, particles have been found that serve for orientation in the magnetic field of the earth.
- For domestic purposes they can be hibernated either in a cold cellar or even in the fridge.
- Reptiles don't sweat.

This information encouraged me to dare to use the prescription on the basis of pure signature (even if I could not confirm the aversion of turtles to making telephone calls....).

After the consultation, her mother called me to say how touched she had felt when Mary described the turtles. Her impression, as well as mine, was that she was clearly talking about something very similar to herself. Something that she could identify with very well.

Some weeks later I got a phone call from the mother who said that the headaches had slowly become better. On one occasion when a friend of Mary's had been at her house, they (her friend and Mary) had had a quarrel during which Mary became very angry and hysterical, went completely out of control, and would not stop. So her mother could not think of anything, but repeating the remedy.

"Immediately after the globules dissolving on her tongue she stopped shrieking and continued to talk in a completely normal way."

Another telephone call on the 31st of January 2007 revealed that Mary had only needed the remedy three times during the last year. She has changed school and was now really blossoming.

The last consultation was on 26th April 2007.

In February 2007 Mary had a very high fever that persisted even after taking antipyretics.

Then her mother remembered to give the remedy and within half an hour the fever came down to normal. Mary fell asleep and woke up in good health.

At school Mary feels well, even if she doesn't participate very actively. She only answers when asked. She loves geography and mathematics.

There is still a fear of robbers.

The only physical complaint is of dry skin.

I prescribed a simple ointment with olive oil, and recommended that she take the remedy when necessary.

References:

– Mangialavori M, Burley V. Remaining in a Safe Environment: the Sea Remedes. Modena Matrix, 2003.
– Vermeulen F. Synoptic Materia Medica II.

Haarlem: Emryss Publishers, 1996.

Summary

This case is an example of how the themes present in a case can point to a specific group of remedies, in this case the sea remedies, and how peculiarities in the case help to find the particular remedy within the family.

Possible expressions of the red-eared slider in patients

If red-eared slider refers to the remedy or patients who need the remedy, suggest:

• General expressions of reptiles—live lives of shy hiding, bask in a group, first impulse to flee and hide when threatened but will attack if cornered

217

- General expressions of semiaquatic turtles—swim, bury, float, sink, hibernate, sensitive to vibrations, strong attachment to home territory

Behavior:

- Slide away

<u>Alert words that reflect the ability to slide away:</u>

Slip away; slip easily

Frantically slide away under safe covers

Quickly dive

Shy away

- Stay within group
- Stack upon each other
- Specific color and pattern: red stripe; ocellate or 'eye-like' markings

Family:
Testudinidae
Tortoises

Homoeopathic remedies

Testudo hermanni [shell of Hermann's tortoise]
Testudo hermanni [blood of Hermann's tortise]
Geochelone sulcata [African spurred tortoise]

Introduction

The family Testudinidae contains approximately 11 genera, and 40-50 species.

Habitat

All are **terrestrial** and inhabit warm areas, ranging from rain forests to deserts. Although they prefer dry habitats to humid ones, they will soak in water when it is available.

Generalised anatomy

They have a **domed shaped shell**. They have **characteristics developed to adapt to a terrestrial life: thick, elephantine, rear legs; short, web-less feet; and short digits.** The forelegs usually have heavy scales on the anterior surface. **Tortoises can fully withdraw their head and limbs into their shell.** Tortoises can be identified by the lack of glands in the axillary and inguinal regions, and the presence of only four digits on the rear feet.

Food habits

Most tortoises are **herbivorous**: eating flowers, seeds, fruits, and grasses. A few species are opportunistic omnivores. Tortoises determine which plant or part of the plant to eat by smell. They have been seen **crushing** plants. This is presumed to release more of the plant's characteristic aroma before smelling them.

Common expressions of the Testudinidae in patients

This group will express all the common expressions of the land dwelling species of tortoises in general (given on page 133).

Testudo hermanni [Hermann's tortoise]

Suborder: Cryptodira (Hidden-necked turtles)
Superfamily: Testudinoidea
Family: Testudinidae (Tortoises)
Genus: Testudo
Species: Testudo hermanni
Common name: Hermann's tortoise
We have remedies made from the shell and blood of the Hermann's tortoise.

Introduction

Hermann's Tortoise (*Testudo hermanni*) is one of eight tortoise species that fall under the genus Testudo.

Two subspecies are known:

- The Western Hermann's Tortoise (*Testudo hermanni hermanni*)
- The Eastern Hermann's Tortoise (*Testudo hermanni boettgeri*)

The eastern species is much larger than the western species.

The Hermanni tortoise is one of the most endangered species today.

Testudo hermanni

Anatomical characteristics

The shell has INTENSIVE COLORATION. Young animals, and some adults, have attractive BLACK AND YELLOW patterned carapaces (shells). The brightness may fade with age to gray, straw, or yellow coloration. The underside has TWO CONNECTED BLACK BANDS along the central seam. The coloration of the head ranges from dark green to yellowish, with isolated dark patches. A particular characteristic is the YELLOW FLECK ON THE CHEEK found in most specimens.

Mating characteristics

Male Hermann's tortoises are often AGGRESSIVE to one another and to other animals. Two males cannot be kept together, or they will fight. A male may even attack a proximate female.

Behavior

The Hermann's tortoises will **brumate** in climates where the temperature drops below freezing. They have VERY SPECIFIC CLIMATE REQUIREMENTS, and a high percentage die in captivity, due to incorrect environmental conditions.

Case (1) of *Testudo hermanni*
By: Sujit Chatterjee

Case of a female with bleeding piles

Introduction: She has been my patient since 1998. She has received *Magnesium muriaticum*, *Collinsonia canadensis*, and *Ambra grisea* with not much improvement.

Retake done on 7 January 2004:

P: **Eyes pain, back pain, spondylitis.** Swelling there, medicine taken, but swelling started again.

    <Work

    <Mental pressure

    Bleeding piles, protruding, and pain while sitting and while walking. While sleeping it **pricks** me **(hg)**, so I sit on sofa cushion. I get tired very fast.

    At office people around me talk, they gossip. My boss especially, he is never at his desk. I have to call him 120 times. Colleagues next to me, being women, they also **play politics**. Why can't I be like them and play politics? The feeling **pinches** me.

I also get upset because of daddy. I don't get along with him very well. He has discouraged me, and insulted me in front of my family and friends. I've become habituated to it. Get hurt. As the role of father, he is not good. He drinks liquor. No happiness to mother.

When I get married I will give 110% loyalty to husband. I have that kind of confidence. Loyalty is no extramarital affair, which is adventure nowadays. I will be truthful to husband, no matter what, good or bad.

D: What else?
P: Boss is a political-minded person. When his work is there, he has tried to flatter me. I respect him because he is a very good father figure. I miss the attention and love from my father.

A friend after marriage stopped communicating with me. When she calls me up, I get so upset, my hands and legs start shaking. I feel she wants a favor from me, but I have done so much already. *Now* what does she want? I don't want to keep my relations with her. If she does not require me in her life, I don't want her in my life.

I realize that she talks almost nonstop and she is at the level of emotions (level 3).

D: What bothers you most out of all your complaints?
P: Piles.

D: Tell about piles?
P: Bleeding a lot, constipation. When I go to pass urine, because of the protrusion I can't even sit, it **pricks**.
   Pains, **pinches, something is poking or pricking (hg)**.
   If a thorn goes in your foot, how it pricks, it's that type of feeling.
   The effect of the chief complaint: pricking pain in hemorrhoids, as if something is poking or pricking (hg).

D: Effect of piles on you?
P: Lose blood. Don't want pain on me. After marriage, it will increase. Now family is doing my work. I don't know how in-laws will be, good or bad. They might not be as caring like my elder sister. When piles pain start, I get weak, don't have the strength; I can't even sit. I have to sit on a soft pillow and rock on it.

223

D: What do you feel that after marriage if people are like that?

P: Will they accept me with this sort of a problem? They will throw me out. They will think, "This girl has such health problems." Health affects my performance. Going to the toilet is a big headache for me. Get tension after toilet bleeding. Can't get up fast immediately, it takes time. Dress gets spoiled.

D: What is the feeling in dress spoiled?

P: I will not like it. I wear all light colors. Office has male staff. So they should not know what problem I am having. I will feel bad. Periods and this bleeding need secrecy. Males should not understand.

D: If they understand, then what is the problem?

P: I will not like it. These are female things. Men should not know. They will give sympathy, I will not tolerate it. All their attention will be on my dress. They will start giving advice, 'you go to good Doctor'. Embarrassing topic to discuss.

Everyone around me is healthy and I am not. I will feel alone. Not that I will be able to cope mentally. Even if my friend asks, how is your health, it **pricks me (hg).** My health is so bad that he has to ask.

D: Not mentally cope, what do you mean?

P: People who have good health are mentally very strong. I can't.

D: How does that feel?

P: I feel very bad. Don't want to put myself down anywhere.

D: How does down feel?

P: Low, **low with them, can't compete at all (hg).**

I am down and they are up. It will really **prick** me like anything.

D: How is the feeling that they are up and you are down?

P: **I feel I will be left all alone behind** *them (hg)*. Because of this problem they will think whether **to include me or not**. I will be left behind them and **they will move ahead of me**. I will feel very hurt.

D: How does it feel; left alone, not included, comparison?

P: **They are neglecting me. Not giving me importance. Not needed anymore. I am good for nothing.**

Here we get a glimpse of the survival issue, of hierarchy, the victim-aggressor themes.

D: Alone, loneliness, good for nothing?

P: It will hurt me, **prick me (hg)** like when you give injection and it pricks the skin. When you are sucking the blood and needle comes out there is pain.

As if someone has put a knife in my heart **(hg)** through and out. That impact will remain life long. Like a knife that pricks in my heart **(hg)** that area will be a vacant **hole, empty** and no blood will fill up, pain that something has happened to heart.

D: Hole, empty?

P: Someone pricks so there will be a space. If something that has to remain filled and if it becomes empty, how it feels. It will be useless. A cushion is there full of cotton. If I take a knife and prick inside, all the inside air will come out. Even if you stitch it, the space will always remain.

Cushion wasted. It will feel very bad. **Aim of life disturbed.**

D: Give one more example?

P: I have a heart and someone **hits** in heart, a hole. I will get it stitched, but that area remains vacant only.

D: Tell feeling of vacant?

P: Vacuum. **I will collapse** mentally and emotionally and **I will fall down.**

D: What is collapse and fall down?

P: **If I fall down, no strength to get up. Strength is power.**

D: What is power?

P: Ability to get up will not be there. **I can't survive.**

I will collapse. I feel as if God has given me this body, but I was not able to take care of it. I could not save myself from the person who stabbed me. I could not defend. I don't have the strength – could not take care of myself. **I should have protected my body** and taken care of all things.

D: Then how would you protect your body?

P: **A person is trying to hurt me. I would have protected.** If he is **stabbing** me in the heart, I would have tried to hold his hand. **Walk carefully if know I am falling. By mistake I know there is a hole, walk carefully, should not hurt myself too much (hg).**

D: What is protecting heart?

P: A person is trying to **stab** me. **I should have protected it.** Like when my piles first started I should have started my medicine then only. Now it is a pretty long time.

D: If someone stabs your heart, how can you protect it?

P: With my hands **(hg)** to stop him.

D: Disconnect yourself. What is protected?

P: Take care of myself.

If I know I have come in this situation by chance, I will avoid it **(hg), I will go out of it.**

Move quickly out of there.

D: What is quickly?

P: **Fast, try to run fast, so much that the person should not be able to reach near me. Use all my will power and run. Later on, even if I face problem** (she meant because of running), **if he reaches to me, I will protect myself by stopping him from stabbing me.**

D: How?

P: **Apply lot of pressure to throw that person down (hg). I'd push him, push him back, pull him down.**

I will try to the last moment whatever little strength I have to avoid and protect myself. If he manages, then mentally I will fall down. I will feel that I could not take care of myself.

Theme of protect:

"I could not save myself from the person who stabbed me. I could not defend. I don't have the strength, could not take care of myself. I should have protected my body. Like when my piles first started, I should have started my medicine that time only" *(relates her to the chief complaint).*

How will she protect herself? "If somebody will try to stab me, I will move quickly or run fast." I thought because tortoise/turtles are slow, they want to do opposite, e.g., snakes want to fly, as they do not have limbs.

D: What are your dreams?

P: In the past I had dreams of **falling from mountains, fear of falling from mountains.** Seen lot of fishes in my dreams. On a seashore a fish was struggling without water. I saw a cat and I could see its dark blue eyes. I don't like cats at all. I don't know how people hold a cat and kiss it. I can't. I don't like to hug any animal. **I feel they should be left free. Let them move where they want to go.**

I want to protect myself is the feeling from my office atmosphere. Sex topics are discussed. But my sixth sense tells me that some problem is there. Always think that boss's intention is not good. **He wants to hurt me emotionally and physically. Whenever I talk to him, my sixth sense tells me he wants to touch me. He wants to touch my body (hg). I want to give him one slap.** Not like it, even when you are walking on the road if someone touches you, you get a sensation.

D: What do you feel?

P: His mind is negative. Corrupt. He wants enjoyment by touching me. **I have to protect myself. Defend, hit him. Apply all my strength to protect.** May take something in my hand and I might **throw** it at him. Protect myself with my hands, **hold** him if he is trying to **hit** me. It does happen on a crowded road, men try to do that. Nowadays I wear bangles, otherwise I have a metal amulet, and I hit quickly like this **(hg)**. Amulet is round, made of 5-6 metals, and when I will hit with it, it hurts. That will be first way to defend myself **(hg)**.

D: What is this hand gesture?

P: Protection for self **(hg)**. This is me; my body has to take care of myself. **Not giving the person the opportunity to touch me.**

I will defend myself either like this or like this **(hg: first showed fist without energy, and then both the hands in front of her chest, as if defending)**. I will not allow boss to come next to me.

D: God forbid…somehow if he touches you, what's the feeling?

P: **I will kill him.**

D: How?

P: Whatever that comes in my hand.

D: What comes to your mind?

P: I have a telephone on my desk, a water bottle, and a paperweight. All can be thrown on his head. No matter where he gets hurt, that's not important.

While describing the dream she says, "Animals should be left free. Let them move where they want to go." Then she says spontaneously – I want to protect myself from my office atmosphere. "Boss wants to touch my body. He wants to hurt me emotionally/physically. I have to protect myself." Here we can see her sensitivity of being touched. Touch means hurt to her. She wants to protect herself from touch.

D: Any more dreams that is very strong in you?

P: One more thing, last week I went for world trade photos. Very nice but photo of a lady, she was naked and part of her hand & chest burnt with caustic soda. I could see the pain in her eyes. Term used for them was *brass wives*. During USSR war, when army people used to stay there, the females were made to have sex with them. If they would try to run away, they would try to **hurt them** with caustic soda. This photo has not gone from my mind. Two different political parties; because of difference of opinion, innocent people are suffering.

D: What touched you maximum?

P: **Her burnt skin.**

In her eyes, I saw the feeling of not wanting to live her life anymore. There is no hatred and sympathy in her eyes for those people, not ready to live her life, after being **tortured** so much.

Not anger or sympathy, not even **strength to revolt**. Her eyes are conveying the message. She does not have the strength to live any moment.

D: What does *brass wives* mean?

P: That was the term; *brass wives* are so many women being tortured. They try and have sex with them and if they are not ready, then torture them. **Try to kill them, hurt them, stabbing them, or hit them more with caustic soda.**

D: What happens with that?

P: **Skin burns, pains when skin comes out.**

D: Any other animal dreams?

P: Had an eagle dream. When I used to see serial on Cartoon Network, eagle takes a small bird like sparrow only. It never came out. Once I saw an eagle in class. I like tortoise and elephant.

D: How did you remember this now?

P: Yesterday, a friend received an e-mail that said how according to ones' birthday, your nature can be described comparing to an animal. My friend got cat. I like tortoise but my nature is described like a turtle. It meant peace loving, I will love the person if the person does not love me back, like to help people. My colleague, cat came out perfectly, i.e., crooked-minded, like to play games with people, political minded. She had habit of playing games. One colleague was on leave, one person from opposite premises wanted some papers. She could have easily arranged for it but she did not because this person in the past had postponed her work. Now she was delaying also. I was zapped and astonished because it was official matter. She did not give the paper only.

She is describing her friend's behavior in reptile terms, attributing to the friend's actions, the reptile trait of desiring to take revenge.

(Interestingly, she sees the eagle who takes a small bird. Tortoises are picked up by birds, carried to a height, and then dropped so that they will crack open, allowing them to be eaten. Actually she said that she likes turtles, but her description of the turtle was more that of a tortoise, more peace loving.)

D: What about turtle or tortoise?

P: **Slow, don't harm any. Do not know why I like their body structure. I like the shell on top *(hg)*, very protective, walk very slow. Turtle or tortoise can live in water as well as on land. He is adapted to nature, to survive in any atmosphere. They can protect themselves very well if an enemy is coming. They put all their legs inside the shell, characteristics of being able to survive and adapt in any area. Some animals can't survive as the climate changes. Don't hurt anybody, peaceful people.**

D: What are the predators of tortoise and turtle?

P: Crocodile eats them up like this *(hg)*. He is also living in water.

Crocodile opens his mouth *(hg)* and jumps on the prey. The tongue quickly goes out, takes the prey and goes in, and chews with teeth, (even) big animals like giraffes. If it gets in water, crocodile will bite.

The tortoise or turtle's shell is very protective; their body structure is such that it is protecting *(hg)* them in water and in land. They can easily mould themselves like a stone, very hard, and **you can't break that** *(hg similar to pricking and hammering)*. Something very protective that can take care of them *(hg with both hands shows similar to rounded structure)*.

D: What is this gesture and protective?

P: It can take care of itself *(hg)*. Take care, like you're nurturing a child, you feed it. **Shell protects tortoise** *(shows with both hands rounded shape)*.

D: Why tortoise needs shell?

P: To protect himself. Otherwise crocodile eat him up in one go with tongue.

229

D: Any other animal you hate or like?

P: Don't know why I hate cats and I am afraid of dogs. I can never dream of keeping cats in the house. I feel when they jump, **their nails will hurt me, it will pain, pinch me, and keep on hurting me.**

D: Hobbies and interests?

P: Knitting, watch films, be alone on beach, like to watch sunrise and sunset. Deep sea, every wave comes and goes. The shellfish come out with water, remain there and water goes back. When a big wave comes again takes shellfish away.

D: Shellfish?

P: Like to eat, it's my favorite. Protective covering is tough. I feel that mentally and emotionally **I have to be very strong. I like shell animals; shellfish, tortoise and turtle, because they can protect themselves.**

D: Tortoise or shellfish; which do you like more?

P: Tortoise! . . . can't eat. Tortoise won't move!

It is like me, slow and steady...winning the race. I also walk very slowly. Friendly with your health is priority. I know you will cure me to be **free and open.**

D: Feeling after sharing?

P: Relaxed. Something is going to happen, sixth sense good.

I had once seen a dream that shark is there and I can see his teeth very well. Zigzag, got scared. If he **bites**, get scared.

At this point, I remembered her sensitivity to pricking and poking from past recording.

Important notes from previous follow-up on 22-1-2002:

(At that time she was on the remedy *Collinsonia canadensis*, and she had spoken about tortoises and turtles.)

D: What is the difference (between tortoises and turtles)?

P: Tortoise; shape wise, is larger than the turtle. If any enemy comes it can cover its legs and hands in the body, and **turn round like a stone. It can sit still.** Basically they are from same breed but there is some difference.

D: What's the main difference?

P: Main difference is that the tortoise is an amphibian. Turtles are not an amphibian. The tortoise can go outside the water to regulate its body temperature.

D: Shell very hard?

P: Compared to the turtle, the **tortoise shell is very hard. He can protect himself. If somebody goes to hit him, he won't get hurt easily. In fact, it will hurt us.** Only turtle is ok. It will be slightly hurt, basically.

Only crocodile can hurt, and no other animal can hurt. On television they had showed that turtle is eaten only by crocodile. Crocodile is big compared to them. The newly born turtle or tortoises are also easily eaten by crabs.

D: How does it eat?

P: **Grabs** and eat it. They have that clams *(hg)*. Clams just pick up and swallow it.

D: Sensation of tortoise or turtle?

P: **He will get, he will die suddenly. Grabs with his pointed nails and teeth. The newborn can't protect it.**

Remedy given: *Testudo hermanni* (blood) 200, one dose.

Her state clearly confirmed the prescription.

Case analysis:

Comparison of the patient's Testudines symptoms with Theales (plant) order sensations:

* Needlelike pricking pain
* Injury, especially to nerves
* Punctured, smashed, penetrating wound
* Cutting; stabbing with a sharp glass, knife, or piece of stone; pierced
* But no victim – aggressor theme

Follow-up on 6 April 2004:

D: How are you?

P: Yes, I am fine, perfectly fine after taking your medicine for 4 years. My bleeding piles have stopped. It has given me more morale, physically and mentally. Mentally, I think I have much improved. **I am able to defend myself. I am able to take care of myself and I think I have got lot of confidence in me.**

D: What way confidence?

P: Confidence in the way that I had lot of suppressed emotions. If anyone used to tell me anything, I would not be able to communicate with the person. I think from this medicine, I have got lot of confidence. **I am easily comfortable to communicate with anyone. I can easily express myself.**

D: How is the office atmosphere?

P: Office atmosphere is okay. Lot of politics is there but it is okay and it is going on. I don't have to see it, though sometimes my blood boils, but it's okay. I can take care of it.

I have to accept them the way they are. I can't change the way they are.

D: Before what was the feeling?

P: Before I used to get confused. I used to get frightened. I used to say I will not be able to do it. **I used to get frightened. I used to tremble.** Piles bleeding used to start. Then I used to get tension. My legs used to **shake a lot**, but now I can adjust. I don't have to give it a second thought about arguing with them, I am right.

D: How you can definitely say that medicine has acted?

P: Skipping. Now in 5 minutes I can do 100 skipping at a stretch. There was a time when I used to jump, and from the 1st step to 2nd step my piles would start to bleed. I was not able to do my skipping ropes. Now in 5 minutes, 100 I can do. So there is definitely lot of improvement.

D: And the pricking pain was there?

P: The pricking pain is also gone. I totally forgot, and now you reminded me (laughs).

Excerpts of follow-up on 22 December 2005:

P: Emotionally I am flowing towards my boss like water is spreading *(hg palm with finger spread outside)*. I am trying to stop that flow of water by holding myself back *(hg closed fist)*. In the past I wanted my friend as a shield, to protect and give me strength. Now I feel I am within myself and I can take care of myself.

Rx: Testudo hermanni 1M one dose.

She is better but still requires the same remedy from time to time.

Authors' comments:

Important expressions of *Testudo hermanni*:

- If I fall down I have no strength to get up
- I should have protected myself
- Walk carefully, should not fall in a hole
- Apply pressure to throw him down, push him down, pull him down
- Fear and dreams of falling
- To be free, able to move around
- Throw, hold, hit
- Skin comes out (molting)
- Slow, not harm anyone, peace-loving
- The shell protects
- Be still

Sensation words:

- Prick, pinch, poking
- Stab
- Break
- Shell, hard shell

Case (2) of *Testudo hermanni*: "As soon as I open myself I become vulnerable"
By: Susanne Sieben

Case of a 20-year-old female, first seen in January 2006.

D: Tell me what are your complaints?

P: My stomach—nausea, especially in the morning, after eating. The last 3 months were really bad, with bloated tummy, flatulence, and belching. You cannot lie on your abdomen. In the night, I usually sleep lying on my abdomen. It is very bad. Not that I vomit but in between, there's retching when I feel nauseous. It is there since 3 years. Sometimes it's better, sometimes worse, and then again it is okay for some time. So morning sickness is there since really long.

233

D: Please describe it more in detail. What does it feel like, how do you experience it?

P: It is very unpleasant because it is like a pressure on the stomach and a real feeling of retching and nausea. I don't know exactly what it is like, but sometimes it feels like there is too much acidity. And I realise then that I cannot take acidic things like juice or wine. My bowel movements are irregular then, and sometimes I have to go to the toilet 5 times a day. It's not diarrhoea, but in the whole abdomen is this **sharp stabbing** pain.

D: Tell me more?

P: I am thinking what to tell, it is difficult. You feel unwell in general. **It is affecting everything.**

This is where I should have continued to ask – but I did not realise at that time that this was the point where she opened the door to generalise.

P: I cannot sit still anymore because everything is so painful. There are these days where it is so bad, so that I can only lie down or that sometimes I weep because of the pain. But that has not happened for quite some time.

D: Please tell me more about your feeling in the abdomen; the sharp stabbing pain, the pressure, the retching feeling, and the nausea. Tell me just a bit more?

So I tried more to understand the chief complaint.

P: It is like stabbing, and it is immense pressure in the stomach. Sometimes it is like very specific stabs, and I can say now it is stabbing. When it is stabbing, there is less nausea. Then it is only latent nausea. The stabbing only comes when I have eaten. And then I can say this is the exact point where it hurts very much. The stabbing and the pressure are connected. There are small areas where it feels **as if somebody is stabbing me with a knife (hg),** so that you bend from pain, flash like, but it comes again and again. It is not that one moment the pain is there and then again not. It is constant for some time. It is hard to describe. The pains last for one or two hours.

D: Describe it more please? I don't understand stabbing and pressure?

P: The stabbing and the pressure belong together. It is a kind of stabbing coming because of the pressure. This is a bit exaggerated, but if someone would take a heavy thing and stand on it, this is the kind of pressure from the outside, and at the same time **something is boring inwards,** so to say.

The sharp thing is for the place where the pain is. It is not the kind of pressure on a big area but on a small area. It is stitching on a small area,

234

and at the same time it is pressure. You get the impression **pressure from outside**. When you take a hand and press hard, a pressure is coming. This is at a specific area, and it is stitching, and at the same time there is pressure. **It is going inside of me. Really, as if somebody would stab with a knife and apply pressure. The stab is constant, because the pressure from outside does not stop.**

D: And how do the pain and the pressure influence you?

P: First of all in everyday life. The days I have this pain I am in a bad mood.

Hint for the potency - 200 – the problem affects her emotions.

P: Many things I cannot do because I have to lie down. **I am limited** if I want to study and go to classes. It is a general feeling of unwell. You don't feel okay; you are constantly concentrated on yourself and feel restless. In a conversation you cannot really get involved with the opposite because you only concentrate on yourself, and sometimes you don't want to. Especially when the nausea is there, you don't just go somewhere quickly to do something. First, I need time and rest, otherwise I don't succeed in anything. I sleep a lot. **When it is there, I am very tired. I am more introverted. I am more concerned with myself.**

D: Tell me more about introverted, concerned with yourself?

P: Because I have to take a rest for myself, I start thinking about my stomach, why it comes, and what causes it. I try to find out if there was stress, if something has annoyed me. I try to find out what has happened.

Pain as reaction to an emotion – another indication for 200 potency.

D: What does it feel like inside when you start to think? What do you experience? How do you experience stress?

P: Very tense, totally tense internally, especially in the stomach area. **Not relaxed, all clenched.** Everything is highly sensitive, it is running high speed. **When I have stress, every part of my body is very receptive for impulses from outside.** No matter what – I take it immediately, take it to my heart. At times when I have time and can relax, I am not so sensitive. When I have stress, it comes close to me.

D: Highly sensitive, body receptive?

P: **Very nervous. It feels inside as if something would come immediately, and you don't know what.** It is complete tension. It is not pain, nor is it nausea. It is as if I had done something wrong, or as if you have to admit something unpleasant. So everything is just muddled.

235

(Fear of sudden attack is a reptile theme.)

Since I could not really see the connection I had to go back to the chief complaint. In retrospective it was of course clear where I should have continued.

D: Please describe the nausea again?

P: It is like too much acidity. It's the feeling like not having eaten for a long time. That is the kind of nausea. I feel unwell, and I cannot really get into the day. It certainly has an influence on me.

D: In what way?

P: Because I cannot participate in a normal day. Cannot engage with something else fully as long as it is there. You always look after yourself, is what it's like.

D: Not engage with something, look after yourself?

P: I start thinking automatically when I have the pain where it comes from. I sit there and think.

I cannot follow a conversation or a lecture because I constantly think, I feel so nauseous. I cannot really get into something.

D: Where is your real point of interest?

P: Mainly when I can do something actively. When I don't just sit and listen. Then I can get into things much easier. When I have a task, where I can do something, or organise something, then I am in my element, and then I don't need to think. And then I like to do it. As soon as I have to sit in a lecture, and it is all theory, for some time it is okay. Then it starts, that **I switch off and am busy with my inner being. So that I am not there anymore.**

D: Switch off, not there anymore?

P: It is that I am **introverted (retreated in myself)**, and then I only think about myself and what is bothering me. I am not present. When someone asks me something, sometimes **I am totally absent, and I did not get anything.**

D: This state; introverted, absent, not there? Tell me more about it?

P: **At this moment you live somewhere in your fantasy.** What I would like to do, what I have to do, what I like and where I would like to be. It's these kind of things. **At this moment you are not there in reality.** You don't sit in the lecture or wherever, but you are at the place you're thinking about. And I am fully there very intensely. So during the lecture only my body is present.

236

("I switch off and am busy with my inner being. So that I am not there anymore."

"I am totally absent. I did not get anything."

"At this moment you live somewhere in your fantasy."

"At this moment you are not there in reality."

These are important expressions differentiating Molluscs and Testudines described in detail on page 134.)

D: More?

P: Well, in your thought you are only busy with yourself. In your thought you do certain things, you have the conversations you imagine, or you want to have later, and you don't realise a thing around you. It is like a small dropout.

And minor things bring me back. Like if somebody next to me is coughing or sneezing. Oh, yes, I am here, and then I try to get into it, and then it depends on the topic whether **I retreat again and go back into my world of thoughts and remain there.** It is the same with conversations as well as with lectures. It's especially true when I am not really interested.

D: Retreat, don't realise what is going on around me?

P: I am so engaged with my own stuff, that I don't perceive what is going on outside, even if it's somebody looking at me. I don't perceive it, **because I have cut off my senses to the outside. I don't look around anymore.** If I speak too loud or disturb somebody, or if something really important is going on during the lecture, I do not look around, and I don't realise what's happened.

I am the kind of person, that if something happens I am very much thinking about it. I allow the things to come very close. Too close I would say. I take things to my heart. When something happens, even minor things, I have the feeling I have to solve it inside of me. I have to bring it into order. What has just happened? **What has this done with me?**

Good animal hint.

P: And then **I start to retreat, to go inside myself** and clarify (hg). **And then I cannot see what is outside, and I do not want to.** I want to resolve it within myself, whatever is there.

D: More about this?

P: I am a very emotional person, which is why my emotions get confused. Be it that I had an argument, or met somebody new, a special person, or had a great experience. Then my **emotions whirl around** and I cannot really tell what it is. And then I have to sort it out and see what this **argument is doing with me.**

The feeling that the illness is doing something to her is another animal hint.

P: Which feeling is it? **Look out of the chaos of emotions**, what is it? What do I want? That means bringing order. To check out. Was it necessary? And does it have to go on like that?

She has, by this point in the case, expressed the concept of looking out of something.

P: Especially when there was an argument. Was it necessary to talk it over another 5 times? Am I really angry or am I sad? All these things immediately lead to a chaos in me, and then I **retreat** (hg: moving backwards with her whole body and moving her hands inwards to her abdomen). And I look out, what has happened? What is it that is really touching me? Or in an argument, what is my part? Which part did I contribute?

Do I have the right to feel hurt, to feel rage or did I go too far? Where **have I maybe hurt the other?** This kind of thing I have to sort out for me. And that takes ages and then it starts, I retreat and it whirls and it does.

D: Whirls and does?

P: **The retreat is a sensation of going into myself. The way I am like now, when you touch me, this part is not there anymore. Even if my eyes are open and I look at someone, I don't really perceive the world outside. When I have my hand on the table here, I don't perceive the table under my hand, because I have gone, so to say, just from outside...inside myself.**

It is difficult (hg: as before, hands going inwards towards her abdomen, her trunk), from the outside into the inside of me. *This* is where I am then (hg: showing the whole area of the trunk). Then I try with this whirling to sort out my emotions. What do I feel there?

D: Whirl?

P: I imagine a can with all the emotions in there, and it is **shaken all the time or rolling**.

You don't have any order. You cannot say it is rage or sadness. It is all mixed up. I feel how the rage comes up. Then again I feel sad and hurt, and then to stop this whirl and to say, I grab the emotions now and put them here and there, and look at each of them one by one and see, **what does it do with me?** Where does it belong to? What has **sneaked** in here which does not belong? That also happens to me often. And then to stop this whirl and see what is going on.

Sneaked is a good reptile word.

D: What is the main sensation with all these emotions?

P: Earlier when I was a teenager it was rage. I hated myself. And I hated everything around me and **I went against myself** *(animal issue).* It was a rage of desperation.

You were desperate and furious, but could not tell where it came from. **It was against me, against everything,** I could have hit against the wall, because I did not know where to go with so much… it has really overwhelmed me. But this is much better since I don't live at home anymore.

I am also very mistrustful. Trust is something I cannot do easily. I get a feeling of mistrust easily. Trust in the sense that I question everything, and I check out. Can this be true? It is hard for me to just let things be as they are. **To really open yourself up to someone, to get involved with someone. I am always careful.**

The ideas of concealment and exposure to danger are important reptile themes.

(The main thing in a reptile is their need to hide or conceal and then attack suddenly. It's an ambush attack. This is their mode of survival.

Each of the different orders of reptiles has a specific mode of hiding, concealing, camouflaging or attacking:

Turtles and tortoises: withdrawal into their shell.

Lizards: fast, agile movements, warning signals to stun their prey by utilizing body morphology (like changing color or enlarging); and autotomy (dropping tails), etc.

Snakes: threatening postures, camouflage, or mimicry to shoo away the predator. Or else attack by biting (venom) or constriction.)

P: **To trust blindly, unconditionally, I cannot do that.** Even with people I really know, it is always a basic feeling there, the fear of disappointment. **If I trust someone and he misuses it**, I feel hurt, sad, rage, and I am depressed.

I retreat myself for days, don't talk much, and am even more engaged with me. I totally give into self-pity, this sadness, all alone and to be disappointed. **I build up a wall around me. I will not trust you anymore.**

239

Other reptile themes are the lack of closeness with his fellows and the inability to trust anyone.

D: Tell me more about this retreat?

P: **It comes all of a sudden**. I am somebody who laughs a lot and I love to meet people and hang out together, to sit in a big round and someone makes a comment. A thought comes, and then immediately I get this,' **I am not there anymore'**.

("It comes all of a sudden ....I am not there anymore." Another reptile-testudines expression: to camouflage, to disappear.)

P: And then **I go inside myself**. Then I can only engage with me. It does not matter which surrounding I have. No matter whether I am in a discotheque or sit in a lecture with a friend, it just happens. And I cannot stop it. Good friends who know me well **try to get me out**, and they may succeed after some time. It is not just that you say hey and I am back. **It is as if you would close the door of a house, and I am inside, and only certain people know the key to get me out of there.** But that is not easy, because I don't want to get out in that moment. **It's as if the body was a house, and I close the door and go inside.** Even if I have just looked out of the window and stood at the front.

D: More, whatever comes to your mind? You retreat yourself?

P: It is not unpleasant. **It is like protection. It is my house, it is my territory, and it's my area. Nobody can enter, and nobody can harm me.** It is my thoughts, my feelings, it is mine. **Nobody can come in, and I don't want anybody to come in. I feel safe in there. When I retreat for a longer time I might feel lonely but safe. A kind of security.** I know my stuff, and I know what I have to do.

D: More, you are doing very good.

P: It is an environment that I know. Where I know my way, where I find my way blindly and nobody tells me what to do. **It is my area, my territory, and I am the master.** I can rule. I can do it the way I want to do.

I am not dependent on anybody. Sometimes it feels good. Sometimes I would like to talk things over with others, and to talk about what is going on with me. **As soon as I open myself, I become vulnerable.** There the story of trust comes up again. I really have to trust somebody. **And that is why I don't really allow anybody to enter my area.** Because it is all about my thoughts and my emotions, it is just natural. **When I let somebody come close, I show him my weak vulnerable spots.**

240

Admitting that made me furious or sad. I feel like this or that. **I show my weak points** to the person. **I fear being abused. That someone could take advantage of me.** The trust, the confidence. **I disclose my innermost from that point on. That is when I would let somebody in fully. Then this person would know everything of me. And I would feel completely without protection. This protection, this house of mine, would be gone.** Or I share my innermost, and this person can at the same time fully **destroy my house,** as I can do it myself. But if he does it, I have no influence. I can only trust that he does not do it. There are certain areas where I can allow people in, but not completely.

D: Describe protection?
P: **Protection is this house. This shell that I don't tell anybody what is going on. That is the protection; that I don't let anyone in.**

D: Protection from what?
P: **To get injured**, knowing someone could take advantage of my feelings, what is going on right now. It is as if I am dressed, and otherwise **I am naked and he can see everything of me. Like a shell**[1] **(hg: one hand up to shoulder region and one down to her hip region with a round movement). I am internally naked and he can see everything of me.** That scares me because I don't know how the other person deals with it.

(Again, the idea of the shell is not only acting as a hard barrier, but without the shell I am naked and I am seen. The protection is more to hide. The shell is seen as a dress or a covering so that you become invisible.)

D: More protection, shell?
P: **It is like a shell, a strong protection, and I know you cannot destroy it, if I don't want this.** Maybe at some special points, but **you cannot destroy it when I don't allow it. It feels completely safe, because I have the control, because I dictate the protection.**

D: You made a gesture when you described the shell?
P: It is like a shell of protection. **When the turtle retreats back into her shell,** which is a good example. She does it because of enemies. **You can knock on the shell. You can push her around. And she lives nevertheless.** And that is how it is with my protection. You can knock and **shake,** but it has no effect. You cannot enter, it is mine and I **decide when I will come out, and**

---

1   She uses the german word <u>Panzer,</u> which is used for the shell of a turtle and beatles, but not for molluscs.

whom I let come close. I have the power to decide. Where I know there is somebody who should not be there, and where I say NO.

D: More – you are doing very well.

P: It is more and more difficult.

D: Tell this again with the turtle?

P: This comparison with the turtle feels good. Because that is how it is. **I can come out. I always carry my shell with me and it is a part of me. I can come out and show myself like the turtle, and stick my head out, and the legs and I can walk around and don't have to go.**

("I can come out and show myself like the turtle, and stick my head out, and the legs and I can walk around and don't have to go." The showing and revealing, itself is again another important reptile-testudines theme.)

P: Inside. **But when somebody comes whom I regard as an enemy, I retreat like the turtle, to sleep.** I don't know if a turtle does this, but like that I can retreat inside myself. **Just like the turtle always carries her shell along and always has the option to retreat, I have it as well. If I would open up for somebody, he would have the chance to come in and could maybe tell others how to get in. And as long as it remains closed, I can be open for everybody. But I have the chance to say STOP, not here, and I am in my protection.** It can happen consciously and unconsciously. Just by having that, this being busy with myself.

Here she is connecting back.

P: Then I don't feel it in this sense, that it is protection from enemies. But there are things I cannot sort out myself, things I cannot talk about with anybody, because I have to check with myself. Then I retreat, and then it happens automatically and unconsciously.

D: Tell me about the process of retreating?
I wanted to learn about the process. Knowing that it is a kind of contraction with the molluscs and snails, I was wondering what it could be like with a turtle. It did not come.

P: Like a little machine inside, it starts running.

The machine is running, you have to do it now. I can hardly resist. It just happens to me wherever I am. I cannot stop it. I cannot say, "No, I'm sitting here with friends and it is good fun and I want to think about the problem later, there is no hurry ". That is not how it happens. But yes, I think, and **Zack…I am in.**

D: Describe Zack! I am in?

P: Well, just like the turtle, head in. I am in my house and start to sort out things and do. Sometimes I catch a few things from outside, but I get the feedback from others, 'what has happened with you'? A minute ago you laughed, and now? That I give the impression of being sad or absent, or **I am really not there anymore as I was before.** I start to sort out things. I am conscious that it is not appropriate and try to sort out things fast. And I try to think okay. It is a bit exaggerated to react like this in this situation. You could talk it over and come out. But this is only possible for a short moment and it comes back. So when I don't solve things properly they come back.

("Zack...I am in."

"I am really not there anymore as I was before."

Note the suddenness, and becoming invisible.)

I could confirm the same pattern of reaction coming from other sides again and again in the case. Two words she had used a few times (edited) and they had energy so I had to ask them.

Fidgety

Whirl

Whirl → due to arguments with friends → feel treated unfair. Cannot sort it out, rage, feel bad. Am overstretched with emotions. Might tell the other when I feel hurt, and might give the same back in return. And when I have hurt the other, I feel sorry a second later.

D: Hurt?

P: My trust/confidence has been misused. When I have hurt him, I know where he is vulnerable and I have abused this.

So although whirl came up in the case a few times, it did not carry energy in the form of a hand gesture. Still, I felt I had to ask about it because it is an unusual word. When asked about it, she comes to mistrust and misused confidence and feeling hurt.

D: Fidgety?

P: Cannot sit still. Think I am **useless** if I do only one thing at the time. Or I think I'll **miss out on something**. Or I do one thing, and in my thoughts I'm doing the next thing already. Not doing things calmly. But that happens mainly when I retreat. Then I am only busy with myself and nothing outside.

D: Useless?

P: When I do only one thing.

D: Missing out on something?

P: When I miss a good party and later meet my friends, who have all been there, and then they talk and laugh about it and I cannot participate. Then I feel **excluded**.

D: Excluded?

P: The point where I retreat into my house is near.

D: Useless?

P: Things should make sense in daily life, otherwise I feel unnecessary. I am not needed. And then I feel lonely and retreat into my house, and don't know when I will come out again.

D: How was the case-taking for you?

P: Difficult. I realised, which was not so obvious to me before, how much I retreat into myself.

Remedy given: *Testudo hermanni* (shell) 200C, one dose.

Follow-up after 5 months:

P: The first week was strange. I was very calm. I don't know myself like that.

And I can clearly say it has changed. **I can coordinate my life much better.** Deal with the stress. I can say NO, and look after myself. No stomach problems at all. No nausea.

I can eat everything. (She was on a special gluten-free diet when she first came in.) I have managed to do many things I always wanted to but never dared to, where I was too lazy. Did many things much more structured. Finding a job, study for university, just get more structure in my life. And I manage to listen to my inner self.

It feels good to know what I am doing. To say NO, when I don't want to go out and look after myself. The feeling of I do what I want. And I have started to do things to fulfil my dreams. I've started to work.

D: Dreams?

P: Go to a foreign country, not Europe, for half a year or a year.

I had these problems with retreating so much. It is not gone completely, there are still moments, but it is by far not as extreme anymore. Because

I am much more coordinated, I check out what is good for me and only do things that do me good. **I don't need to retreat so much anymore.** I realise it comes back when I am overstrained, but it is much better. It never comes for minor things. In situations when I am tired and don't have enough control about myself, it can happen that I fall back into my old pattern. But I realise consciously what is going on and come out of it consciously. I realise it starts, and by realising it I can deal with it differently, because I don't want it anymore, and I have much more fun going outside.

Susanne:

A few months later she did leave for South America to fulfil her dream to travel for 6 months. She had a good time and no major problems

Short follow-up in August 2007:

She is still well. She's had no repetition of the remedy, since the single dose in Jan'06. Very stable, no stomach problems. No problems with withdrawing into herself. Pregnant now with a bit of nausea.

Remedy: *Testudo hermanni* (shell) 200C, one dose repeated.

Follow-up on 29 May 2008:

In March she had her baby. The nausea of early pregnancy was no problem anymore, after the redose in August.

P: I had a dream of pregnancy. I am perfectly fine and healthy. The stomach problems completely disappeared. I am happy.

No more problems with withdrawing, and she feels she is present in life.

She is too busy with a 3-month-old-baby and university to come and see me for a longer follow-up, especially since there are no problems.

Authors' comments:

Important expressions of *Testudo hermanni*:

* I switch off and am busy with my inner being. So that I am not there anymore.

* This shell, that I don't tell anybody what is going on. That is the protection, that I don't let anyone in... I am naked and he can see everything of me. Like a shell... I am internally naked and he can see everything of me.

- I can come out and show myself like the turtle, and stick my head out, and the legs, and I can walk around and don't have to go.

- Zack… I am in.

- I am really not there anymore, as I was before.

- As soon as I open myself I become vulnerable.

- Tired, introverted, concerned with myself.

- I retreat.

- I have cut off my senses to the outside.

- I don't look around anymore.

- I go inside myself and don't know what is happening outside, and I don't want to.

- Look out.

- Retreat is a sensation of going into myself.

- Sneaked in.

- Protection, my house, my territory, my area.

- Nobody can enter…nobody can harm me.

- Nobody can come in, and I don't want anybody to come in.

- Inside is lonely but safe.

- Security.

- I don't let anybody enter my area.

- When I let somebody come close, I show him my weak vulnerable spots.

- Feeling completely without protection, this house of mine is gone.

- Protection, shell, don't let anyone know what's going on.

- You cannot destroy if I don't allow.

- I am in control, I dictate the protection.

- You can knock the shell, you can push, but she (turtle) lives nevertheless

- Where I know there is somebody who should not be there, and where I say NO.

- I can come out. I always carry my shell with me and it is a part of me. I can come out and show myself like the turtle, and stick my head out, and the legs and I can walk around and don't have to go.

- I can be open for everybody, but I have the chance to say STOP, not here, and I am in my protection.

- Feeling excluded.

Physical sensations:
- Sharp stabbing

- Immense pressure

- Stabbed with a knife (hg)

- Something boring inwards

- Pressure from outside

- Constant stab with pressure

- Shaken, rolling

- Knock, push

Case (3) of *Testudo hermanni*
By: Staria Manos

First consultation: February 3, 2007

Case of a 44-year-old male suffering from depression, low self-esteem, and addictive personality.

Observation: He arrived right on time and stayed 3.5 hours. When I tried to finish, he kept adding information. He loves to talk, and did not want to leave. As soon as he comes in, he starts talking. "I have too many X chromosomes, (female chromosome). I bring my wife flowers. I walked through the shop and these two women are conversing, and I bought them flowers. I wanted to do something nice for them. It cost me $20. I am wired up to feel for women. I like to talk too much. I am intelligent and **extroverted**, but I want to be helpful to a fault. I used to be generous to a fault, but now **I am more guarded**."

D: Main complaint?

P: **Help me insulate myself against the world**, or people's indifference. I just have a need for **thicker skin**. **(HG all his finger tips downward touching my desk palm arched up)** I wish I had more energy, and a little more sleep. I would like to wake up, go out, and feel better about life overall. I would like to improve my attitude a little. I am fine, I am blessed, but when life crashed, people were like, "Screw you — you are the worst of the worst."

*He later describes this as a **crushing** defeat.*

P: I am very emotional. I think that is a little bit of a war of the X chromosome.

D: Insulate?

P: **A cocoon, just to rebuff, or to make things bounce off, like an outer shell. Where you don't think, or I want to NOT care if people are hurting.** I know I am intelligent. I like my qualities. I have things that are not so great. Like my **tenacity**... wrong word, tenacity. It's something I do have. **I have been able to keep my own integrity**. Like with drinking (alcohol), but, I made a promise. It hurt me deeply that no one took me seriously. I expected something back. There was no deal made to help me to regroup. I thought, let's go forward, but NO....they thought, **"Let's bury you."**

He got in some sort of trouble drinking and driving and was seeking help from a group of friends.

I shut it off. I could sit here and make you a margarita...me, I'm done. I have turned that off. That will not become a factor. I will not break my word. I have had to take another vow to keep myself out of trouble.

D: Outer shell?

P: A transported **shield**, not visible, but **repels all negativity, a multipurpose shell**. It has to allow me to keep my self-esteem and repel any negativity from **this dangerous world** and people's careless thinking.

D: Thicker skin is like what?

P: That is a tough one, to be honest. My mind goes back to the bionic man (reference is to the main character in the movie *The Six Million Dollar Man*), when he reached into a toolbox and he had all these fish hooks sticking in his arm. He took them out. He did not bleed; that is thick skin. **I am unable to deal with unjust cutting terms.**

D: Tenacity?

P: If I need to accomplish something, I get it done. I set out what I need to accomplish. I don't say, "Oh this is so hard" (he sighs). Like, when a pit bull **latches on** to something, it latches on and it won't let go. I want… **I may get rebuffed temporally, but I will keep trying**.

D: Dangerous world?

P: People don't seem to care. If another person has any distress, it does not register, or they minimize your distress or respond with something unkind. It hurts your heart.

D: Transparent shell?

P: Invisible shell; not like I have a piece of cardboard around me. Like a **force field** you cannot see, like in *Star Trek*, and the lasers did not get through it. **The shield is not there until the enemy shoots.** I expect the same level of performance, high performance.

D: High performance?

P: I expect things to be done in a certain way, 2+2 is never 5. At least, I don't take an apathetic stand. Show me that you tried. I edit all the term papers to make sure they are up to snuff. My instructor is more cold and sterile; I have a talent for speaking and writing, I have to come to realize that.

D: Tell more about the person that is cold and sterile.

P: Frustration, it just kills me. Don't you see this, don't you understand!? It is the black spot on the white wall, it is right there. I feel like my head is going to explode. I get tense in my body; I want to go, move on. "Let's go, come on!" I do the same thing when I drive. I am impatient all the time when I drive. That is an oxymoron. I have all the patience in the world. If I am helping someone at work and they say 'Oh I am so stupid', I say, 'No, you are not'. I would not have a problem if someone does not have a clue, but if someone already knows, I lose my patience.

D: Tell me more, 'I lose my patience'?

P: Frustration, I start to get angry. I can get enraged. Not like where **I could kill them**. When I am driving I would like to go to their car window and say **'I want to move forward, I want to go'**. That is when you have to **retreat into your shell**. I am stuck behind them, the bus is only going 29 mph. I get tense in my neck, my upper body, head and shoulders. You are stopping me. You are limiting my behavior, my purpose. You are putting a damper on my desires. **You are holding me back.**

D: Holding me back?

P: **I can't move forward quickly, at the speed I desire. Limiting, not allowing,** not accomplishing what I want to. **Albeit, I understand that moving forward fast runs the risk of a policeman pulling me over. That would severely limit my movement forward, but I want to get there. I need to move. They could be on the freeway. I am doing 70 mph and I come on someone doing 55 mph. That is constrictive, that limits your movement.** They are Neanderthals.

D: Childhood?

P: I love my dad, but the guy was a prick. They did not call him Dick for nothing. **Harsh.** Now this is where I have to draw a line of discrimination. When I was young he taught me to read far better than anyone, and it helped my intelligence. When I was young, when I started to come of age and think for myself, **he became harsh, unyielding, and unreasonable.** There were moments when **our worlds came together (HG snaps fingers).** I started smoking dope, I have an addictive personality. My mom was nurturing, caring, overprotective, and a mediator between me and my dad.

My father is harsh and unyielding. It is almost like you are only as good as what you can do. When I did have his approval, it was like throw the dog a bone. What can I do to make him happy or stay out of his way? It was a war, when I started my own way of thinking. My father, **he can castrate you. I have to fight so hard** to get any recognition at work and at church. I want everyone to get along, that is what I think would be so appealing. Everyone getting along, no war, no one will pick on one another. We all want to have this ideal-like life.

D: Ideal-like life?

P: Paradise, everything in harmony, balanced. Everyone is getting along, no malice, no strife, and no division. No one thinks another person is lower or higher. That is my ideal.

D: Opposite?

P: Fighting in the streets, where **people are out to assail or attack you**, put you down, and laugh in derision. They don't care. You could be lying there **bleeding from an assault**, and no one cares.

D: Dreams?

P: I have to think about that one…in *Star Trek* they were in a shield where they could not dream. I've had dreams where I could fly. Well sometimes **I would want to fly, but can't get off the ground**.

D: Flying?

P: It was like you can fly, but you can't. I cannot get off the ground. **I cannot get up enough speed to get off the ground.**

D: Not get enough speed?

P: I can't describe it. When I am driving, I can drive 120 mph and it is not enough speed.

D: Childhood fears?

P: I was afraid I would not be well liked at school. I did not fit into that environment. There were more bullies. That was not good. In middle school and high school, like any teenager, it was a time of change and upheaval. I did not have much fear of authority. I don't remember a major fear. I wanted to move around, have a car.

D: What in nature do you enjoy?

P: I like nature, in general. It can be uncomfortable; like that time we went camping. That day just dragged on forever, **just sit and warm yourself on a rock**... do nothing. I like people and I like to be around people, if they are friendly. We were amongst all those college kids. **I might be quiet and reserved for a bit, but, once I get warmed up, I am comfortable. I don't like snow and ice.** I can tolerate heat more than cold.

Staria's evaluation:

Right from the beginning he talks about the 'dangerous world' from which he needs insulation. He refers to a thicker skin, or an outer, multipurpose shield, that repels negativity. *Harsh* is the word he uses to describe his dad.

Theme of testudines, which I understood from Divya Chhabra:

- To survive in the competitive predatory world outside, the testudines have a protective shield for their soft, vulnerable bodies – effective against most predators (except humans).

- However, they cannot come out of their shells, as their backbone is fused to the shell (see the figure).

- Every adaptation comes with a price. What is the price the turtle pays for its shell? It is expressed as the conflict of the patient in the testudines state.

- These patients have a sensitive emotional state. They get hurt, tortured, wounded, and injured easily by the harsh, rough world.

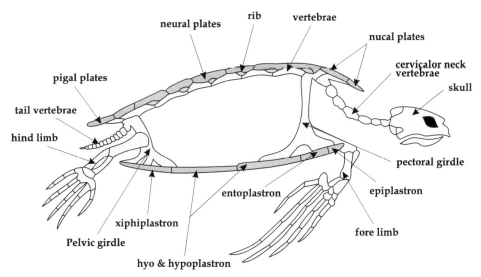

Lateral or side view of a generalised sea turtle skeleton

- Being blamed or humiliated is how they perceive their treatment by the world around them. They then withdraw, detach, become hard-hearted, and unfeeling like stone (withdraw into their shell).

- This shell then is protective and strong. It is often symbolic of dependency on guidance and advice (reptilian themes), during decision making.

- The conflict then arises as this comfort zone also implies restriction, suffocation, claustrophobia.

- They then yearn for the freedom of open spaces. This is expressed in hobbies such as: dancing, sport and desire for flight.

- The guidance which they had relied on and sought, now seems a force, a control, an intrusion into their space. And they desire to be independent and free.

- Yet the world seems harsh, and difficult to face. They feel unprotected and vulnerable if they come out of the shell.

Staria:

The key for me that made this case different from the other turtles was his feeling that the world and his father are harsh. As Divya Chhabra says, 'they feel hurt and wounded from the harsh, rough world.'

Testudines = need to be protected from the harsh world outside.

Rx: *Testudo hermanni* (shell) 12C

January 2008 phone follow-up (11 months after his initial visit):

He said he had been laid off from his job, but surprisingly is handling it quite calmly. He said he was doing volunteer work and had returned to public speaking, after 5 years. He feels more content with his life,.

It may sound crazy that I start my clients out on such a low potency, but in my experience, when you find that true simillimum, even a low potency can have such a powerful effect on the system.

Follow-up February 16, 2008:

P: I am taking the 12C. I took it some days back.
I had trouble with things; drinking and other stuff. I knew I needed to make a change. I knew it in my heart of hearts. I paid the price.

The worthless and self-esteem issues are gone, it disappeared somewhere along the line.

I use to think *Wow, if I can perform, they will like me!* Now I could give a rip about that. The first week I took the remedy, the body was like *Hey, you are giving me something I need.* I remember everything. I feel very vanilla, very natural.

D: Vanilla?
P: Natural is good in that I can resist the negativity. All the crap is gone. The only thing I have done different is the remedy. I have only taken the 12C.

Fear of moving forward gone.

Recommendation: Wait.

He says he does not want to move to the 30C. He still gets irritated when driving behind someone slow, but not as much. He has lost his job. He got laid off with the cutbacks in this slow economy, but he is surprisingly calm about it.

Authors' comments:

Specific reptile features:

- Sit and warm yourself on a rock (illustrating basking of the reptiles)
- Don't like snow and ice (indicates sensitivity to extreme cold)

Specific *Testudo hermanni* features/expressions:

- Help me insulate myself

- Thick skin

- Cocoon, to rebuff, to make things bounce off, like an outer shell

- People are hurting

- Bury you

- Shut it off

- Shield, repels all negativity, multipurpose shield

- Dangerous world

- Thick skin

- The enemy shoots

- Retreat into a shell

- Stuck behind

- Slow moving

- Progressing

- Tenacity

Possible expressions of the Hermann's tortoise in patients

The remedy *Testudo hermanni*, will express all the expressions of tortoise, mentioned on page 133.

Apart from these features there are few specific features of the Hermann's tortoise:

- Primarily terrestrial (to be on the ground)

- Aggressive

- They could also express an affinity towards their specific coloration: black and yellow

Geochelone sulcata [African spurred tortoise]

Suborder: Cryptodira (Hidden-necked turtles)

Superfamily: Testudinoidea

Family: Testudinidae (Tortoises)

Genus: Geochelone

Species: Geochelone sulcata

Common name: African spurred tortoise

Family: Testudinidae (Tortoises)

Explained on page 219.

Genus: Geochelone

Geochelone tortoises, which are also known as *typical tortoises,* can be found in *Africa, America, Asia* and several Oceanic islands. They **primarily eat plants,** specifically **dark greens.** Measured by the length of their shell, the species in this genus are some of the LARGEST tortoises in the world, especially the Galápagos island tortoise *(Galapagos nigra)*, which can grow as long as 1.80 meters/6 feet.

Geochelone sulcata

Introduction

The African spurred tortoise is the THIRD LARGEST TORTOISE of the African mainland, and is surpassed in size only by the giant island species from Aldabra and Galápagos. Both belong to genus Geochelone. It is the largest tortoise not found on an island, and is the largest continental tortoise.

Some African cultures regard the Sulcata as a mediator between man and the gods. As a result, the tortoise is often kept in villages to intercede between the head of the village and the ancestors. Even today in Dogon countries[2], the tortoise is kept with the village leader at all times, to allow him to communicate with the village ancestors.

---

2. **The Dogon** are an ethnic group of people living in the central plateau region of Mali, south of the Niger bend near the city of Bandiagara in the Mopti region. They are best known for their mythology, mask dances, wooden sculpture and their architecture.

Habitat

The African spurred tortoise is native to the Sahara desert and the Sahel, a transitional ecoregion of semi-arid grasslands, savannas, and thorn shrub lands. They are found in the countries of Chad, Eritrea, Ethiopia, Mali, Mauritania, Nigeria, Senegal, and Sudan. This species CANNOT TOLERATE DAMP OR COLD WEATHER.

Anatomical characteristics

Adults are usually 18 in/45 cm in shell length, and weigh 32-45 kilos/70-100 lbs. They grow from hatchling size, 2-3 in/5-7.5 cm, very quickly reaching 6-10 in/15-25 cm, within the first few years of their lives. The oldest known of this species was 56 years old; although it is believed they can live up to about 80 years.

Geochelone sulcata

This DESERT-DWELLING tortoise is well camouflaged. This is due to its overall SANDY COLORATION, with a THICK GOLDEN TO YELLOW-BROWN OR SANDY IVORY coloration of the shell. The broad, oval carapace displays PROMINENT SERRATIONS at the front and back margins and CONSPICUOUS GROWTH RINGS on each scute. These become particularly marked with age. LARGE, OVERLAPPING SCALES cover the front surface of the forelimbs. The

256

hind surface of the thigh bears two or three LARGE CONICAL SPURS, from which the species earns its name. The skin on the legs is well blended into the shell color. Their THICK SKIN may serve to reduce fluid loss through transpiration.

Food habits

They are VORACIOUS EATERS and purely **herbivorous**. They are often described as 'eating machines', as they can GRAZE AND FORAGE FOR HOURS daily. They graze similarly to cows or sheep. Desert vegetation is usually coarse and of poor nutritional quality. Therefore they also produce a large amount of waste. These tortoise's are also known to eat their own and other animals' feces.

Characteristic behavior

Sulcata's are ACTIVE tortoises, and they like to DIG, CLIMB, ROAM ABOUT AND WANDER FREELY. If they climb over a steep surface, they are likely to **fall and topple over onto their back**. If this happens, it is difficult for them to flip over, due to their large size. This can even lead to death.

Sulcata's do not hibernate, rather they aestivate. IF MUD IS AVAILABLE, THEY WILL FLIP IT ONTO THEIR BACKS to cool themselves. When temperatures reach more than 40 degree C/104 degree F, they salivate and smear the saliva on their forearms to help with cooling. Research has shown that tortoises raised in dry conditions are more likely to develop a shell abnormality called "pyramiding", which is an abnormal hump-shape of the scutes.

They like to BURROW and are well adapted at doing it. Burrows may average 30 in/76 cm in depth. Some may even DIG TUNNELS extending 3 m/10 ft or more underground.

Sulcata's are VERY STRONG and are known to BREAK DOWN FENCES AND EVEN WALLS. In captivity, all fixtures and fittings must be firmly bolted down. All fences and walls must be sufficiently resilient to resist the effort which will undoubtedly be directed at overcoming them! Sulcata's are also very AGGRESSIVE TOWARDS EACH OTHER. This aggression starts right from the time they hatch and reaches its peak when they sexually mature. **Ramming** into each other and attempts to **flip each other over** are commonly seen in the males. Since they are very POWERFUL AND PERSISTENT, housing more than one, especially the males, should be avoided.

They also GROW VERY QUICKLY. They are very ATTRACTED TOWARDS BRIGHT COLORED OBJECTS and will attempt to move through anything between the attraction and themselves. Sometimes in captivity a bright colored flower or object is used to lure them, in order to move them. They become very EXCITED JUST BEFORE IT RAINS AND START RUNNING ABOUT.

Specific method of attack and defense

Adult males HISS when approached too closely, and **retreat into their shell** or **burrow**, where they **wedge** themselves in. Females do the same, as well as make CROAKING noises. Another peculiar behavior is they RAISE THEIR SHELL UP OFF THE GROUND AND DROP IT WITH A VIOLENT THUD.

Materia medica

Excerpts from Todd Rowe's proving of *Geochelone sulcata*

Reptile themes:

Reptile themes that emerged in the proving include: constriction and compression, attack and defense, violence, conspiracy, suspicious, antagonism with himself, sexuality, loquacity, sudden unpredictable attack, fear of death, desire to kill and lethal. There was a strong theme of killing, particularly around cutting off the head. Turtles are particularly vulnerable in the head area. There was a strong theme of split and divided that came out during the proving. This is a common animal theme, which is particularly strong in the reptiles.

Proving symptoms indicative of testudines:

- Several physical sensations experienced by the provers:
    - Compression by a circular band accompanied by a hand gesture of circular tightening.
    - Aching in arms like being grasped very hard.
    - Beside myself with worry about my son. Feel gripped by this. It is pressing in on me.
    - Felt like I wanted to crawl out of my skin.
    - First night within one minute had a physical reaction; started in right breast; crushing pressure radiating down to my breastbone.
    - The compression tended to be circular.
    - Restriction is not able to move or deep breathe; being confined.
- Sensation of being an upside down turtle. Like I am on my back and cannot turn over. Like I am contained in a shell (general testudines sensation).

- Interestingly, slowness was not seen at all in the proving (which is a quality commonly associated with tortoises).

Proving symptoms specific to *Geochelone sulcata*:
- Several provers experienced lovesickness during the proving. The feeling was one of romantic excitement. One prover had not experienced this for many years and the other prover had never experienced this. The feelings were intense.

- The core sensation that came up in this proving was the sensation of tingling/prickling/burning as if something was coming alive.

- Desert themes:

  One desert theme that was particularly strong in this proving was that of prolonged torpor followed by hyperactive energy, excitement, and hurry. This relates directly to the core sensation. In the torporous state, there was a desire for dark cave like places (the animal spends much of its time aestivating during summer heat) and photophobia.

  Other desert themes that emerged in the proving are: water themes, distension and contraction, violence, attack and defense, large and small, wandering, restlessness, isolation, death and dying; strong thirst, without a desire to drink is characteristic of desert remedies. Formication is also typical of desert remedies.

- Aggressiveness marked by irritability, anger and a strong desire to kill (this was surprising considering the placidity of the animal, and tortoises in general, and its vegetarian diet). The most common descriptor of the irritability was "snappy".

- Compassion and benevolence; a need to protect others. This also came out in a maternal protective role with many provers having dreams of protecting babies and others. This is interesting in that the animal does not protect its young.

- General characteristics: Right sided symptoms, tends to be warm and associated with hot flushes, night time aggravations, tendency towards injuries, weight gain, swelling, and lassitude.

- Miasm: Miasmatic classification is difficult to do based on a single proving. However, there are suggestions of the Leprosy Miasm with suicidal tendencies, homicidal tendencies, self contempt and loathing, disgust, helplessness, hopelessness, self-torture, feeling violated and dirty, and not feeling good enough. The syphilitic miasm is also a possibility.

Some dreams that suggest the miasm:

1. 'I dreamt that I sat down in the dark on my own toilet. I discovered it was filled up with someone else's shit and was so full of shit that it got all over my ass. I turned to look and then I couldn't decide if it was really someone else's shit or my own.'

2. 'On a bus somewhere in Texas and could not find a bathroom. Every one I approached was disgusting. I finally found one, but part of the door was broken out and little girls kept sticking their heads in and waving their American flags in my face.'

Case of *Geochelone sulcata*
By: Ben Ta'ati

Case of a 34-year-old female, suffering from chronic Bi-polar depression and severe anxiety, first seen in November 2007.

She has been hospitalized on several occasions in the past and has persistent suicidal thoughts.

D: When it comes to your health what concerns you the most?
P: My depression; I've had a bad drop; I am in a crisis mode. I was ready to go to a Psychiatrist, but know that it hasn't worked in the past. I was diagnosed with bipolar several years ago.

D: What has this experience been like for you?
P: I feel trapped. My life is good, I have two good jobs, I am healthy, I have a good boyfriend...but I can't function, my mind won't stop, I am not sleeping, I feel helpless.

D: Tell me about trapped?
P: It sucks me back in, I'm trapped in this cycle; it will never let me be okay. I am trapped in my own mind. It won't let me enjoy what is good. It is going to trap me to be this lonely person.

D: What is lonely?
P: I am very happy with my boyfriend. He has not witnessed my depression. I am afraid it would push him away, like I am always going to be alone in the world, you're on your own. I don't even feel worthy of saying a prayer, GOD, I just feel so alone.

D: What is it like to be alone?
P: It can be good. I'm very proud of becoming a strong individual. This year I was divorced, it just feels sad.

D: How do you experience sad?

P: I don't feel worthy of the company of others. I feel burdened.

D: What is it like to experience sad?

P: I don't feel very present, kind of vacant, not in the world, not a participant.

D: What is it like to experience that?

P: You feel like you're on the side line. Why am I here? What am I doing wrong? It looks like you're weak.

D: What is it like to look weak?

P: I am a very capable person, and letting myself fall into this pattern makes me feel weak. Why can't I snap out of it?

D: What is it like to be weak?

P: Draining; it is so hard to function, hard to be part of the world when you don't have the strength.

D: What is that like?

P: Helpless, lonely.

Like I am being pulled away from everything that I love. I feel like I am going to die, the end, I feel this total nothingness. As if life is being pulled away from me.

My soul, who I am, is being sucked out of my body.

D: What is this experience like?

P: Like I will die. I will be in this shell, and the world will be twirling around, and I will not be involved in it.

D: What is it like to be in this shell?

P: That is the trap thing; like I am sitting there and I can't participate. I can see everything and can't be part of it.

D: Tell me about the shell?

P: Like that person who doesn't have that energy, who just cries, who can't function in the world, not much mobility. Inside there is that fire, this neat person, the shell is my body. If I could get out and light up that person and be the whole person, not just the spirit inside that no one can see. I feel that the 'shell' is me, and that I am trapped.

D: Is it good or bad?

P: It has protected me at times. It is secure.

D: What is it like to be secure?

P: I used to be. I used to go inside. Now I want to be free from that. I picture myself not moving, like a cadaver.

D: What does the shell feel like?

P: Before it was like armor, and now I picture it as something lighter. You can break it, but I am not able to do it.

D: What is the sensation inside?

P: Very quiet, it feels like clouds over me. It is not restful. Like being under water, I would sometimes lay in bathtub, because you can't hear and communicate.

D: What are your fears?

P: Forever being trapped in a cycle that I will not be a happy person. I am afraid of deep water. I went to the ocean this year, it is the vastness of it. I am afraid of dying, fear of the unknown. I feel that I am going to die young, and not being able to share my life.

D: What is it about deep water?

P: The vastness, don't understand what is beneath me, can't comprehend, there is so much. I was date raped in high school, and also later on by my husband. Can't do anything about it.

D: How does that make you feel?

P: Angry, makes me so mad. Helpless, I could be very violent in my feelings, I would hurt myself. When I am angry at something, I like to scratch myself or pull out my hair.

D: What is that like?

P: Total helplessness.

D: Food cravings?

P: All salads, peanut butter, chocolate, salt.

D: Food dislikes?

P: Meat grosses me out! Oysters and peas.

D: Dreams?

P: They can be vivid, and in color. I have a lot of sci-fi dreams.

D: Tell me about your childhood?

P: My parents divorced when I was 10. They split up me and my brother. I felt like I was a loner of a child. I was not happy. I remember having to learn that I need to do things on my own.

D: What was that like?

P: Lonely; being inside of a house, knowing stuff is going on outside.

D: Relationship with your father?

P: He was very demanding, not very accepting, very judgmental. I could never be good enough, never loved or accepted for who I was.

D: What was that like for you?

P: Frustrating; I didn't have anybody to go to, I tried to solve things on my own. That is why I was trying to go inside myself.

D: What is that like?

P: It is that shell thing.

D: How was your relationship with your mother?

P: Awkward; she has trouble relating. I don't feel connected to her.

D: Have you had any weight issues in the past?

P: Parents divorced when I was 10. That is when weight issue started. I over ate and felt lost in the shuffle. I used to be huge. I have lost over 70 pounds, and I used to be 201. I feel like I am always hungry.

D: What is it like to be lost in the shuffle?

P: Detached; not being part of the world,

D: Describe your sleep?

P: I have NEVER had good sleep. I am not someone who could settle down. Even when I am sick, I don't sleep well. I wake up too early. I am a horrible sleeper. I don't wake up refreshed, but then I go to the gym. I like the activity; I do a lot of cardio. The word REFRESHED would never be in my vocabulary!

Remedy: *Geochelone sulcata* LM1

Follow-up on 2 January 2008:

D: How is your anxiety/mood?

P: I can actually smile for no reason! I feel freer and more confident and OK with myself, even if something around me doesn't work out. I still have occasional anxiety but I am able to bounce back much quicker. I feel I can stop and get a better perspective on things.

D: How is your sleep?

P: I can actually fall sleep! That is HUGE! And now I am sleeping pretty solid and also can fall back to sleep. I may still get up once.

Continued with LM1 as patient is still improving.

July 2008:

P: I have left my shell behind! Sometimes though I feel like I could crawl back into that shell. I sleep well and usually wake up once, and I am able to fall back sleep. I am stronger and feel more confident.

By **December 2008** she had no major anxiety attacks. Decided to have a child.

In **April 2009** she reported being pregnant. Said she was feeling even keel.

Gave birth in October of 2009, and by this time she was no longer on the remedy.

As of Jan 2010 she has not needed the remedy, and remains depression/anxiety free.

Important rubrics of *Geochelone sulcata* (derived from the proving by Todd Rowe) confirmed in this case:

- Desire for activity
- Anxiety about future
- Desire to stay in bed
- Beside oneself
- Aversion to company
- Concentration impaired
- Thoughts of death
- Desire death
- Delusion, is about to die
- Delusion, he is a failure
- Delusion, knives
- Dream, as if in a
- Escape, desire to
- Helplessness feeling
- Kick, punch in sleep
- Sensitive to light
- Suicidal disposition
- Suicidal disposition from knife
- Thoughts wandering
- Heat flushes
- Obesity
- Weariness morning

Possible expressions of *Geochelone sulcata* in patients

These are similar to *Testudo hermanni*, and we will see the common characteristics of the land dwelling tortoise (as explained on page 133).

Specific indications of this species are:

Body parts and functions:
- Specific affinity towards: sandy coloration; thick golden to yellow-brown or sandy ivory

Behavior:
- *Inactivity (aestivation) alternating with periods of increased activity*
    - *Desire to remain hidden (images of hole/cave) alternating with hyperactive state of excitement and hurry. This is a general reptile feature of hibernation, but perhaps this feature is more pronounced in this specie.*
- *Connection to desert dwelling*
- Aggravation in cold and damp weather
- *Voracious appetite (in patients, expressed as various eating disorders and also issues with weight)*
- Dig, climb, burrow
- Strong; can forcefully break things, powerful, persistent, resilient
- Grows fast
- Attraction towards bright colors
- Excitement before rains
- Hissing, croaking
- *Desert themes: water themes, distension and contraction, violence, attack and defense, large and small, wandering, restlessness, isolation, death and dying, strong thirst without a desire to drink, formication*
- *Compassion, benevolence, need to protect*
- *Tingling/prickling/burning as if something was coming alive*

Method of attack and defense:
- *Aggressive, desire to kill*

Chart illustrating the differences

Sea/marine turtles

Flat, streamlined shell to aid swimming and prevent sinking.

Inability to withdraw into the shell (nonretractile).

Flippers.

Glide, paddle.

Swimming, diving (very well developed).

Come to land only for laying eggs.

Difficult/laborious movement on land.

Submerged in water for long while holding breathe; dash to the surface.

Sensitive to smell, sound and vibrations.

Quick burst of speed.

Do not hibernate.

Migrate.

High sexuality.

Ambush attack.

Severe injuries; profuse bleeding.

Crush, grind.

	Characteristic body feature	Dwelling	Locomotion	Characteristic behavior & Type of attack/ attacked feeling
Eretmochelys imbricata [hawksbill sea turtle]	Beaklike mouth, sharp and hooked (more than the other sea turtles').	Rest in caves and ledges.		Habitat containing sponges; feed more on sponges with silica. Highly migratory.
Lepidochelys olivacea [olive ridley sea turtle]	Flippers. Large sea turtle. Olive gray color. Thin shell.	Shallow, soft-bottomed waters.		Mass nesting, come ashore in large groups.

266

Terrestrial/land based tortoises

Able to withdraw completely into the shell.

Generally slow-moving, awkward, lumbering gait.

Heavy-dome shaped shell.

Restricted movement due to the shell.

Short, club-shaped, sturdy feet.

High sexuality.

Hibernate.

Do not migrate.

Good sense of direction.

Home-range; homesickness.

Generally calm, peaceful, docile, gentler disposition.

	Characteristic body feature	Dwelling	Locomotion	Characteristic behavior & Type of attack/ attacked feeling
Geochelone sulcata [African spurred tortoise]	Large size, large conical spurs, serrations, prominent growth rings, thick skin, large overlapping scales, sandy coloration.	Desert dwelling. Hide in holes and caves.	Dig, burrow, climb. Not slow (unlike the usual nature of land tortoises).	Prolonged torpor and inactivity alternating with hyperactivity. Voracious appetite. Strong, resilient. Grows fast. <cold, damp. Attraction towards bright colors. Excitement before rains. Highly aggressive.
Testudo hermanni [Hermann's tortoise]	Dome shaped shell. Black and yellow patterns.		Slow, lumbering, awkward gait.	

267

Semiaquatic/freshwater turtles

Partial/complete ability to retract head into the shell.

Swim, sink, float, wade, soak, and paddle in the water.

Walk or come to land to lay eggs; dig, burrow, etc.

Do not migrate over long distances.

Hibernate.

High sexuality.

	Characteristic body feature	Dwelling	Loco-motion	Characteristic behavior & Type of attack/ attacked feeling
Chrysemys scripta elegans or *Trachemys scripta elegans* [red-eared slider]	Red stripe. Ocellate or 'eye-like' markings. Low, streamlined, flattened carapace.	Freshwater; quite, soft flowing, muddy bottomed.	Slide off, slip easily. Quickly dives; fast.	Stays within a group. Bask in a group; stack upon each other. Poor hearing, sensitive to vibrations. Flutter, vibrate. Frantically slide off under safe covers.
Ovum *Chelydra serpentina* [Common snapping turtle]	Primitive appearance. Huge head, sharp and hooked jaws, sharp claws. Rough skin: keels, knobs, tubercles, serrations. Long neck: swings forward. Partially developed shell.	Highly aquatic. Submerged in muddy water; partially exposed. Prefer freshwater; shallow depth, slow-moving water bodies. Bottom covered with soft mud.		Not social. Grazing, emitting bubbles, hold on with long claws, biting the neck. Scratch, kick, fling sand. Males live in established territories. Aggressive and ferocious (since not enough protection from the shell). Hidden, camouflaged. Ambush hunt. Quickly snapping. Lunging forwards. Speed and accuracy. Powerful bite. Drag prey into water. Grasp, slice, tear, bite.
Terrapene carolina [box turtle]	High vaulted/ domed/ arched shell. Shell with regenerative powers. Hinged shell. Yellow to orange colored palmate patterns.	Require plenty of fresh, shallow water.	Not much adept at swimming and diving.	Boxing in or retract completely. Leave no space or crack or any part exposed. Clamp, pinion, bind, shackle. Not very aggressive, mild. Produce loud sound while snapping its jaw shut. Strong homing instinct, homesickness, need to come back to the birth place. Stay within group.

268

Crocodylia
(Crocodiles, alligators, caimans and gharials)

Homoeopathic remedies

- *Alligator mississippiensis* (Alli-m.) [American alligator or Mississippi alligator]

- *Crocodylus acutus* [American crocodile]

- *Crocodylus niloticus* [Nile crocodile]

- *Crocodylus novaeguineae* [New Guinea crocodile]

Introduction

The fierce and powerful ambush hunter

The order Crocodylia includes the **largest** of all the living reptiles. They are amongst the largest of all the vertebrates that still venture on land.

The order name Crocodylia comes from the Greek word 'krokodeilos', which originally referred to a type of lizard. Its Latin cognate 'crocodilus', originally referred to a land reptile, or the Nile monitor. Both words over time came to refer to the crocodile. During the Mesozoic era, 65-245 million years ago, the Archosauria (refer to the classification table on page 73) dominated the land. The only **giant** archosaurs that have survived, with body structures similar to those of their ancient ancestors, are today's crocodilians. The archosaurs, the "Ruling Reptiles" of the Mesozoic, have left only crocodilians, turtles and birds as today's reminders of the majesty of the time, when the giants of their kind roamed the earth. Since then, the crocodilians have evolved as the most advanced surviving reptiles. **Many of their features are more similar to those of mammals or birds than other reptiles.**

Man has always feared these large, **flesh-eating** reptiles, and with good reason. Alligators' and crocodiles' intimidating, massive appearance suggests **predatory ferocity and danger**.

Crocodilians are a persistent presence in human culture and mythology. The ancient Egyptians considered the crocodile symbolic of not only power, protection, fertility, and treachery, but also the destruction of the unworthy soul after death. It is still regarded as sacred by some groups in Pakistan. Crocodilians have symbolized greed, hypocrisy, treachery, darkness, and death in Western culture. Crocodile symbolism in the East is more positive. There the crocodile is connected with initiation, judgment and the rhythm and harmony of the world. In all cultures they are **strongly connected to death**. They are often called the **lord of the underworld**. They also are strongly connected to water symbols, lightning and rain.

Classification

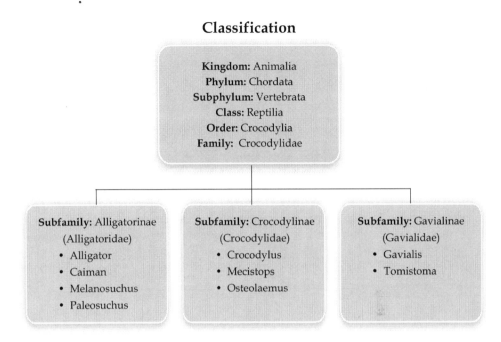

Kingdom: Animalia
Phylum: Chordata
Subphylum: Vertebrata
Class: Reptilia
Order: Crocodylia
Family: Crocodylidae

Subfamily: Alligatorinae
(Alligatoridae)
- Alligator
- Caiman
- Melanosuchus
- Paleosuchus

Subfamily: Crocodylinae
(Crocodylidae)
- Crocodylus
- Mecistops
- Osteolaemus

Subfamily: Gavialinae
(Gavialidae)
- Gavialis
- Tomistoma

Generalized anatomy

The external characteristics that differentiate crocodilians from other reptiles are mainly adaptations to a **semiaquatic** lifestyle.

Their length ranges from 1 meter (3.3 feet), to over 7 meters (23 feet). All species of crocodilians have powerful jaws, a wide, slightly flattened body, and a long vertically flattened muscular tail.

The characteristic position of crocodilians' eyes and nostrils is set high on the head so they remain above the water's surface, while the rest of the animal is completely submerged. This allows these carnivorous reptiles to keep a close watch on what is happening on shore.

Most of them are dull olive, grey, or brown, although juveniles have lighter markings that disappear with age. The skin is covered with non-overlapping **scales, which are shed in flakes**. This is unlike the shedding patterns of other reptiles. The crocodiles do not molt their entire skin all at one time as snakes do. Although crocodilians' water absorption through the skin varies by species and

Crocodile position of eyes and nostrils

size, they do share the general reptilian trait of **reduced skin permeability**. This prevents crocodilians, other than alligators, from inhabiting cooler climates. Alligators can live where the seasonal temperature variation dips below the freezing point.

The crocodile's skin has small plates of bone, called osteoderms, under the scales (also called *scutes*). These cover its body from head to tail, and form a **tough, protective armor**. Like the scales covering the shell of a turtle or the cross section of a tree trunk, crocodile osteoderms have annual growth rings, and by counting them it is possible to tell their age. Beneath the scales and osteoderms is another **strong** and **flexible** layer of armor, built of rows of bony overlapping shingles, called osteoscutes. The combined strength of these structures makes crocodile hide so **tough** that light ammunition, even a 22 caliber bullet, will bounce off the dorsal and lateral portions of a crocodile.

In fact, throughout the world's history, war shields have been made from crocodile hide. In the ancient world, Beja archers from Sudan, carrying shields made from crocodile hide, served in the Egyptian army. Crocodiles have **tough armor,** similar to that of the tortoise for protection. In the case of crocodilians, this armor is thought to play a role in the animals' thermoregulation. The heavy vascularization of crocodilian cervical osteoderms is thought to transfer radiant heat absorbed during basking into the body core via blood vessels spread throughout the bone.

Crocodilians' **large, extremely powerful and lethal jaws are armed with powerful teeth.** Crocodilian **bite power** has been measured at an upper figure of approximately 3,000 pounds. So powerful are their jaws that these creatures can **break open** and eat even a hard-shelled turtle. The teeth are conical spikes and designed to **grip and hold the prey** and then **tear the prey into pieces.** Unlike the shark, whose sharp or serrated teeth are made to rip and saw its meal apart, **the crocodile's teeth are made to shatter, then break its prey with its powerful bite.** Once **impaled on the sharp teeth,** the prey is swallowed whole. Sometimes the crocodile will **dismember** a large prey by holding part of the carcass in its jaws while **violently spinning about a horizontal axis** underwater. If the prey is still too large to be consumed at one sitting, the crocodile might **stash** it away, if it made the kill alone. If two or more crocodiles are present, the victim will be **torn to pieces,** as each crocodile attempts to **devour** as much as possible.

(Stash: 1. Hidden store, a secret store of something such as money or valuables.
2. A secret hiding place.
3. To put something somewhere, e.g., in a convenient place or where it belongs.)

Most crocodilians, like Homo Sapiens (humans), have thecodont dentition. Unlike mammals, **the crocodiles replace their teeth throughout life,** except in extreme old age. The result of this is that a single crocodile can go through at least 3,000 teeth in its lifetime. Each tooth is hollow, and the new one is growing inside the old. In this way, a new tooth is ready once the old is lost.

The crocodilians **do not have lips, so their mouths leak when closed.** Located on the gular (throat) and paracloacal areas of the crocodile are glands which secrete an odorous, oily substance used during courtship rituals. The male alligator gives the female a **head and back rub** with his jaw.

The muscles that close the jaws are exceptionally powerful; however, the muscles for opening their jaws are relatively weak in comparison. As a result, an adult man can hold an alligator's jaw shut with his bare hands. A strip of duct tape is enough to prevent an adult alligator from opening its jaws and is one of the most common methods used when alligators are to be captured or transported.

Crocodiles' skin is covered with sensory pits known as DPRs (dermal pressure receptors). These are small, black speckles on the skin. These pigmented nodules encase bundles of nerve fibers that **respond to the slightest disturbance in surface water. In detecting vibrations and small pressure changes in water, it is possible for them to locate and capture prey. With this special ability they can detect danger and intruders even in total darkness**. While alligators and caimans have them only on their jaws, crocodiles have them on almost every scale on their body.

Crocodilians have a secondary bony palate that enables them to **breathe when partially submerged in water**. This is possible, even if the mouth is full of water. Their internal nostrils open in the back of their throat, where a special part of the tongue, called the 'palatal valve', closes off their respiratory system when they are underwater. They can then **open their mouths underwater without getting choked**. Their ears are covered by flaps which close to prevent water from entering them.

Crocodilians' eyes are immobile spheres covered by three eyelids. The third eyelid, or the nictitating membrane, is transparent, yet it protects the eye from water. They have vertical, cat-like pupils which dilate to allow them to **see well in the dark**. A layer of tapetum at the back of their eyes greatly increases their **ability to see at night** as well. This also makes their **eyes glow in the dark**. Crocodilians cannot see well underwater.

Crocodiles eyes glow in dark

Crocodilians have two pairs of short legs with five toes on the front feet and four on the hind feet. The toes are partially **webbed** which allow them to make **fast turns and sudden moves** in the water, or to initiate **swimming**. A webbed foot has advantages in shallower water where the animals sometimes move around by walking.The front legs are weaker, smaller and shorter than the hind legs. They also use their feet to **hold the prey down while tearing out** large chunks of flesh with their strong claws. The **strong claws** are also used for **digging and dredging**.

Crocodile propels vertically

They have a **powerful blade-like tail** used for locomotion in the water and for communication. The tail is capable of **propelling the whole body vertically out of the water to snap** prey from overhanging branches. The tail is able to **power the thrust,** as **a large crocodile explodes out of the water to take a mammal that has ventured too close to the bank. Flying prey is flicked through the air towards their wide gaping mouth.**

The **stones swallowed** by crocodilians, that aid various body functions, are called gastroliths. This term literally means 'stomach stones'. These serve as counterbalance. They enable the crocodile to **hold its position in mid-water, while it is floating with its body suspended at a slight angle to the surface, lurking underwater in ambush**. Gastroliths also aid in the digestion of crocodilians' prey. The crocodilian stomach is divided into two chambers. The first stomach is a powerful, muscular pouch, like a bird gizzard. This is where the gastroliths, it is believed, aid the churning action of the stomach to break up the food. The second stomach, which has the strongest acid of any animal digestive system, can digest almost everything from their prey. This includes: bones, feathers, shells and even horns!

Crocodilians have kidneys, but no bladder. Urine and stool are mixed together in the process of excretion through the cloaca.

Food habits

Crocodilians are carnivores that eat a mixture of live prey and carrion. Crocodilians are opportunistic hunters; they eat whatever they can catch when they are hungry. Some larger crocodilians may also eat humans. Birds, small mammals, and fish are **swallowed whole**. Their **powerful sense of smell** enables them to smell carrion even from great distances. If an easy meal, like a dead mammal, presents itself, they will readily consume it.

Crocodilians need not feed often. 60% of what they eat is stored as fat, hence they can survive for long periods of time without food. It takes several days for complete digestion of a large meal.

In places with extreme heat, such as Africa, the flesh of the crocodile's prey might start to rot, but this does not seem to bother them. Instead, it may be to their advantage to have slightly decayed meat for easier digestion. Such behavior has given these **fierce predators** a bad reputation. They actually perform the very useful clean-up service, in the lakes and rivers, that vultures and hyenas do on the land.

Reproduction

Male crocodiles are **polygamous** and mate with several females. They display **increased aggressiveness during the mating season**. Females use the **submissive snout-lift** to signal the beginning of courtship.

The female lays her eggs near water either in a mound of vegetation and mud or in an underground chamber. The females **guard the eggs** and **help the hatchlings out of the nest when they hear them calling**. Often their guarding is quite **ferocious against the intruder, where they will pursue the intruder, normally for a short distance, until the intruder has sufficiently retreated.**

The crocodilians don't abandon the young as other reptiles do. The female gently picks up the hatchlings in her mouth and takes them down to the water for their first swim. The young can find their own food from the onset, but they will stay in groups and in the vicinity of the mother for variable periods in different species. They will benefit from the protection she provides. During

Crocodile lifting a newborn

this period the hatchlings communicate among themselves and with the mother by means of audible grunts. The adult crocodilian will **respond to distress calls made by the young, and defend them fiercely from dangerous intruders. This behavior sets them apart from the other reptiles.**

Behavior

Crocodilians, **highly formidable, semiaquatic** predators, are called the **'monsters of the swamp'. They do not venture far away from estuaries, swamps, lakes, streams, or rivers; although all species must venture onto dry land to lay eggs.**

Crocodilians will bask in the sun during the day to raise their body temperature; while at night they retreat into the water. When overheated they will lie on the banks of a river with their **mouths wide open** to evaporate heat. They will remain in this position for a long period of time. Some crocodilians also estivate (sleep out the summer). After feeding, crocodilians tend to seek more heat, as it speeds digestion.

During cold weather alligators, which can live in temperate regions, remain completely submerged (except for their nostrils), alongside steep-sided shorelines. This is so their body and tail can remain in deeper, warmer water.

Another crocodilian environmental adaptation concerns the ability to eliminate salt. Many species of crocodilians have special salt-secreting glands which permit them to survive in brackish or saltwater habitats. Alligators do not have this capability, so they do poorly in saltwater environments.

The crocodilians are **especially adapted to survive in their restricted area. This is in comparison to limbless snakes that are adapted to survive in a wide range of habitat, capable of moving anywhere on land, trees, and in water.** The crocodilians' **high intelligence, good vision, hearing, and smell make them successful aquatic predators.**

Crocodilians are **extremely inactive**, since they have a very low metabolic rate. They primarily **move only to feed, mate or fight.**

Crocodiles feed by allowing their food to rot, or when ambushing prey in the water, by biting and then spinning or convulsing wildly until bite-size pieces are torn off. This is referred to as the **death roll**, a hard-wired response developed over millions of years of evolution. Even juveniles are able to execute death rolls when presented with chunks of meat. Critical to the crocodile's ability to initiate a death roll is **tail flexure** at a **significant angle relative to its body. Immobilizing a crocodile's tail incapacitates its ability to perform a death roll**.

Territoriality

Adult crocodilians are **highly territorial and disputes are waged largely with sound.** Alligators are particularly noisy. Both male and female will **lift their head** above the surface of the water and **roar** a **loud throaty bellow** that lasts for a few seconds. A male establishing or maintaining a territory will **bellow repeatedly** half a dozen times, at intervals of ten seconds or so. He also makes a **deep infrasonic (very low frequency) call**, hardly heard by humans, that **shakes** his **body with its vibrations**. This causes the **water to dance in droplets on his back.**

They also mark their territory by **loudly slapping** their head down on the water, or **snapping** their jaws on the surface of the water. **The sounds produced are challenges to contenders.**

Dominance is determined by size and aggressiveness. The arguing, bellowing creatures proceed to spar with **open jaws** just above the surface of water, with **mouths wide open,** displaying their teeth, and **lunging** at one another. They also **thrash** their tails from side to side, making a great splash. Rival males, though capable of delivering a **powerful bite,** fight one another by **violently striking** their heads together, at times with such **force** that the **thud** can be heard from many yards away.

The dominant male **swims lordly and confident,** with his head and back clear of the water's surface. The vanquished admits his rank and remains **submerged,** low under water. The submissive male also adopts a special gesture when approached by the victorious, dominant male. He will **lift** his head clear of the water and remain motionless for several seconds, with his pale neck exposed, and his jaws shut. He is then allowed **to slink off** without encountering further aggression from the dominant male. Such behavior doubtlessly serves to reduce physical violence, lessening injury and mortality in the crocodilian world. Occasionally fights between rival males do cause **severe injuries**. Usually the **base of the tail** is injured, not the more **vulnerable chest region,** and rarely will part of a limb be **chopped off.**

Crocodiles have a **remarkable healing capacity**. In captivity only severe injuries need external intervention. (This information was provided from the zoologist at the Chennai Crocodile Park, India.)

(An interesting observation was made by Dr. Meghna Shah, while visiting the Chennai Crocodile Bank, in order to observe crocodilian behavior and further homoeopathic prescribing knowledge of reptile remedies: "We observed a dominant male crocodile in captivity take over a water area, and disallow any other crocodile, male or female, to enter his domain. When a nearby crocodile on the surface would try his luck, in no time he was thrown out with a loud grunt by the ruling giant, asserting his dominance. The other crocodile simply dashed out in order to save himself from the attack. This behavior also showed how fiercely the crocodiles guard their territory.")

Dominant animals control access to mates, choice nesting sites, food, basking sites, and living space. During drought, territories are forgotten as crocodilians crowd into the smaller remaining inhabitable area, although hierarchies are still observed.

Crocodilians are **normally solitary animals, but plentiful food may bring many individuals together**. Some species have been observed to **hunt cooperatively**.

Crocodiles coming together

Locomotion

Crocodilians' normal land gait is the "high walk". Of all reptiles, only crocodilians have an ankle structure that can **swivel** to allow a 90° foot rotation. This enables the legs to be placed almost under the body, which is raised **high off the ground**. The high walk resembles the locomotion of mammals. No other reptile moves in this way. However, they cannot maintain this position at speed. When their legs get out of sync while running, most species revert to a typically reptilian splayed-legged, belly-slide gait. They also use this mode of movement while **sliding** up or down a river bank or moving across mud.

Crocodilians can also **run** by simply speeding up their walk. In smaller crocodilians this may change the gait into a '**gallop**' in which the animal appears to be **bouncing**. Some may achieve speeds of 17 kph (10mph). They're able to **move quite rapidly when being chased or chasing** a prey. Due to their large size and short legs they can be **agile** on land only over very short distances. Generally they are **slow** and **awkward** on land.

Crocodilians are known to accelerate into short-distance **bursts of speed**, but they cannot maintain this acceleration for long, as they tire very quickly. Within one body length of the crocodile, this **short burst of explosion** is enough to **capture an unaware** victim before it even has time to react. This is where crocodiles excel; **launching themselves into motion from a standing start**, hoping to cover the short distance between themselves and their prey, **before the prey can react.**

They can also do the '**tail walk**' like dolphins do, in which their head and body are held vertically out of the water.

In water the crocodilians are superbly adapted predators. Their streamlined body allows them to **swim swiftly**. They spend much of their time **cruising or drifting,** while holding their legs against their body to reduce drag. Crocodiles can swim at the rate of 40 kph (25 mph) with the help of their powerful tails, which **propel** their bodies to such speeds. While cruising leisurely, the motion of these same tails moves the crocodiles slowly, apparently **effortlessly** through the water. This type of locomotion is very efficient, because some species have been seen at sea hundreds of kilometers from land. Crocodiles **swim fast only to escape from danger or to pursue** a prey.

Crocodiles **submerge** and remain underwater for a variety of reasons. During most voluntary dives, crocodiles stay underwater for between 10 to 15 minutes.

If the crocodile is trying to **hide** from a threat, dive length may be longer, up to 30 minutes or more. Most crocodiles can actually remain underwater for up to 2 hours if pressed, or if the surface freezes in extremely cold temperatures. This is possible as the heart rate reduces to 2-3 beats per minute. This in essence reduces the oxygen consumption, and the heart functions, in a way where it restricts the oxygen supply only to the most essential areas.

Communication

Crocodilians **communicate with each other by means of sounds, postures, motions, odors, and touch**. Vocal sounds are made by forcing air through a voice box (larynx) in the throat. Young **bark** out, or make distress calls to adults when in danger. They can also be very vocal while being fed. Sounds, made by the hatchlings themselves or by adults, also seem to keep young together. Communication in crocodilians starts even before they are hatched. The most common adult sound is a **loud roar** which is repeated, and may be echoed by other adults. During mating, **softer purrs or bellows** are made. Threatened crocodilians may **growl**. Adults also **grunt** to signal to juveniles that they will help, and they may **hiss** while defending juveniles. They also communicate by **slowly lifting** their jaws off the ground with their mouth closed. This also is a **contagious behavior** and helps to maintain long-term social relationships.

Crocodile tears

Everyone has heard the phrase **'crying crocodile tears'**. It means that the person doing the crying is **expressing the most insincere remorse. Either their sadness is not genuine, or they're simply using the tears to gain sympathy where none is deserved.** Is this just a fanciful phrase, based upon the ironical concept that a crocodile could cry, or do crocodiles actually cry crocodile tears? In reality, crocodilians' lachrymal glands produce tears which mainly function to lubricate the eye and check bacterial growth. When the crocodile eats, air is pushed through the sinus and mixes with the tears in the lachrymal gland which empties into the eye, resulting in an aqueous display of **'fake remorse'**.

Early sources of the "crocodile tears" myth can be found, and it's easy to see why the idiom has persisted to the present time. The image of such a stealthy hunter as the crocodile weeping over its victims is memorable for its contrast and irony. A 14th-century book, that over time was translated into many languages and made its way around the globe, is called 'Mandeville's Travels'. Its tale, of a creature that wept when it killed and ate men, seems primarily responsible for the promulgation of this popular myth.

Method of defense

Crocodilians are **highly efficient predators and exist at the top of their food chain**. However, hatchling and juvenile mortality from predators is high. Predation of eggs by other species is also very high. Alligator nests are subject to visits from raccoons, opossums, skunks, pigs, black bears, otters and Gila monsters. Young are preyed on by large frogs, water snakes, snapping turtles, great blue herons, American egrets, wood storks, anhingas (similar to egrets), raccoons, alligator garfish, and black bear.

Method of attack

Crocodilians have an **undeserved reputation for ferocity**. Most crocodilians **do not chase their prey as they cannot maintain speed.** They are **very agile** in the water. Crocodilians typically **hunt by stealth: lying in wait, lurking underwater**.

The wary hunting crocodile **lies in wait** in shallow water, relying on camouflage. With **only eyes, ears, and nostrils exposed with the rest of the body submerged,** it **moves within striking range without being seen**. They rely heavily on their **terrifying ability to explode into sudden violent**

Crocodile attacking a goat

activity. **This is completely unexpected in such an otherwise lethargic seeming creature.** The **sudden lunge** of a crocodile can **lift it almost entirely clear of the water.**

The prey is usually a thirsty animal that has come to the water to quench its thirst. The crocodilian will detect its presence by its **acute sense of smell**. While waiting, it has been holding its webbed feet splayed out to give it stability in water. It then moves them slightly upwards and its body, in response, **sinks** slowly. Muscular flaps close its nostril and the three bumps (eyes and nostril) disappear from the surface with barely a ripple. The prey, unaware that it has been spotted, starts to drink. Below water, the crocodile gently undulates its huge tail and **slowly drifts** towards the unwary prey, approaching very **cautiously,** hoping to **catch it off guard.** Suddenly the river in front of the victim **explodes** with a huge splash and the crocodile **lunges out** of the water, **propelling itself** with its legs and hugely powerful **thrash** of its tail. It will **seize** the prey by its muzzle or foot, **capturing it in a single fluid movement** and then **dragging it under the water.**

Lunge:

1. Sudden forward movement, a sudden strong attacking movement forward.

2. Quick thrust in fencing, a sudden thrust made at an opponent.

3. Move suddenly forward, threateningly, to make a sudden attacking movement, thrusting forward.)

After the deadly attack, the crocodilian, with a twist of its head, **thrashes** its victim from side to side (often **rolling it**). The crocodile **breaks its limbs or spine,** and then **holds it beneath the surface until it is dead.** No amount of struggle can release the prey from the crocodile's **powerful grip.**

Small creatures are regularly preyed. They are often **snapped up with a sudden sideways movement of the head before the creature realizes it is in danger.** Animals at the shoreline are more vulnerable because the muddy terrain makes it difficult for them to reverse their direction in time to escape. Animals migrating through rivers are also easy prey. Larger species of fish are **beaten** against rocks or tree trunks to kill them first. They can also bring them to the surface of water and juggle them around until their heads point downward. Crocodilians can also **slam** their heads into a large mammal, **breaking** limbs or **knocking** them into the water. They then are able to **swallow their victims headfirst**.

Crocodiles prefer to **swallow their prey underwater**, as it becomes difficult for the struggling prey to escape.

Humans sometimes fall victim to large crocodilians in boating accidents and other unfortunate circumstances. Usually this occurs when the crocodiles learn of a regular water activity place, where they then lie in wait for the human prey, in the same way as they wait for animals coming to drink water.

The 3 groups of crocodilians—for all their similarities—can be differentiated from the chart given on page 330.

Kingdom – Animal kingdom

At sensation Level A the main issues are:

- Survival – the need or instinct to survive
- A process and a life story
- Struggle with self or situation, a conflict
- Me vs you, competition
- Hierarchy
- Comparison
- Sexuality

Subkingdom – Reptile

At sensation Level B, for a case indicating a crocodilian remedy, we can appreciate the following general reptile features:

- Attack from a hiding, concealed position
- Camouflage
- Attack with stealth, speed, and surprise
- Sudden, ambush attack
- Violent attack
- Basking
- Tough, protective armor/shield

Excerpts of *Alligator mississippiensis* from Todd Rowe's proving

(The following themes and proving symptoms are also indicative of the crocodilian issues in general.)

This was a powerful proving for many of the participants. The issues of power and will, self-confidence, and unwavering self-assertion were elicited by the proving.

Many of the provers described a feeling of self-reliance (self-assured) and an ability to do things that they felt uncomfortable with before. This was associated with a feeling of increased alertness (watchful, keep enemies off guard). There was a strong feeling of freedom, fearlessness, majesty and beauty associated with that power. Along with the concept of power, there were issues concerning situations under control, authority, and domination. The proving also elicited a feeling that there were no limits to what one could do (lack of inhibition, no stipulations, wanting to be myself). Some examples: 'More aware of who I am and my defenses and deceptions.' 'No longer afraid of looking foolish or fearful of being seen.' 'To do what I want and not care what others think.'

Some provers experienced this as a mania, while other provers experienced significant depression, even to the point of feeling that life was not worth living.

The negative side of this power issue came out in the form of greed and anger. The greed was best exemplified through themes pertaining to stealing and theft. There were strong fears of robbers, dreams of robbers, dreams of espionage, dreams of crime families, and urges to steal coupled with a lack of remorse.

The anger could be intense and sudden. Mostly it manifested as irritability, coupled with intolerance and impatience. Several described it as a 'chip on the shoulder'. The anger was easily triggered, especially by noise. Many of the issues here relate to feeling attacked and having to defend oneself, especially from other's stupidity. Several described it as being 'touchy' and 'snappish', while another said, 'My terror was that I could not control my anger. If not, everything would explode. Infinite anger; so angry that I could destroy everything around me.'

Many of the provers described a strong connection to death.

The energy of the proving was often intense, sudden, and violent. Many described a feeling of panic or terror which was intense and overwhelming. Two of the provers described this as being similar to how it felt when suddenly abandoned as a small child. This feeling was accompanied by persistent hypertension in one prover: 'I was asleep for one hour and woke up paralyzed with fear and total terror. I was frozen and could not move. It was the most fearful that I have ever been in my life. If I moved a muscle I would be in real trouble. I felt my heart would pound out of my chest. I felt the terror when I was six years old and left alone when my dad had to take my mom somewhere in Chicago, and I was left alone. It was very similar to that.'

Many of the provers experienced increased sexuality and themes of competition.

There were many experiences and dreams of animals, dreams of dinosaurs. (Alligators are thought to be directly related to dinosaurs.) Several provers also dreamt of the death of large animals and looking at their bodies.

Water themes were strongly present throughout the proving. They manifested through images of diving, swimming, floating, and fish. Many of the provers had a strong craving for fish and in particular salmon. Provers spoke of feeling peaceful and at home in the water. Another interesting aspect of the water theme had to do with irrigation. This may have to do with the importance of water levels for the alligator nests. These nests are precarious and with even small amounts of flooding they can be destroyed.

The sensitivity to noise in many of the provers was fairly profound. This produced significant irritability that was most strongly provoked by voices. One prover described it as follows: 'There was an extreme sensitivity to noise. I felt like blowing up and screaming with loud noises. I'm doing everything I can do not to smash it or choke it when it is going on. I felt like the noise was an intrusion onto me. Don't come near me and bug me.'

In contrast to the violence and angry eruptions, a feeling of peace was also elicited by the proving. This seemed particularly associated with water, darkness, floating, and creeping slowly along.

The proving of American alligator also brought up issues of death, killing, and pursuing/being pursued:

Several provers described dreams full of death, guilt, and secrets. Examples:

'The woman confides in me that she has another side to her. She killed her daughter's infant son by putting a hose down his mouth. She is sorry she did it and no one else knows. Everybody thinks she is wonderful.'

'A friend and I decided to go to dig up an old corpse. We dug until we found a body. It was of an old man. We dug him out and he sprang to life and he chased us. We never knew what happened to him. Later, I am visiting an old man and he is showing us his guns and knives, and how to kill with them. I think he is the man we dug up some years back.'

'A conspiracy that I was involved in. I was being chased by a woman who wanted to kill me. She would use martial arts and shoot at me. She never caught me or killed me, but she gave me hell in the process. I felt scared.'

A prover expressed the idea of functioning in a family.

'An image of my great aunt and it made sense to me that she was the structure or the glue that held my extended family together, and after she died, they were never the same.' This crocodilian proving elicited the same concern with belonging to a group that the mammal remedies have.

One prover said, 'I became fearful of my dreams; dragging me down.' (Interestingly, the crocodile drags the prey into the water, drowning and tearing it by spinning before devouring it.)

Strong general themes include better exertion (the crocodilians are very lethargic), and icy coldness (they are sensitive to extreme cold). The amelioration from exercise is interesting in that after crocodilians have extremely high levels of exercise, they take a long time to recover from any exertion. Strong physical characteristics included lack of appetite during the day but dramatically increased appetite at night, and explosive frontal headaches accompanied by nausea. The increased appetite at night is related to the nocturnal activities and feeding of most alligators. Several provers described a feeling of enormous weight and pressure on their shoulders.

Method of attack:

The main thing about crocodilians is their terrifying ability to explode into a sudden, violent activity, completely unexpected from something which is seemingly lethargic and inactive. They have remarkably adapted to survive in their restricted (aquatic) habitat, unlike the versatile snakes and lizards. Being opportunistic hunters, they can wait for a long time until they plunge into a deadly attack, completely taking over the unwary prey.

Specific human expressions of their type of attack are a combination of various expressions related to their powerful musculature, jaws, claws, teeth and tail, and specific method of attack.

• *Powerful (or power) and strength*

Patients that require a crocodilian remedy will exhibit characteristics of being *extremely powerful, massive, and dominating* (from the sheer strength of their huge musculature, powerful jaws, teeth and tail). They are *fearless* as they have no predators. *They have no inhibitions or limits. Extremely aggressive and attacking rather than escaping or running away.* Their attack is very vehement, and ending in complete destruction (indicates the syphilitic miasm).

Crocodilians are very self-confident, self-assured, assertive, and unwavering. They know what they want and don't care what others think about it. They are very self-reliant (independent, self-sufficient). No limitations on their freedom – this is very important in them.

• Powerful within its limited area

In the crocodiles, unlike a land creature which can roam freely, or a sea creature which can swim freely inside the water, their area is limited. It can only live in a very specified area. And it cannot go outside a specified radius. It has to wait for the creature to come to him in order to attack. So it is very, very powerful; but in a very small, limited territory. If you go within the territory, then you are in danger; but if you avoid that territory, it can't do anything to you.

One could think of a local mafia or a local gangster who operates in his small territory. Powerful in a limited territory is the main difference between crocodiles and snakes.

- Hidden, concealed, partly submerged, stealth, lurking, lie in wait (also indicative of a general reptile theme)
- Completely motionless, still
- *Agile, alert, and watchful*
- *Sudden explosion into a violent activity, short outburst of violent activity, completely unpredictable*
- Sudden lunge, sudden ambush
- *Takes over* (the prey), *in control*
- *Grab* and pull (the prey with powerful and strong claws and jaws)
- Power around the bite, to clench, grasp, hold, grip, seize (the prey with their powerful teeth)
- Twist, thrash (the victim from side to side)
- Slam, knock, break apart, roll
- Spin violently
- Tear into pieces
- Drag under water, giving no chance to escape
- Drown
- Powerful grip
- Swallow whole

Here we would like to cite the common alert words of each feature mentioned above. These words are collected from cases, the natural history of the crocodilians, and the dictionary.

Alert words that describe the power and strength:

Aggressive	Gigantic
Dangerous	Huge
Dominating	Mammoth
Dreadful	Massive
Fearless, courageous	Monstrous
Ferocious	Oversize
Fierce	Powerful
Formidable	Terrifying, fearsome
Frightening, fear-provoking	Titanic

Alert words that reflect the lack of inhibition:

Lack of inhibition

No stipulations

Alert words that describe the seemingly motionless and lethargic nature:

One would not imagine the hidden strength and violence lurking under the surface behavior of these patients, as they will characteristically exhibit a very silent and unmovable nature.

Frozen	Silent
Immobile	Soundless
Indolent	Static
Inert	Stationary
Lethargic	Still
Motionless	Unmoving
Noiseless	Unspoken
Quiet	

Alert words that describe the sudden lunge and sudden explosion into a violent activity:

Catch off guard	Aggression	Bite (with great force)
Catch unaware	Bloodshed	Break
Pounce	Brutal	Bust
Short burst of explosion	Cruel	Chop off
Spring at	Destructive	Crush
Sudden launch	Fierce	Cut
Sudden leap	Killing	Dismember
Sudden lunge	Mayhem	Flick through air
Sudden outburst	Merciless	Hit
Thrust	Murder	Impale
Unpredictable	Ruthless	Mutilate
Violent outburst	Slaughter	Pierce
	Vehement	Tear apart
	Violence	Tear into pieces

While giving his case, the crocodilian-remedy patient may describe situations which display some kind of outburst:

1. Sudden display of strong emotion.
2. Intense period of activity, a sudden burst of energy or growth.

The crocodilian-remedy patient's case may have interesting expressions of violent spinning which relate to the crocodilian practice of spinning the prey underwater to kill and break it apart.

Alert words related to this feature are:

Roll	Whirl
Twirl	Swirl
Twist	

Alert words that describe the crocodile's terrifying ability to take over and be in control:

Conquer	Situation in hand
Get the better of	Take control of
Overcome	Win over
Overpower	Vanquish

Alert words that describe the characteristic ability to grab, drag, or pull (under water) with the powerful grip and drown:

Charge	Hold beneath the surface
Clasp	Immerse
Clutch	Latch on
Drag	Powerful grip
Drown	Powerful sweep
Escape (difficult to escape)	Pull inside
Force	Pull under
Go under	Seize
Grab	Sink
Grasp	Snatch
	Take hold of

Characteristic expressions that indicate their asserting dominance and can be possibly seen as source words:

- Various sounds like: bellow, grunt, roar, deep call, bark, hiss, or purr
- Shake the body, vibrate
- A peculiar expression of water droplets dancing on the back
- Slapping, lifting (their head on the surface of the water)
- Snapping (their jaws on the surface of the water)
- Mouth wide open
- To lunge at one another
- Thrash (tails from side to side)
- Violent striking (of their heads)
- Thud, bang, knock, slam, smash
- Powerful bite

Behavior:

Crocodilians come close to mammals and birds when we talk about:
- **Territoriality**
- **Parental care**
- **Issues of territoriality and hierarchy**

Fight for dominance (and mating rights) within a group. The tough and dominant remains at the top position (surface), while the weaker becomes submissive and retreats (submerged). Crocodilians also exhibit the feeling to be part of a group (*family, togetherness*) and the opposite of being left out or excluded. *There is a fear of sudden abandonment, such as a child would feel.*

- **Parental care**
    - Maternal instinct, motherly, tender, affectionate, warm
    - Caring, responsible
    - Defensive, shielding, protective, guard
    - Guarding fiercely

- **Locomotion – indicating semiaquatic lifestyle**
    - Short burst of speed or movement
    - To launch with a sudden motion from a standstill position

- Turn fast, move suddenly
- Awkward, sprawl, walk, swivel (on land)
- Run, gallop, bounce (on land)
- *Swim, slide, slink off, swim swiftly, cruising*
- *Float, to counterbalance, drift, suspended* (opposite is *sink*)
- *Images of water/sea*

- **Heightened sensitivity**
  - Powerful sense of smell, hearing and vision
  - *Sensitivity to noise*
  - Sensitivity to slightest environmental changes
  - Ability to detect slightest vibration and pressure changes
  - Heightened sensitivity or alert in dark
  - Ability to see in the dark
  - Eyes glow in the dark

- **Sensitive to cold**

- **Stash, hide away**

  This feature is possibly understood as storing in humans; like storing wealth or food for future use.

- **Death roll**

  The significant energy in the crocodile while performing the death roll is 'rolling' which can be seen in patients.

- **Good healing capacity**

  In the Complete repertory there is a rubric with the remedies:

  Generalities; WOUNDS; heal; quick tendency to (2): lyss., manc.

  Crocodile is a possible addition to this rubric.

- **Vulnerable chest region**

- **Ability to breathe underwater without getting choked**

- *Dreams-animals, cats, insects, large animals, alligators, dinosaurs*

- *Desire-fish, salmon*

- **Mating characteristics**
  - *Increased aggression, sexuality, competition*
  - Violence (fighting for a mate)
  - Polygamy

Body parts and functions:

- **Tough and flexible (skin with the bony plates)**
  - Body armour
  - Breastplate
  - Bulletproof vest
  - Defend
  - Guard
  - Semi permeable
  - Protective armour or covering
  - Shield
  - Strong
  - Tough

- **Molt or shed** – in single pieces

- **Absence of lips** – increased salivation

  For further difference between the alligator and crocodile refer to the chart on page 330.

Comparison with snakes and lizards

Compared to snakes and lizards, crocodilians have a restricted and confined habitat. The snakes and lizards can be spotted anywhere. They are universal by nature, except in extremely cold places. The crocodilians are extremely powerful in their limited territory, dominating and fearless. They have no inhibitions. They don't have the sophistication (planning, scheming, etc.) of the snakes or various signalling instincts (autotomy, change color, etc.) like the lizards. They simply lie in wait, patiently. From a completely inactive and lethargic being, they can explode into a terrorizing violent creature whose activity ends in complete destruction. To grab, hold and pull under (the water) is also very specific for crocodilians. Also they show a parental care that is lacking in most snakes and lizards.

Comparison with *Lac leoninum*

The crocodilians' mode of attack comes close to *Lac leoninum*. They both have: sudden violent activity, sudden lunge, power, hierarchy, fight till the finish, complete destruction, etc. The main difference in *Lac leoninum* is that they usually hunt in groups and stalk the prey.

In the following section we will be studying remedies from the following families:

Subfamily: Alligatorinae	Subfamily: Crocodylinae
Remedies:	Remedies:
Alligator mississippiensis (Alli-m.) [American alligator or Mississippi alligator]	*Crocodylus acutus* [American crocodile] *Crocodylus niloticus* [Nile crocodile] *Crocodylus novaeguineae* [New Guinea crocodile]

Subfamily:
Alligatorinae

Homoeopathic remedy
Alligator mississippiensis (Alli-m.)
[American alligator, Mississippi alligator]

Introduction

Two species of alligators are identified under this family:

1. *Alligator mississippiensis* (American alligator); native only to Southeastern United States.

2. *Alligator sinensis* (Chinese alligator); native to Yangtze River, People's Republic of China.

Alligator mississippiensis (Alli-m.) [American alligator or Mississippi alligator]

Order: Crocodylia

Family: Crocodylidae

Subfamily: Alligatorinae (Alligatoridae)

Genus: Alligator

Species: Alligator mississippiensis

Common names: American Alligator, Mississippi alligator, pike-headed alligator, "gator"

Habitat

American alligators are found from the southern Virginia border, along the Atlantic coast to Florida. They're also found along the Gulf of Mexico as far west as the Rio Grande in Texas. Their PRIMARY HABITAT IS FRESHWATER SWAMPS AND MARSHES. They also live in rivers, lakes and smaller bodies of water.

Anatomical characteristics

The American alligator is **large and powerful,** with a large, slightly rounded body, thick limbs, and a BROAD HEAVY HEAD presumably adapted to LIVING IN HEAVILY VEGETATED SWAMPS. IN OPEN AIR OR IN WATER, THIN SNOUTS WOULD BE MORE MANEUVERABLE, BUT A HEAVY HEAD HAS MORE MOMENTUM TO CATCH PREY, BY SMASHING THROUGH THICK VEGETATION.

THE ALLIGATORS' LOWER FOURTH TOOTH FITS COMPLETELY INTO A PIT IN THE UPPER SOCKET, SO THAT IT IS NOT SEEN WHEN THEY CLOSE THEIR MOUTH (UNLIKE THE CROCODILES).

Males average 3-4.5 m/10-15 ft in length and can weigh 450 kg/1000 lbs. Females grow to a maximum of about 3 m/10 ft.

Both adult and juvenile American alligators are black, but the juveniles have bold yellow crossbands. The eye color of American alligators is generally silverish.

Mating characteristics

The most OBVIOUS NESTING BEHAVIOR IN REPTILES is seen in the **mounds built** by the American alligator. **The female remains near the nest to protect it from intruders. She may also assist the young in hatching and escaping from the nest.**

A recent study has revealed that ALLIGATORS ARE NOT AS PROMISCUOUS as previously thought. Up to 70 % of female alligators returned to the same mate for several years. This illustrates mate fidelity.

Characteristic behavior

They can tolerate a reasonable degree of salinity for short periods of time, though they LACK THE LINGUAL OR BUCCAL SALT-SECRETING GLANDS FOUND IN CROCODILES.

The American alligator is especially notorious for its BONE-CRUSHING BITES. Some sources claim that they have the strongest bite force of any living animal on land or sea.

American alligators are the MOST VOCAL AND NOISY of all crocodilians. Alligator communication begins early in life, while still in the egg. THEY HAVE AN EXTRAORDINARILY VARIED VOCABULARY WHICH CONVEYS A WIDE VARIETY OF SOCIAL MESSAGES.

Alligators **do not feed during the cooler months**. Studies in captivity have shown that alligators generally begin to lose their appetite below 27°C /80°F. They stop feeding altogether below 23°C /73°F. They can easily last the winter on their energy reserves.

Adult alligators can SURVIVE FREEZING CONDITIONS, if they are in water. They **submerge** their body but keep their nostrils projecting above the water surface, so that when the surface freezes they can still breathe. This is called the 'icing response'. They can also survive by lying in shallow water and maintaining a breathing hole through the ice. Occasionally their snouts are frozen into the ice, and provided their nostrils are not covered, they usually survive. Most other species of crocodilians would be killed by such low temperatures. Occasionally alligators may be TRAPPED COMPLETELY BELOW ICE, and have been known to survive for over 8 hours without taking a breath. The freezing water slows their metabolic rate down to very low levels. This is yet another example of their amazing ability to survive!

Adult Alligators are roamers with the unique characteristic that they have a strong instinct to RETURN TO HOME TERRITORY. They also have EXCELLENT DIRECTIONAL CAPABILITIES.

Gator holes (Alligator holes)

The alligator's greatest contribution to the marsh and the other animals that inhabit it are the 'GATOR HOLES' ('ALLIGATOR HOLES'). This is not the alligator's nest but merely a way for the reptile to survive the dry season and winters when they are used for SHELTER AND HIBERNATION. Alligators normally prefer to float partially submerged, though during mid-summer, as the water table falls, they RETREAT INTO THESE HOLES. They keep a small body of water open by DIGGING out the sand or mud at the bottom. It will also feed on the fish and other visiting animals that are trapped in this diminishing pool. During the dry season, and particularly during extended droughts, gator holes PROVIDE REFUGE to other animals as well. The holes supply vital water for: fish, insects, crustaceans, snakes, turtles, birds and other animals, as well as the alligator itself. Sometimes the alligator may expand its gator hole by digging beneath an overhanging bank to create a HIDDEN DEN. After tunnelling as far as 6 m/20 ft it enlarges the end. This makes a chamber with a ceiling, high enough above water level to permit breathing.

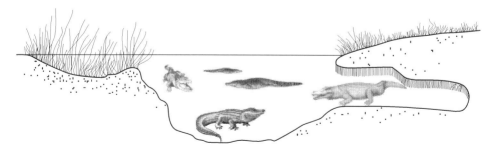

Gator hole

300

Specific method of attack and defense

The American alligator was widely hunted for its skin until the 1950's, when it became seriously endangered. Since then it has been under legal protection and has experienced a recovery.

Alligators are capable of killing humans, but they generally fear humans. **They will not purposely perceive humans as prey,** yet they will **attack in self-defense when provoked.** THE ALLIGATOR'S TAIL ITSELF IS A FEARSOME WEAPON CAPABLE OF KNOCKING A PERSON DOWN AND BREAKING BONES. EVEN THOUGH THEY RARELY KILL, THEY SHOULD BE LEFT ALONE.

Alligators are FAR LESS DANGEROUS THAN THE INFAMOUS NILE CROCODILE AND SALTWATER CROCODILE. Alligator bites are serious injuries due to the risk of infection. Inadequate treatment or neglect of an alligator bite may result in an infection that necessitates amputation of a limb.

Alligators hunt primarily in the water at night, **snapping up small prey and swallowing it whole.** It's BLUNT, BROAD JAWS HELP IT CATCH PREY IN THICK VEGETATION. **Large prey are drowned, by dragging underwater, and then devoured in pieces.**

Materia medica

Excerpts from proving by Todd Rowe

Themes and proving symptoms indicative of specific alligator issues:

Images of cave in the sea, den. 'I felt closed; did not want anyone to bug me; felt closed in on myself, cocoon around myself; wanted to be home all the time; would have been happy if I did not have to leave the house.'

This is similar to the gator holes made by the alligators.

One prover had an unusual dream: 'I was a carbon atom and could not bond to another carbon atom; two dimensional forms; kind of that graying cream background; would not stop; trying to find any place that I could go to and could not bond anywhere; this was odd because carbon bonds with everything; I was running; feeling of total panic; could not sleep much; strangest dream I ever had.'

Melinda Leeson's observations about alligators from the proving and cases (who also participated in the proving and has lived besides the alligators for 20 years):

'Admiration for their toughness and ability to survive even under the most adverse conditions. A certain primitive curiosity and appeal, similar to the interest and curiosity we have for dinosaurs or nightmarish reptilian creatures in films.

I suspect that the deeper fears we have about the alligator have more to do with his magic muscular ability to submerge and move out of our view. If I cannot see my enemy, while he can see me, and he moves within striking distance without my awareness, I am powerless to defend myself... and I am very afraid.'

Case of *Alligator missippiensis*
By: Melinda Leeson, DOM, AP

(Case taken from Reference Works and further edited for better readability.)

A Case of Obstructed Respiration and Anger
Male, Age 34

He owns and manages a tree-trimming business. He presents as a **heavyset, powerfully muscled** man, 5 feet 9 inches tall, with completely grey hair, which is thinning, making him look 15 years older than his age. He arrives at the appointment in his work clothes, covered with chain saw dust and dirt. He has a rudimentary manner, and interacts easily. He gives me the impression that he is a hard worker, **strong and tough**, but fair in his dealing with his men and his customers.

2 July 1997:

His appointment had been arranged by his wife. His chief complaint is obstructed respiration while sleeping, accompanied by loud snoring and occasional moments of apnea. On examination, his tongue is so **large** that when I press on it with a tongue depressor, he begins to **choke**. He noted that the dentist found it impossible to perform any dental procedures in the back of his mouth for the same reason. If pressure is applied to his tongue he begins to choke. Respiration through his nasal passages is severely restricted. The airflow on the right side is 90% restricted.

Examination also reveals multiple deep scars on his right lateral chest, neck and shoulder. His intake form describes these signs, as resulting from a series of accidents from which he barely escaped with his life – an anchor mistakenly thrown into his shoulder, 2nd degree burns by the fire from an explosion, a near drowning incident, and several deep chain saw injuries, where flesh was cut to the bone. About the injuries, he says **'I heal unbelievably quick. I'm an old alligator. I keep on going. I don't have time to be sick.'**

The first thing he tells me is a joke about a female dog in heat. He laughs in a cheerful, **robust** way. It's as if he's **trying to win me over**.

D: What stresses are you experiencing in this life?

P: Stress of; dealing with my business 6-7 days a week, equipment failures, meeting schedules, working with 'rough cut' employees, and a wife who doesn't do what she is supposed to. His wife works as the office manager for his business. She forgets stuff and I feel helpless. I am counting on her and she doesn't follow through. I try to get it off my chest and talk to her about it, but I end up getting angry and tense. If I say I'm going to do it, I do it. If she says she'll do it, she doesn't. It's like I'm being **lied** to. I hate that. I don't like to look **incompetent** to the customer. Work is what is important.

D: Is there more?

P: Financial stress. I have a huge mortgage on the house we bought, and my wife insists that our kids go to private school. She wants so much out of me. It costs a lot. I like nice things but they are not that important to me. **I just like to go outside and be in nature.**

D: How do you get on with the men you employ?

P: I get out there with them and sweat with them. I'm there to help them as well as to be their boss. A lot of my men have been with me for years.

D: What in your life would you describe as stress free?

P: I enjoy playing with my kids. I wish I had more time with them.
I like to fish. I like to watch the light dance on the water. I like to hunt. If I sit down, I fall asleep real easy. I like to go out of my body, five minutes and I'm gone.

D: What were you like as a child?

P: I was one of five kids, too many for Mom to deal with. When I was too much for her she would put me in my playpen in a room at the other end of the house, and then lock the door as she left. It would drive me crazy, like put in a cage and locked up in a room all by myself, **far away from my Mom,** and not able to get out.

303

I was afraid she had forgotten me. It made me so mad, I just thought to myself that I am going to **destroy** this. So I **broke** every single bar of the playpen all the way around, and started **beating** on the door with one of the pieces, **furiously** screaming for her to come get me. When she finally came to get me she was so mad. Four other kids had been in that playpen. At two years old, I had broken it to smithereens.

My Dad was gone all week driving a truck. **I was very independent**, and when I decided I wanted to do something I would do it. Mom would save up all the things I'd done wrong for my Dad to deal with when he got home at the end of the week. He was a hard man. **His way to control me was to beat me, over and over, then lock me in my room. I wasn't scared of him. I wouldn't back down. My older brothers would try and control me too. They were really mean, and they beat me up every other day.**

Once they tied me to a tree for 12 hours. I was furious. I made up my mind I would get them back. I wanted to make them afraid of me. So I hit one brother with a baseball bat. When I was twelve, I shot the other brother with an arrow in the butt. I had an inner knowing that there was only so much my parents and brothers would do to me. My family used to think I was crazy, that I had a violent nature. So I thought, if they think I'm crazy, I'll just show them I'm crazy. Once they expect it, it's OK, you can do anything.

I grew up very fast. I left home when I was 15. I quit school, and had to learn to be a man instantly. I had to learn how to eat and house myself, how to pay my bills, make a workable business, **organize, and plan ahead**. I've always been business minded. I'm a good planner, good organizer. I check off things as I go, replan when things change, and don't get behind. You gotta accomplish something! The only opponent is time. I used to drive everywhere a million miles an hour, until I got too many tickets. Now I try to go with the flow, but stuff has to be done in a timely fashion.

I married when I was sixteen, a girl from a wealthy family. Her Dad made life unbearable so she moved back home with her parents. Her Dad and her brother were always **belittling me**. One day her brother said something bad about their sister. **I took a shovel to him, and beat the living tar out of him.** The marriage was annulled.

D: Do you have any fears?
P: Rats. I hate them. If I see one I want to kill it. Big cities. Visiting New York made me feel real small and congested. It was too noisy, all that horn honking. Policemen; they are like Gestapo agents, and not loyal to the people they serve. They are only loyal to the government. **Don't ever trust them.**

304

D: For example?

P: When I was dating my first wife, her father and four cops came to my house at 2 a.m. and banged on the door. All of them **jumped on me**, handcuffed me to a chair, and **beat** me up. They threatened to plant drugs on me and take me to jail if I didn't stop seeing that girl. I told them anything they wanted to hear. I was at their mercy. All that did was make me madder.

D: Can you tell more about that?

P: When the police did the beating, **they threatened to put me in a cage** for something I didn't do. It would be something I couldn't get out of. It felt like being locked in my room as a kid. I couldn't even imagine what it would be like to be locked away for ten years. When I contemplated on it, I remembered that I had a past lifetime as a prisoner. I can't stay in one small place for a long time. I have to get outside. Then I'm better.

D: You have an awareness of other lifetimes?
(He has frequently referred to his memories of living other lifetimes during the case-taking, so I chose to ask him this question.)

P: Yes, ever since I was little. My family said I had a great imagination, but I could remember doing things from before this life, knowing people from before, stuff that happened.

D: Any other fears?

P: I worry that the business will fail.

D: What about dreams?

P: Sometimes I have dreams that are like visions, with strong emotions that are burned into my memory. A year ago I had a vision that I was a bird, a hawk flying. All I could see when I flew was barely the tops of trees. Everywhere was underwater. I had to fly long ways before I could find land and I was tired. I was looking at all this water, wondering *where did it come from?*

D: Can you tell something about your shoulder injury?

P: It's karmic. I was out on a boat with two friends. We had finished catching all the grunts we needed, and were getting ready to set out to fish for grouper. We stowed the anchor, but it fell out and caught on something in the shallows, as I was putting the motor in reverse. The rope stretched taut and then slung the anchor back into my right shoulder. It was extremely painful.

In the hospital I had a dream explaining how my friend had forgotten to tie up a sail line correctly in a previous life. The boom had come crashing down on my shoulder. In that life I got gangrene and died. I knew I would be healed when I felt this warm breeze going through me. I think it was about forgiving each other. It took over a year to get movement back in that arm. **The doctors said I healed much faster than expected.**

D: And the fire injury?

P: A year ago, my best friend accidentally ignited an explosion when I was working under the hood of a truck he was trying to get started. The fire burned up the right side of my body, chest, neck, shoulder and the side of my face. It was extremely painful. In the hospital, I was given codeine, which didn't work. It just made me angry, like I wanted to **bust** heads. Another doctor gave me morphine. It was like heat going through my body. It felt good. Then I slept. I wanted to blame my friend for the accident, but I knew I was supposed to learn not to blame. The burn healed very well and quickly. I've learned to be calm and collected about pain each time, a common sense response. I just take care of myself. **I'm an old alligator, I just keep on going.**

D: Was there a time when you felt you couldn't take care of yourself?

P: I almost **drowned** one time when I was about twelve years old. A friend of mine **knocked** me overboard by mistake. The anchor rope was around my leg. When the propeller hit it, I was really **tangled** up. I lost control of my mind. The rope was keeping me down. **I could see the surface, but I couldn't get there.** I panicked, started to lose it. Then I heard a voice inside me saying, 'you have a pocket knife, cut the rope.' I got my knife and started cutting. I got free just as I ran out of air.

D: Do you remember any significant dreams?

P: Dreams about working, jobs needing to get done, organizational stuff.

Dreams about healing me when I've been injured, about spiritual things, about going to places in other worlds. Sometimes they are prophetic dreams, things that happen later on.

Dreams of **water, and a flood. A wall of water coming toward us, crashing into houses. It is so powerful. It is going to destroy us.** We had to drive very fast to outrun it.

Recurring dreams about earth changes, water where land used to be, **danger** to my family; I need to pack them up and move them to the mountains.

Dreams of **being underwater**.

Dreams of **alligators**. Both my daughters and I dream about them. They are being chased. I am talking to them or hunting them for food.

Generals

Thermal/Perspiration: Easily overheated working outdoors. Perspires heavily. Thirsty, drinks a huge amount of water daily. Prefers to be outdoors in nature.

Food Desires: Red meat and potatoes with lots of butter, fried steak or chicken, biscuits and gravy. Coca-Cola.

Food Aversions: Milk. Never liked it, even as a baby, tofu, sauerkraut, food that tastes too vinegary.

Sensitivities: I **don't like the noise of car horns blaring, or children squealing.**

Physicals

Head: Frontal/temporal headaches in am on waking, weekly. Pulsating and pounding.

Stomach: No appetite in am. Hunger begins between 11 am and 3 pm. Always thirsty while working. I like ice cold water.

Rectum: I pass a lot of smelly gas after I eat; twice daily stools that are regular. Occasional loose stools after eating salads.

Chest: When I get real upset, I get really bad pain in my chest. It feels like a heart attack, pointing to his sternum.

Back: Pain and stiffness, sometimes radiating down right leg. Intermittent sharp pain in feet. <Metatarsophalangeal joint of big toe. Coinciding with pain in ankles, worse after eating red meat.

Kidney: Sometimes pain surrounding my right kidney, worse in morning and on waking; better hot shower and stretching.

Seven years ago had kidney stone colic, with sharp stabbing pains in my right kidney, as if getting stabbed with a hot knife.

Male: **Very high sex drive**, 'I like sex as often as possible.'

Sleep: Deep sleep, and easy to fall asleep. Snores loudly, and stops breathing periodically. Then wakes with a start, inhaling as if gasping for air. Remembers many dreams clearly and in detail.

Assessment: The remedy I wanted to give him, *Alligator mississippiensis*, did not exist as a remedy at that time.

I suggested extensive diet changes, and gave him a single dose of *Kali nitricum* 200C on the following elements: Explosive nature, family orientation, work ethic, rudimentary reliance on logic and perseverance.

And the rubrics:
- Respiration arrested during sleep
- Kidney pain; burning/cutting

Kali nitricum appeared to reduce the frequency and severity of the apnea, but did not affect his nature in any noticeable way.

There followed a time gap of one year, due to difficulty of obtaining his remedy for him. He received his first dose of *Alligator mississippiensis* in May 1998.

Rubrics included the following:
- Mind, anger, violent
- Mind, talks, business of
- Respiration, difficult, sleep during, awakened to avoid suffocation, must be
- Respiration, arrested, sleep during
- Mind, dreams, danger/floods/water/drowning
- Delusions, visions
- Mind, forsaken
- Mind, fear, rats
- Head pain, forehead, temples
- Kidney pain
- Nose, obstruction, right

Themes in the case included the following:
- Childhood failure in defense
- Childhood failure in love/trust
- Themes of aggression/attack, rejection, isolation, survival level responses to circumstance
- Fear of failure in performance and work
- Intimate relationship with nature

Within three weeks of the remedy, his wife left him, taking the children with her. Over the next year, he struggled with the consequences. He received additional doses of the 200C potency in October 1998 and again in November 1999. After a recurrence of right-sided kidney stone colic in September 2000, he was given a 1M. After a recurrence of sleep apnea, the 1M was re-dosed in November 2001. All symptoms resolved. The following notes were taken over the period of time he was taking the *Alligator mississippiensis.*

Follow-up in July 1998:

D: Can you tell more about your emotions?

P: **I hate being separated from my kids.** I feel an emptiness, real lonely, as if I've been robbed of something irreplaceable, something I can never get back. Worry; I feel that in my stomach, like butterflies. Angry; **I feel a swirling sensation**.

D: Can you tell more about this?

P: It's energy in and around me. I'm part of the **swirl**. It starts at the top of my head when I get mad, so I push it down into my solar plexus. I keep it there, building it up, **spinning it into a vortex of power**. The madder I get, the faster it spins, until I can throw it out at whoever makes me angry. It used to be that the anger got so powerful it would control me. Sometimes I would have blank outs in certain circumstances I couldn't remember because the anger became so powerful.

When someone penetrates, I don't feel anything. Morphine was like that. **People can't hurt me**, and I can't feel any pain. Then I am invincible. **Watch out here I come.** The madder I get, the more its there. I call it the Iron Curtain. Its purpose is **destruction**... anything that is in its way.

(Swirling, spinning — indicative of the death roll.)

D: What makes you angry?

P: Betrayal, or lying to me.

D: Betrayal?

P: My wife left without telling me, secretly took my kids away from me, found a place and didn't tell me where they were. **It caught me off guard.**

D: Can you tell me more?

P: It was like she **attacked me when I wasn't expecting it**. I was afraid I would lose my kids. I felt the same swirling in my stomach, **anger building up**

power. Now I'm reasoning it out a bit. I still get rid of it by saying what's on my mind, but now it's the same force. The anger is more mental now than emotional.

Report from his wife: He is able to negotiate for the first time ever. He is not using swear words at me since I asked him not to, but this is the first time he has done anything because I've asked. He talks even more about 'Earth Changes' since the remedy. He is convinced that a ring of fire is going to set off a chain reaction of volcanoes and earthquakes which will send enormous floods to cover us in water. He wants to take the kids up to the mountains and build a house and raise food. He's buying guns to shoot anyone who tries to take what he is going to grow.

Follow-up in August 1999:

His youngest daughter is living with him. The older daughter is living with her mother. Communication is poor. The older daughter has been experiencing some troubles of her own. He and his wife have not agreed on all the details necessary for the divorce or childcare. Each is working with lawyers to accomplish this.

P: I have spent a lot of time this year looking at myself.

I've seen that the mental and the emotional are two different bodies. They don't mesh. The perception from each is going to be different. I know I have a big personality, and I know I have a big energy around me. I know that I can be extremely delightful to people, or **I can be extremely frightening to people**. Now I have to learn to balance out that energy within my bodies. I've been stepping into my emotional body and saying it's OK for myself for the first time in my life.

D: Any more flood dreams?

P: No. But I have to say that when I saw all those earth changes I thought a flood was going to crash down on me (laughs). It wasn't the flood, it was my life crashing down on me. Now if I dream about water, **I'm at this beautiful pool. It's so nice and warm there.** In one dream, my wife comes into the pool, but she goes to the other end by herself. My older daughter is there, but I can't see her. The youngest stays close by me. There are some spiritual masters in the pool with us, and one of them goes over to my wife. I realized that we're all on the same pool of life together, just at different ends, not communicating very well. We all have our problems, and at the same time we are all being taken care of, and we're all loved just the same, no matter where we're at. We all have karmic situations that we got to work through. I just have to go with it.

Follow-up in September 2000:

P: I seem to be clearer within myself since I got the remedy. My energy has held together stronger.

Melinda: I have been treating him for ten years or more. He does well on the same remedy. His issues on the physical plane are still WORK, he must work, and eat. He eats way too much of all the wrong foods, producing inflammatory pain all over his body, and phlegm on laying down to sleep, which produces snoring and occasional sleep apnea. The food seems to be a compensatory strategy to avoid making ultimatums in his relationship with his common law wife. She is incredibly demanding and can be quite negative with regards to her own experience of life. Every now and again, he'll sit down with her and explain what aspects of her behavior disturb him, requesting that she work on them, but he continues to tolerate her negativity, and uses humor to ease the more difficult moments.

I lived on the banks of the Myakka River, in Southwest Florida, from 1983 to 2003, along with pet goats, chickens, dogs, and cats. Parts of the property were fenced, but wild animals freely roamed the unfenced areas along the river. After witnessing neighbors toting rifles, and shooting at the water whenever they saw an alligator, I noticed that the alligators always returned later on and ambushed the shooters' pets. It was almost as if the smell of gun oil, eradicated all trust and good will. I decided to find another way where we could all peacefully co-exist, at least along my property lines. During that first year, I spent considerable time contemplating the issue while sitting under a tree near the river, whether or not there was an alligator basking nearby. I made a focused inner promise to stay out of the water and the lowlands, and asked that the alligators not encroach unless the boundary line between water and dry land became obscured. I stopped carrying a gun, and I trained my pets to stay behind an invisible four-foot safety line between the land and the water. In twenty years, we never had a conflict, not even during the yearly floods where the land/water boundaries were completely erased. It never occurred to me that I would meet a patient who needed a remedy made from an alligator. Nor did I imagine that he would be the person to provide the alligator.

(Just a thought: This could be a model for world peace.)

Possible expressions of the American alligator in patients

One will see the general features of the crocodilians and then have to differentiate between the two species—alligators and crocodiles.

Method of attack/defense:
- Very strong crushing or biting force (as compared to the crocodiles)

Behavior:
- Less salt tolerant (unlike crocodiles)
- Very strong parental care. They get violent and ferocious defending the young, as compared to the crocodiles.
- *Gator holes (caves, den)*

Alert words:

Hole

Burrow

Hideaway

Hideout

Refuge

Secret place
- Very noisy, talkative, vocal (more than the crocodiles)
- Less dangerous than crocodile
- Ability to survive freezing conditions underwater, at times even without breathing.
    - More tolerance to cold, unlike the crocodiles
    - Images of being trapped below ice (possibility)
- Strong instinct to return to home territories, homesickness
- Excellent sense of direction
- Fidelity, loyalty, faithful

Crocodylinae

Homoeopathic remedies

Crocodylus acutus [American crocodile]
Crocodylus niloticus [Nile crocodile]
Crocodylus novaeguineae [New Guinea crocodile]

Introduction

The name crocodile comes from the Greeks who observed them in the river Nile. The Greeks called them *krokodilos*, a compound word from *kroke*, which means 'pebble' and *drilos*, which means 'worm'. To the Greeks this 'worm of the stones' was so named because of the crocodile's habit of basking in the sun on gravel-covered river banks.

Generalized anatomy

The size varies between species. CROCODYLI POSSESS SALT GLANDS ON THE TONGUE WHICH EXCRETE EXCESS SALT IN SALINE ENVIRONMENTS. This is in order to maintain an appropriate salt to water balance. Crocodiles are SALT TOLERANT. Alligators are less salt tolerant. The reason for this has to do with the physiology and role of their lingual or tongue glands. The lingual glands are present in crocodiles, alligators, caimans and gharials. The cell structure, shape and salt-secreting function of these glands differ according to species. Only the true crocodiles (subfamily Crocodylinae members) have glands capable of any significant salt concentration or secretion rate.

Common expressions in patients

This will include all the common expressions of the crocodilians and the following, specific for the crocodiles:

Method of attack:
- More gripping and tearing (alligator has more of crushing)

Behavior:
- Inhabit wider areas (unlike the alligators which are more restricted to thick vegetation)
- Migrate over longer distances (unlike the alligators)
- More aggressive and dangerous (than the alligators)
- Inability to tolerate colder climate (unlike the alligators)

Within the subfamily Crocodylinae we have three remedies from the genus Crocodylus.

Crocodylus acutus [American crocodile]

Order: Crocodylia

Family: Crocodylidae

Subfamily: Crocodylinae (Crocodylidae)

Genus: Crocodylus

Species: Crocodylus acutus

Common name: American crocodile

Habitat

American crocodiles inhabit freshwater coastal areas of southeast Florida, in the USA, as well as Central and South America, and the Caribbean islands. They prefer freshwater, but they can survive in brackish conditions.

Anatomical characteristics

Compared with other crocodile species, the ARMOR IS LESS PROMINENT.

Reproduction

This species is mainly a HOLE NESTER, but populations without access to suitable nest sites which can be excavated (relatively well drained) will build mound nests using whatever nesting materials are available. Flooding creates high mortality. Nesting occurs during the dry season. This tends to minimize flooding, especially in hole nests which are in danger of falling below the water table after heavy rains.

The degree of parental care seems to be variable. Some sources note minimal protection of the nest and the newly hatched juveniles. Other sources report a higher degree of parental attention. This includes guarding the nest (a burrow is constructed nearby) to assist the hatching juveniles and subsequently protecting them. Predators include birds, wild cats, raccoons and even large fish. It appears that the juveniles move away from the nesting area within a few days of hatching. It has been suggested that this lack of parental care and early juvenile dispersal is a direct result of the rigorous hunting that the species was subjected to in the second quarter of the twentieth century. This produced a rapid adaptation to survive.

The juveniles have also been noted to vocalize less than other species during the first few weeks of life.

Characteristic behavior

American crocodiles are MORE SUSCEPTIBLE TO COLD than American alligators. Unlike the American alligator, which can survive in water of 7.2° C/45° F for some time, an American crocodile would become helpless and drown. It is thought that this intolerance to cold is the reason that American crocodiles never spread as far northward as the alligators. American crocodiles, however, have a FASTER GROWTH RATE than alligators.

While accounts of crocodilians having their teeth cleaned by birds and fish have been repeated often enough to have acquired the veneer of truth, they must be approached with caution, for the accounts from centuries back that recount observations and stories of birds cleaning the teeth of Old World crocodiles have not been verified in modern times and the fact that the American crocodile RELIES ON FISH FOR PARASITE REMOVAL comes from a single expert writing in 1972.

Crocodiles: Their Natural History, Folklore, and Conservation (1972), by C.A.W. Guggisberg. Quoting from the book (page 79):

While there are no records of birds attending any of the New World crocodilians, the American crocodile has recently been found to be 'cleaned' by a fish.

Possible specific expressions in patients

The American crocodile will manifest all the common expressions of the crocodiles. Their specific indications will be:

- Faster growth rate
- Connection to fishes (possibility)
- Builds nesting holes; makes a house
- Less vocal

Crocodylus niloticus [Nile crocodile]

Order: Crocodylia

Family: Crocodylidae

Subfamily: Crocodylinae (Crocodylidae)

Genus: Crocodylus

Species: Crocodylus niloticus

Common name: Nile crocodile

Introduction

There is a long history of reverence for the Nile crocodile. Their history dates back to the time of the pharaohs, when hundreds of crocodiles were mummified along with dead kings. Today there is less reverence, and more fear and intolerance towards these crocodiles, which sometimes prey on livestock and humans. The Nile crocodile and the saltwater crocodile are the top two of the eight crocodilian species known to make UNPROVOKED ATTACKS on humans. It is a SOCIABLE species, as large numbers can be seen on river banks, lying side by side.

Habitat

They live throughout sub-Saharan Africa and the Nile Basin. They're also found in Madagascar in both fresh and brackish rivers, freshwater marshes, and mangrove swamps.

Anatomical characteristics

The Nile crocodile is the largest crocodilian in Africa and is sometimes regarded as the third largest crocodilian, after the saltwater crocodile and the gharial. It averages 5 m/16 ft in length and 750 kg/1600 lbs in weight.

Nile crocodiles' brains and hearts are more advanced than those of any other living reptile.

Food habits

Hatchling Nile crocodiles begin their lives eating insects, and then move to a diet of aquatic and smaller land vertebrates. The diet of the Nile crocodile is mainly fish, amphibians, and reptiles; but it will attack almost anything unfortunate enough to cross its path, including zebras, small hippos, porcupines, birds, and other crocodiles. It will also scavenge carrion, and can eat up to half its body weight at a feeding.

Reproduction

Female Nile crocodiles are hole nesters and BURY THEIR EGGS IN SAND, rather than incubating them in rotting vegetation. A female will USE THE SAME NEST SITE FOR HER ENTIRE LIFE. After burying the eggs, the female then **guards** them for the 3 month incubation period. The father-to-be will often stay nearby, as **both parents will fiercely attack anything that approaches their eggs.** The attending mother will only leave the nest if she needs to cool off (thermoregulation) by taking a quick dip, or by seeking out a patch of shade. Despite the attentive care of both parents, the nests are often raided by humans, monitor lizards, and other animals while the mother is temporarily absent.

Nile crocodiles have temperature dependent sex determination (TSD). This means the sex of their hatchlings is determined not by genetics, but by the average temperature during the middle third of their incubation period.

Characteristic behavior

The stories of the Nile crocodile having their teeth cleaned by birds (having a symbiotic relationship with the plover bird), all come from ancient history and don't seem verifiable in modern observation. The story is repeated as gospel truth, especially in children's science articles, but modern herpetologists' accounts or photos are nonexistent.

Christopher Perrins' *Firefly Encyclopedia of Birds* says on page 253:

The Egyptian plover's alternative common name, Crocodile bird, arises from an account by the Greek historian Herodotus, telling how certain birds on the Nile — which later commentators took to be this specie — fed on the scraps left between the teeth of basking crocodiles. Despite being corroborated by anecdotal evidence from two eminent German ornithologists in the 19th and 20th centuries, this alleged behavior has never been properly authenticated!

Specific method of attack and defense

Adult Nile crocodiles use their bodies and tail to HERD GROUPS OF FISH TOWARDS A BANK, AND EAT THEM WITH A QUICK SIDEWAYS JERK OF THEIR HEADS. THEY ALSO COOPERATE BY BLOCKING MIGRATING FISH IN FORMING A SEMICIRCLE ACROSS THE RIVER. The most dominant crocodile eats first. Groups of Nile crocodiles may travel hundreds of meters from a waterway to feed. When groups of Nile crocodiles are sharing a kill (COOPERATIVE FEEDING BEHAVIOR), they use each other for leverage, biting down hard and then twisting their bodies to tear off large pieces of meat. This twisting is seen as the characteristic crocodile **death roll.** They may also get the necessary leverage by lodging their prey under branches or stones before rolling and ripping. They will also scavenge other animal's kill, although they avoid rotting meat.

Nile crocodile: cooperative feeding behavior

319

Case of *Crocodylus niloticus*

By: Staria Manos CCH, RSHom (NA)

Middle-aged woman.

Main complaint is migraines.

Her first husband was <u>not</u> a good man. She is still affected deeply by the hidden abuse. She is currently married to a man with serious health issues and she's the only one working.

HG= HAND GESTURE

BL= BODY LANGUAGE

24 December 2007:

'I drive a long way to work. I have to have benefits I provide for my family'.

Observation: She looks older than she is. She sits on the floor instead of the chair and cries most of the intake.

D: Main complaint?

P: I would like my migraines to go away. They control my life **point blank**.

I have a shoulder injury. **It pops up** and I have to pop it back in. I would like to do things without my shoulder popping and aching. There was a time I could not get my arm over my shoulder. I have a catch; I know it is there (HG- pressing her fingers into her shoulder). A chiropractor worked on pressure points. I have a 5% disability.

D: Shoulder?

P: The shoulder is a prolonged injury from working with the children. This injury happened when I was working with a boy almost as tall as I am, he had cerebral palsy. He lost his balance and he pulled me down. Then all at once you are hurt. Another day, the bus driver handed me the back pack. It was full of baby food jars; I thought my arm would fall off. If I could put my hand in here (again pushing her fingers deep into her shoulder). If I could rub deep inside. My fingers are numb and tingling and it affects my head, how tight and irritated it is.

D: Deep inside?

P: It feels like a blockage, like you could not pull your hand through it (crying).

It is the size of an orange and you can never get to it. The muscle behind the breast, it is better than before car accident. I sleep with a pillow, just enough to keep it elevated. If it is too high and too low it hurts, and it catches. It is down in here (points to axilla) kind of behind here (top of breast).

Kind of like when you have a migraine beginning sensation. That leftover drunken stupor. You are just hanging on (HG), and you don't feel clear. If I get those kind of feelings with my head I know when there is an emergency situation. (BL- arms crossed over chest. Wiggling whole body, while still sitting on the floor.) It's when that foggy stuff comes in, or when I'm extremely tired and don't sleep well. I am down for 3 days, down for the count.

D: Orange?

P: I can't tell you that it is hard or mushy, it is always there. It would be, (HG-rolled out) it's not round, more smashed, it is not just here (points to that same area), but it has fingers that go out. Flatter and it could go in the other direction. Numbness goes down my arm if I have done a lot of cutting or writing. I feel that numbness going out. It hurts behind . . . if I could just get to it, and lay a different way or something! If I could rub it, it would relax like a charley horse in your foot. The pain was like a burning sensation, but this underside side, just the underside was burning.

D: Burning?

P: I know when I am sewing, I get that same hot burning sensation. Not like walking on broken glass. It is stingy. I guess . . . kind of like, if you thought of your head as a balloon and **it popped, that fast** . . . air gush, burning. In a couple of days I am stiff all over.

D: Fingers are like what?

P: Wires that spread out a lot of little ones. No color, just seem to be sharper, some ends seem to be sharper. What's amazing me, is I live with this all the time. It hurts to talk about and think about it.

D: Tell me more about the migraines?

P: I have had them since I can remember. I used to think I had a sinus problem. I would take over the counter sinus medicines and I would get tingling, **crawling** in my head. They did a CAT scan of my sinus problems. They misdiagnosed the problem. Then we started checking off the food list. I am susceptible to weather changes especially when the fog comes. If it is hot and I go to a cold room. I hate going into the pool. I have a headache. I feel robbed. **They control my life.** There are days when I wake up, my balance is off. I feel separated, and part of me is going through the daily routine, the other part is disconnected. **There is something odd about me.** I don't see spots, but my balance is off. My right eye, but not my left eye, gets real droopy. I am quieter. I can lie down and have some peace, and then the severity will not be as bad.

D: Separate part?

P: God…it is like I am just not all there. I guess kind of like a star that does not have its full brightness (HG). I have this…and that is just…just not there. It is not a hurt. I just don't feel right. I don't know. I don't know what I feel. I don't know…

D: Brightness?

P: Brightness is me. I wake up in a good mood and I love life. Sometimes you just don't have that sparkle, and **the edge is rough**.

D: Weather, fog coming?

P: **Dread**. I know that when the humidity… I feel the pressure, and it is pressure. Pushing above my eyebrow, and it will be down in my ears. On the right back side of neck, and it is like the size of a golf ball. I feel that there is a ball right there. If I could just rub it out. But my head pounds so much. My head will hurt so bad I don't want to breathe, and just the movement of breathing hurts. It takes me so long to be able to relax. My neck and shoulders hurt. Feels like a **wrecking ball hitting** the side of your head. My husband will put ice on a wash rag. When it is cold, it is better for me to have cold up against my skin, I guess.

I would not wish a migraine on my worst enemy. When I wake up my voice will be real crackly or raspy. **Controls you** like this. It takes **dominance over everything** else. It has the final say.

D: Dominance?

P: Something against my will. Something I really loathe (crying). This is going to sound really stupid, but **my ex-husband was very controlling**. In fact he is a pedophile, and I have a son and a brother who are two of his **victims.** Everyone in the family is a victim, making you feel like **you are less** than a woman, or you have less importance. You are not worth anything.

D: Dominance?

P: It would be like being in a boat in the ocean, and there is a horrible storm, and the waves are so tall, and you are afraid. One wave will just **consume you** and it takes your breath away. I am going to die. I am cold and I can't breathe. I just can't get my breath (BL-shaking head).

D: Ball on neck and head?

P: It is really hard, and it does not matter how much you rub on it, it does not decrease. It is so tight, kind of like...um...sounds silly, but my mom use to have a clock that would wind for the week, a 7-day clock. I feel like I've been wound too tight, I am a 10-day clock, **twisted** too hard. I don't remember feeling like it is hot. **More like a rock. It would be cold and it is hard**. The sensations are **twisted and claw, and pulls, pinching. It is hard**. It is a clawing, pulling, kind of like the skin on this side of your face is shrinking. Everything just feels out of place.

D: Twisting?

P: Twisting would be more like (HG- going around) around like a funnel cloud in a smaller scale but like that: **whirling, and twisting with strength**. Yeah, yeah!

D: Pull and pinch?

P: It has that control, it's just taking my head. You **twist someone's head** and make them do it, it is a dominance, it truly is.

D: Dominate and pull, like what?

P: Like a wolf or a **wild animal, that would rip and tear, and pull and shake something with those long sharp teeth.**

Here she is describing the substance in nature taking her head and twisting

D: Wild animal that would rip and tear?

P: Coyote, a bear.

D: Dominate like what?

P: Be like a tiger or a lion that would dominate. That is what comes to my mind.

D: Childhood?

P: Happy, I am the oldest of 5. My mom and dad are compassionate people. We grew up on a farm, and we had chores to do. We would play ball or swim at the end of the day.

I have a brother, that he and I were very completive always. Girls could not play on the team. I was just as good as anyone of them, but girls could not play.

D: Completive?

P: Keeping up with someone, side by side (HG). Being in sync with someone else (HG- always in a circle).

D: Swimming?

P: We did not have swimming pools, but down the road we had **a pond that you could swim in**. All the neighbors met there, so it was an extension of the family. Just going to **relax and cool off**. I watched for the weeds, I did not want to get my feet tangled in them. So they don't tip me over. Where I swam there were no weeds. I was afraid of the weeds.

D: Weeds?

P: **I would drown, I would get tangled, and I thought you could not get out.** There were so many of them. I guess I have a phobia of being tangled. (She pauses and is thinking.)

Twenty years ago we rode the trolley or maybe it is called a tram, it's one of them. I remember **I could not breathe.** If we are making a road trip, and there is a tunnel, and if I have to go into a tunnel where I can't see out, it is a panic.

I can't breathe. I get tightness in my throat, and I am short of breath. I feel like everything is going to close in on me and I am going to **suffocate** (HG-inward). Knowing that the **water was above me,** I just wanted to get out. I just knew the walls were going to close in on me, like that wrecking ball, here it comes.

D: Physically what is the sensation?

P: I don't feel the water, but **I am afraid it is going to rush in on me. I don't want to drown. I imagine the cold, and the dark water, and I'm going to drown.**

I don't know why it bothers me if I drown.

All this talk of water with strong sensations indicates the substance you choose has to have a connection or be in water.

D: How would you describe yourself?

P: I have so much energy. I laugh a lot, I like to cook and sew and knit. I love life, color, and birds singing. I like to hear the wings of a dragonfly, or a humming bird. I feel exuberant. On my worst day there is that **darkness and it is all around me. I can't get out from underneath it**. I feel **ugly,** maybe even angry.

D: Dreams?

P: I have dreams about something on TV; child that has been abducted, things that take me back. I wake up screaming and my husband will just hold me. It is the kids. (Now she is crying very hard). Recently I read a magazine on predators, that has upset me so much. (She is talking about men who sexually molest children). That has upset me so much, because neither the kids nor the adults know how to handle the predator.

I was not expecting it. I was not prepared for it. Everything that article described was what I lived with. I guess it upset me that much inside. I did not protect him, my youngest son. I was raw nerves. We moved, we were **hiding so we could get out of his grasp**.

D: Ex-husband?

P: **There are two sides that I see**. One side that is likeable, warm, and entertaining. But then there is the **dominating** side (crying), the **ugly** side of him. He is **mean and hurtful.** He is selfish and I hate him. And obviously he has never left my life.

(The two sides, a good indication of reptile.)

D: Predator?

P: Always a man. **Predators are sneaky. They know how to get around the obstacles** to get what they want, and they always win, because **they are stronger than you are**.

D: What is your perfect environment?

P: I like the warmth of a sandy beach with a soft breeze... warm, breezy, with palm trees swaying back and forth. No boats. I don't want to hear boats. I like just the warm sun, not hot, and the pleasant Santa Ana winds, (a weather condition that happens in southern California; a warm, dry breeze). Tropical.

I like the colors and unusual plants. I like the greenness of the water. Yeah...

D: Anything else?

P: The last report from my doctor is that I have a fatty liver. I don't think I am overweight. Then she talks about some minerals she takes that 'give me energy, and help to give me sharpness or clearness'.

Case analysis:
The indications of Crocodile remedy were as follows:

Fear of drowning, being pulled under, can't breathe, dread, dominance, and feeling cold. The hand gesture which always went in a circle was also important. It is really interesting that she preferred to sit on the floor instead of the chair, she seemed to like being lower than me.

The question 'What is your perfect environment?' It has helped confirm a remedy many times for me. In this case she does not say crocodile but by asking about the environment she very much paints the picture of where this predator would live. In a warm tropical place with unusual plants and green water. It is a good question.

Remedy once every week: *Crocodylus niloticus* 6C.

[Please note: I always start my clients on a low potency, usually a 6C or an LM1 where possible. I have found this to be very successful. The benefits are fewer aggravations, more consistency in follow-ups. I have gotten amazing healing right from the beginning on these low potencies. I believe it is because with the sensation method we have a greater ability to find the 'simillimum' which can encourage healing on a very deep level.]

Follow-up on 11 August 2008 (6 ½ months after initial consultation):

Crocodylus niloticus **6C, taken every 6 days (she is putting 2 pellets in 4oz of water and taking 1 tablespoon of the water, then discarding the rest).**

P: When I first started seeing you I was having migraines 2-3 times a week, but I am much better. I have not really had a migraine. I've had headaches, but not a full-blown migraine.

D: Blockage deep inside?
P: I don't think so, I can't think of anything that makes me feel locked in. .

I have read about sexual predators. Me and my husband recently sat and talked about it for a long time. I told him feelings I had not expressed. I think you feel guilty for not protecting your children. I feel really bad that I did not protect my children.

D: Stiff all over?
P: I can tell you that I am not feeling stiff. I have been doing a lot of walking.

I am trying to stay healthy. When I went to physical therapy, I learned things I can do on a daily basis. It keeps my strength going and I am not feeling like I was. This is not the first time I have had therapy on this shoulder. I did not make progress last time. This time I benefited from the therapy.

D: Separate/odd?
P: No I don't remember feeling that way. No I don't feel that. I am just feeling better as a person, myself, just me.

I have not had the migraines like I had before.

D: Internal coldness?

P: (Laughs) I don't feel cold, no, I am not. I am not feeling negative. I never thought of myself as having low self-esteem…it… the catch… my shoulder does not catch.

Staria: This patient says she feels so much better when she comes in for the follow-ups, but she still cannot afford to come more often. I am still having her take the remedy in water to soften it and make it more like LM potency.

I know most homoeopaths might think it is crazy that I would start a patient off on a 6C, but this is a perfect example of how much healing can come on a low potency when it's the simillimum. She rarely takes her prescription medicines for migraines now. She is off of the sleeping pills, and has started dreaming. Emotionally she is opening up about the abuse from the past.

Follow-up on 12 August 2009 (one year and 8 months after initial consultation):

By this time I had stepped up her potency to *Crocodylus* 12C every 7 days.

Sometimes she takes it after 6 days.

She reports getting an acute illness in which she had a bad cough, and raspy voice that lasted for 6 weeks. She went to the medical doctor several times, but nothing seemed to improve her condition. I am thinking she had a healing crisis.

D: Have you had more migraines?

P: I think if you look at the paperwork (she keeps notes and brings them to me), there has been a decline. I have not had to take my migraine medicine as much; only once a month. I get a dull headache, which is great! I was having 2-3 migraines a week, and now I get headaches about once a month and they are not as intense. I take my migraine medicine, and they do not turn in to migraines.

D: How are you sleeping now?

P: I have been sleeping really good.

She is not having any trouble at all with her shoulder. No problems with numb tingly feeling in her fingers. She is still having hot flashes but not as often or intense.

She has had one dream which she had in July. She could not remember anything else, but it was about snakes, which scared her. Emotionally she feels she is able to deal with her adult children better, and stay calm even when dealing with her husband's health issues.

Recommendation: Take remedy 12C every 6 days.

Staria: I have also found that patients that have suffered abuse in the past have to be dealt with very carefully and they tend to heal slowly. Even taking the remedy one day sooner can be too much for their system.

Possible specific expressions of the Nile crocodile in patients

The Nile crocodile will exhibit all the common expressions of the crocodiles as well as their specific indications which are as follows:

- Cooperative behavior; need each other, working in groups or partnership
- Homesickness, coming back to your origine
- Ability to exert a stronger bite force
- Unprovoked attack
- Social
- Burying

Crocodylus novaeguineae [New Guinea crocodile]

Order: Crocodylia

Family: Crocodylidae

Subfamily: Crocodylinae (Crocodylidae)

Genus: Crocodylus

Species: Crocodylus novaeguineae

Common names: New Guinea crocodile, New Guinea freshwater crocodile

Introduction

Crocodylus novaeguineae (New Guinea crocodile) is a species of the Crocodylidae found in New Guinea. The genus Crocodylus includes 13 fairly similar species.

Crocodylus novaeguineae

Habitat

Crocodiles live throughout the tropics in Asia, Africa, Australia and the Americas. Although tolerant of saltwater, it is rarely found in brackish coastal waters, and never in the presence of the competing saltwater crocodile (Crocodylus porosus).

Behavior

Primarily NOCTURNAL by nature.

Possible specific expressions in patients

Crocodylus novaeguineae will also have all the common expressions of the crocodiles. Its only specific feature that is available is its nocturnal nature.

Chart illustrating the differences

	Alligator and caiman	Crocodile	Gharial
Snout shape	**Wider, shorter head** is U-shaped, with a more **obtuse snout** than the crocodile's. Broad and flat snout design for **strength**. **Head bones** must **withstand stress from the force used to crack open the turtles and hard-shelled invertebrates** which form part of their diet. Broad snouts can power through **thick vegetation** to **catch prey**.	**Longer, narrower head** is V-shaped, with a more **triangular snout.** A more forward eye placement than the alligator's. Pointed snout isn't quite as strong as the alligator's. The crocodile is still capable of exerting massive biting power.	**Long, very narrow snout.** The end of a mature male gharial's snout develops a **lobe** that enlarges with age. This **bulbous lump** has a flap inside. When the male gharial breathes, it makes a **buzzing noise.** The male gharial uses the lump during courtship to make **bubbles** against the belly of the female. This bump gives the animal its name. *Ghara* in Hindi, (Indian regional language) means 'pot'.

Comparing snouts of alligator, crocodile and gharial

	Alligator and caiman	Crocodile	Gharial
Teeth	An alligator's fourth lower tooth fits into a pit in the upper jaw which conceals it when the mouth is closed. **Only the upper teeth** of an alligator are visible when the mouth is closed.	A notch in the crocodile's upper jaw accommodates the fourth lower tooth so that it remains visible when the mouth is shut. **Both the upper and lower teeth** of a crocodile are visible when the mouth is closed.	The gharial's teeth are larger near the tip of the snout. **Both the upper and lower teeth** of a gharial are visible when the mouth is closed.
Jaw function	Alligator jaws are meant to **crush bones** and can deliver a **bite force** of up to 450 kg/ 3000 lbs.	Crocodile jaws are much narrower, and are used to **grip and tear** prey.	Long, thin gharial jaws allow the **swipes and snaps** necessary to catch prey underwater.
Head physiology and diet	Thanks to their broad, heavy snouts, alligators can feed on the widespread **hard-shelled creatures**, as well as the softer prey.	Crocodiles' neither-thick-nor-thin snout shape can be thought of as generalized. Ideal for the **wide variety of prey** in the crocodile's environment.	Thin gharial snouts are extremely hydrodynamic. It creates less water resistance to the **sideways whipping motion** the animal uses to catch fish underwater. The thin jaw shape does not endure the stress of capturing mammals and large prey that other crocodilians feed on. This is why gharials are **primarily fish eaters**.

	Alligator and caiman	Crocodile	Gharial
Dermal pressure receptors	Dermal (sometimes called 'dome') pressure receptors are dome-shaped papillae which appear as small dots or pits on the skin of crocodilians. They function as sensing organs for water motion or air-water interface disruption. They allow crocodilians to orient towards pressure or motion changes of the surrounding water in order to locate prey.		
	Found on only the jaws of alligators.	Found all over the bodies of crocodiles.	Found on the jaws and lower sides of gharials.
Salt water tolerance	Alligators lack salt excreting glands. They have **limited tolerance for salt water** and **are restricted to fresh water**.	Crocodiles **can tolerate salt water** due to specialized glands that filter out salt. This explains their **ability to migrate** across marine bodies and live in salt water for extended periods of time. Crocodylus porosus, the species known as the estuarine or saltwater crocodile, has a high tolerance for salinity. It breeds in freshwater and then moves between the fresh and saltwater bodies of the coastal regions where it lives.	Salt excreting glands on gharials' tongues allow them to **tolerate some salt water** exposure.

	Alligator and caiman	Crocodile	Gharial
Thermal preference	Alligators have more tolerance to cold. They are able to survive in freezing conditions.	Crocodiles, unlike alligators, are purely tropical. They need consistent warm weather year round and are intolerant to cold.	
Temper-ament	**Less aggressive** than crocodiles. Alligators **would rather avoid than attack humans** unless provoked.	Crocodiles are **very aggressive**. They would rather flee at the sight of a human. They do **attack large prey animals** and will sometimes attack humans.	Gharials are **not very violent or aggressive.** Nervous and shy. They are **highly aquatic** and tend to **submerge in deep water for safety** when encountering humans or danger.
Parental care	**Extreme degree of parental care.** The mother alligator watches over the nest until high pitched noises from inside the eggs prompt her to remove the nesting material. She carries the young alligators to the water in her mouth. They stay with her up to a year for protection.	**Extreme degree of parental care.** The mother crocodile protects the nest. Once the eggs hatch, she carries the young crocodiles to the water in her mouth. They stay with her up to two years for protection.	**High degree of parental care.** The mother gharial visits and protects the nest at night but remains in the water during the day. She will protect her hatchlings but does not carry them to water. This may be due to the unsuitable shape of the jaws.

	Alligator and caiman	Crocodile	Gharial
Vocalization	Crocodilians are the most vocal of reptiles. Their habitats contain thick vegetation making it difficult to see others, so they communicate by sound. Baby crocodilians make noise while still in their eggs, to elicit their mother's help and protection while hatching. Baby crocodilians make high-pitched noises to call for their mothers. These calls are sometimes answered by nearby adults.		
	Alligators: **chirp, bellow, and hiss**.	Crocodiles: **hiss, growl, and bellow.**	The bulb-like protuberance at the end of the male gharial's snout makes and amplifies a **buzzing sound**.
Facts of interest	'Gator holes' are deeply hollowed out depressions in the marsh muck that alligators make with their mouths, claws, and tails. They then become small ponds during dry seasons and droughts. The holes remain wet and keep alive the alligator and other animals that are attracted to the 'gator holes'. A strong instinct to return to home territories with excellent sense of direction. Not as promiscuous as previously thought (fidelity).		Compared to other crocodilians, the gharial's legs are poorly developed. It is **unable to lift its belly to walk on land** and can barely manage to push itself along the mud. This is why it rarely leaves the water.

	Alligator and caiman	Crocodile	Gharial
Specific character-ristic of crocodilian species	*Alligator mississippiensis* [American alligator, Mississippi alligator] (Given in the column above.)	*Crocodylus acutus* [American crocodile] *Crocodylus niloticus* [Nile crocodile] *Crocodylus novaeguineae* [New Guinea crocodile] (Further differences between the crocodile remedies are given in the table below.)	

Crocodylus acutus [American crocodile]	*Crocodylus niloticus* [Nile crocodile]	*Crocodylus novaeguineae* [New Guinea crocodile]
– Faster growth rate – Connection to fishes (possibility) – Builds nests/holes; making a house	– Cooperative feeding – Forming a semicircle – Bury eggs in the sand – Use the same nesting sites throughout their life – Ability to exert a stronger bite force – Unprovoked attack – Social	– Primarily nocturnal

Squamata
(Lizards, Amphisbaenians, Snakes)

Introduction

Squamata is the largest and the most successful group of reptiles. It comprises 95% of all the reptiles. The geological history of the extant (still existing) squamata families and near relatives begins in the Late Jurassic (ca. 150 million years before present*). Squamata consists of the snakes, lizards and amphisbaenians. Currently there are about 7200 species[1] of squamates. This is more than the number of all the mammalian species. Of the squamates, half are lizards, 130 are amphisbaenians, (limbless, "worm lizards") and the rest are snakes. Members of the squamata are found in all continents except Antarctica.

Classification

Kingdom: Animalia
Phylum: Chordata
Subphylum: Vertebrata
Class: Sauropsida (Reptilia)
Subclass: Diapsida
Order: Squamata

Suborder:
- Lacertila or Sauria (Lizards)
- Serpentes or Ophidia (Snakes)
- Amphisbaenians or Amphisbaenia (Worm lizards)

Classification

Kingdom: Animalia
Phylum: Chordata
Subphylum: Vertebrata
Class: Sauropsida (Reptilia
Subclass: Diapsida
Order: Squamata

Suborder:
- Lacertila or Sauria (Lizards)
- Serpentes or Ophidia (Snakes)
- Amphisbaenians or Amphisbaenia (V

Generalized anatomy

The squamates are characterized by their skin, wh **shields**. They all possess movable quadrate bones, w **the upper jaw relatively with the brain case**. This e flexibility, gape, and power of the jaws which help to capture a prey. This pliable jaw structure is particularly striking in snakes. It allows them to **accommodate and swallow a comparatively larger prey**. This kind of adaptation has been the key to the success of the squamates.

---

1   Ref: Herpetology, the definitive college text by Laurie Vitt

The male members of the squamata are the only vertebrates with a hemipenis.

Squamata tongues are **notched or forked**. The squamates are **limbless** or have **very reduced limbs** and an **elongated body** (biological evolution).

Recent studies suggest that most of the snakes, and more lizards than previously believed, have evolved **venom** delivery systems (modified salivary glands connected via duct to fangs). This shared feature is believed to originate from the squamata phylogeny. The Gila monster and beaded lizard were previously believed to be the only venomous lizards. Venom toxins have now been identified in monitor lizards and the Iguania clade as well.

Reproduction

This is also the only reptile group which has both viviparous and ovoviviparous species, as well as the usual oviparous reptiles.

Most squamata mothers provide **no care for their young and leave almost immediately after they lay their eggs or give birth**. Some lizards and snakes (like the python) are exceptions. The pythons, mud snakes, and skinks, for example, stay with the eggs until they hatch. The female wraps her body around the eggs and protects them.

While most species reproduce only after the male and female mate, some ⋅s are **parthenogenic.** In many of these species, such as the lizard known desert grassland whiptail, only females exist. The female's young are all cal copies of her. Like the whiptail family of lizards, seven other families rds and snakes have some all-female species.

Behavior

The squamates display diverse modes of life: **climbers, burrowers, crawlers, aquatic forms, and even gliding types**.

339

Possible squamata expressions in patients

- Easy mobility and flexibility of jaws

- Wider gape

- Important words of locomotion:

  Climb, burrow, swim, crawl, glide, slither

The following features are found more commonly in snakes and lizards:

- Poison, venom (for many snakes and some lizards of the Heloderma, Varanus and Iguania groups).

- Notched or forked tongue (all snakes and a few lizards, like the monitor lizards).

- Flicking of the tongue (all snakes and some lizards, e.g. the monitor lizards). This is commonly observed as a protrusion and retraction of tongue in patients.

Lizards

Homoeopathic remedies

Iguania remedies

- *Calotes versicolor* [Bloodsucker]
- *Chamaeleo zeylanicus* or Chamaeleon (Divya) [Indian chameleon]
- *Chlamydosaurus kingii* [Frilled neck lizard]
- *Furcifer oustaleti* [Oustalet's or Malagasy giant Chameleon]
- *Iguana iguana* [Green iguana]
- *Pogona vitticeps* [Central bearded dragon]
- *Sceloporus occidentalis* [Western fence lizard, Blue-bellies]

Scleroglossa remedies

- *Anguis fragilis* [Slow worm]
- *Heloderma horridum* [Mexican beaded lizard]
- *Heloderma suspectum* (Helo.) [Gila monster]
- *Varanus komodoensis* [Komodo dragon or Monitor lizard]
- *Lacerta agilis* (Lacer.) [Sand lizard or Green lizard]
- *Lacerta vivipara* [Common lizard]

- Lizard (Divya) [species unidentified]

Introduction

Have you ever observed a lizard **scurrying** across the wall as though in a **big hurry, suddenly stopping in the middle of nowhere, deadly still**, and then starting to **chirp?**

Lizards have been the subject of superstition and speculation for thousands of years. They form one of the most successful and fascinating groups of reptiles. They have evolved over 314 million years and constitute the largest group of living reptiles. There are more than 4,300 species, in a **wide variety of shapes, sizes, form and behavior**, that continue to fascinate us even today.

Lizards (and other reptiles) differ from amphibians. Because of their dry, scaly, impermeable skin, the lizards have been able to cut all ties with a watery environment. There are many specialized body adaptations that aid in their survival. Lizards have colonized almost the entire world, and are able to live in diverse habitats: from swamps to rainforests, from woodlands to the arid, dry hot deserts. This makes them the most widespread of all the reptiles, found on all continents except Antarctica.

Lizards are notable and noticeable for their **bright colors, quick movements, and almost bold tolerance of human presence (up to a point).** One can't hold back astonishment at the lizard's remarkable ability to **scurry** on vertical walls and across the ceiling, or to simply **dart off** and **swiftly scamper** over old fences, logs, tree trunks or rocks. They can be **ground dwellers, burrowers of the underground,** or **gliders!** Still others are **slow-moving**, relying on **cryptic coloration** rather than speed and agility for protection.

Unlike its fellow reptile, the turtle, we never see the lizard depicted as a fun, lovable creature which inspires children's movies and stories. In fact, most of us even despise its mere sight! This is quite understandable, given the fact that when you closely examine their tiny little faces, you see the remnants of the fearsome dinosaurs, which were capable of eating up a human in one dainty bite. Unfortunately, the diabolic powers attributed to lizards have made them objects of fear in many countries. Mankind has always lived with reptiles, so from the Dragon in the Garden of Eden to Godzilla in Japan, the lizard represents a slightly alien yet familiar archetype.

Classification

Kingdom: Animalia
Phylum: Chordata
Subphylum: Vertebrata
Class: Reptilia
Subclass: Lepidosauria
Order: Squamata

Suborder: Iguania (includes the iguanas, chameleons and relatives)
- **Family:** Agamidae (Agamid lizards)
- **Family:** Chamaeleonidae (Chameleons)
- **Family:** Iguanidae (Iguanas)
- **Family:** Corytophanidae (Helmeted lizards)
- **Family:** Crotaphytidae (Collared and leopard lizards)
- **Family:** Hoplocercidae (Hoplocerids)
- **Family:** Opluridae (Madagascar iguanians)
- **Family:** Phrynosomatidae (Scaly, sand and horned lizards)
- **Family:** Polychrotidae (Anoloid lizards)
- **Family:** Tropiduridae (Tropidurids)

Suborder: Scleroglossa (includes the geckos, skinks, poisonous/venomous lizards, legless lizards, and monitor lizards)

Superfamily: Gekkonoidea (includes the geckos)
- **Family:** Gekkonidae (Geckos)
- **Family:** Eublepharidae (Eyelash geckos)
- **Family:** Pygopodidae (Australian flapfoots)

Superfamily: Scincoidea (includes skinks and relatives)
- **Family:** Lacertidae (Wall lizards, true lizards or lacertids)
- **Family:** Xantusiidae (Night lizards)
- **Family:** Scincidae (Skinks)
- **Family:** Dibamidae (Dibamids)
- **Family:** Cordylidae (Girdle-tailed and plated lizards)
- **Family:** Gerrhosauridae (Microteiids)
- Family: Teiidae (Macroteiids or whip lizards)
- **Family:** Gymnophthalmidae (Microteiids)

Superfamily: Anguoidea (legless and alligator lizards: includes the poisonous lizards and monitor lizards)
- **Family:** Anguidae (Anguids; glass and alligator lizards)
- **Family:** Helodermatidae (Gila monster and Beaded lizards)
- **Family:** Varanidae (Monitor lizards)
- **Family:** Lanthanotidae (Earless monitor lizard)

General differences between Iguania and Scleroglossa:

Iguania	Scleroglossa
Group sharing a fleshy tongue and lingual prehension of prey.	The name is derived from the Greek, 'skleros', meaning *hard* and 'glossa', meaning *tongue*. These lizards' use of jaw prehension for prey capture has freed their tongues to act as a well-developed chemosensory system. Their sensory tongues and wide foraging provide access to more sedentary and hidden prey than is available to lizards of the Iguania family.

Generalized anatomy

Lizards form a large and varied group that is not easy to concisely define. They show various body modifications that help them adapt to their diverse habitat. Although they closely resemble snakes, **a typical lizard has a distinct head, four well developed limbs with claws, and a long tail**. There are exceptions to these generalizations. Lizards can range from tiny, delicate and secretive creatures to huge, dragon-like marauders. Some may have two legs or no legs at all!

They range in total length from geckos that can measure 3 cm /1.2 in to monitor lizards that measure over 3 m/10 ft. The tiniest of them is the dwarf gecko which can easily fit on the tip of a human finger! The adult lizard can weigh from less than 1 gr/0.04 oz to more than 150 kg/330 lb!

Lizards have dry, scaly and impermeable skin which they shed or molt **in large flakes**. A lizard's **scales** may be large, smooth, and overlapping or small, rough, and stud like, in almost any combination. They may also have irregular scales, or large scales that can be scattered amongst many smaller ones. None has the single row of wide ventral scales which are characteristic of snakes.

A tiny gecko

Lizards exhibit a variety of **skin modifications or ornaments**, like extensible throat fans, tail crests, horns or casques on the head, a frill around the throat, and spikes. For example, the anole lizards have a brightly colored patch of skin on the throat called the *dewlap*. Usually hidden between scales, it is displayed only to scare off a potential threat or to attract a mate.

Anole lizard displaying the brightly colored throat (dewlap), which also makes it appear much bigger than its size

Most lizards have **movable eyelids**, unlike snakes with immovable eyelids. There are also some forms that have no eyes and even no ears, while some have eyes covered by a transparent scale rather than movable lids. In lizards their lower eyelid moves upwards. This is opposite to a human eye.

Lizards don't have an external earflap like mammals, but they have an external ear opening and an eardrum just beneath the skin which **hears airborne sounds**, unlike the snakes. Thus, **lizards hear better then the snakes**.

The lizard's tongue may be short and wide, or slender and forked, or highly extendible. The **tongue conveys particles from the environment to the chemosensory organ** opening in the roof of the mouth.

Most lizards have **sharp teeth** which primarily help in **grabbing, holding,** and **crushing** their food, and less for **chewing**. Some herbivores, like the iguanas, have tooth crowns expanded to a leaf shape with serrated cutting edges. The teeth of some large predators are conical and slightly recurved.

Some lizards, like iguanas and bearded dragons, have a third eye, called the 'parietal eye'. This is actually a photosensory organ located on the top of their heads and connected to the pineal gland. The parietal eye detects changes in light with its very basic lens and retina. This allows the lizard to thermoregulate it's body. The parietal eye also acts as a defensive measure, as an approaching predator will cause the light to change.

Many male lizards have enlarged pores on the underside of their thighs, which they rub against objects to **mark their territory**.

Most lizards have five digits on each foot. Lizards' limb modifications facilitate their various forms of locomotion, and help them adapt to their habitats aiding in their survival. They can then be burrowers, ground dwellers, tree climbers, or aquatic/water dwellers.

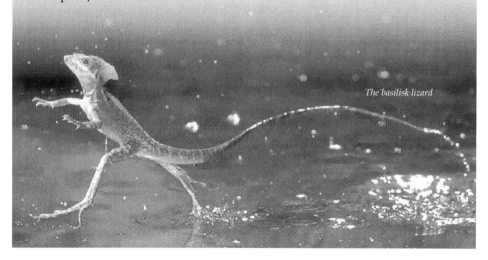

The basilisk lizard

Ground Dwellers

Lizards that live on the ground have large, heavy feet. Their legs are short and powerfully built. In many cases, terrestrial lizards with large feet are also able to **dig and borrow** into the ground. Some species with no limbs, or poorly formed limbs, may simply **force their way** through loose soil and sand with **rapid 'swimming' movements**. Some lizards with small and weak legs **move slowly**. Several terrestrial iguanids and agamids are able to run with bipedal locomotion. Amongst them is the peculiar basilisk lizard *(Basiliscus basiliscus)* that is actually able to run across water for short distances. Because of this unique ability, it is nicknamed the 'Jesus Christ lizard'. During bipedal locomotion the tail is held out backward and upward, acting as a counterweight.

Tree Climbers

The **climbing** species have complex, multi-jointed legs. The bones in their legs are relatively fragile. Some lizard species are **agile climbers** and have **long, curved and sharp claws** that provide a **tight strong grip** on the branches.

Aquatic/Water Dwellers

The water dwellers have short but very strong legs. With webs in between their toes they are able to **swim quickly and efficiently.** The tails of these lizards are also adapted to assist in swimming. It is important to note that the aquatic lizards are actually only semiaquatic and live both on land and in the trees.

Specialized foot adaptations in lizards

Flying dragons

The most highly adapted of gliders are the agamid lizards called 'flying dragons' (genus Draco). They have extensible lateral expansions of the skin, supported by elongated ribs. Some other species have similar flaps between their toes. These flaps of skin enable them to move from tree to tree by GLIDING, rather than powered flight, and make soft landings.

Geckos with tenacious climbing skill with the super-sticky feet and tail

Gecko claws vary from no claws to fixed claws. Some geckos have retractable long claws with flattened and ridged pads at the end of each toe. These pads are made of millions of microscopic structures adapted for GRIPPING SMOOTH VERTICAL SURFACES. Their

A flying dragon with its brightly coloured wings spread wide

retractable claws have hundreds of lamellae (fine plates) on the undersides of the toes. Each lamella is made up of brush-like setae (hundreds to thousands) with multiple split ends, with a final strand less than 0.25 micrometre (1/100,000 in.) in diameter. These fine hair-like processes MESH WITH EVEN THE TINIEST IRREGULARITIES IN THE SURFACE THAT THEY ARE CLIMBING and provide the gecko with it's grip. These structures are also able to generate an ADHESIVE

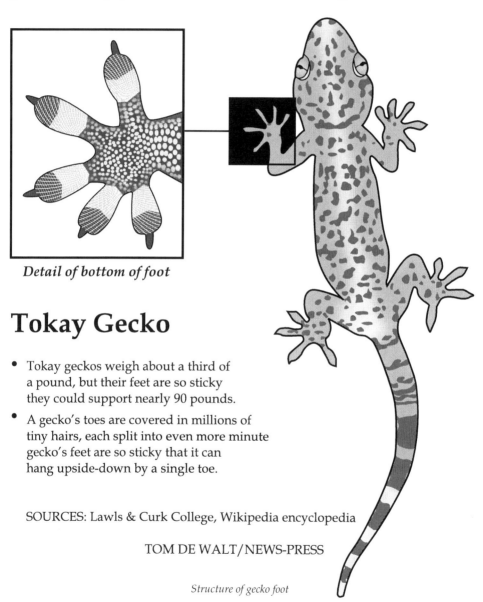

Detail of bottom of foot

Tokay Gecko

- Tokay geckos weigh about a third of a pound, but their feet are so sticky they could support nearly 90 pounds.

- A gecko's toes are covered in millions of tiny hairs, each split into even more minute gecko's feet are so sticky that it can hang upside-down by a single toe.

SOURCES: Lawls & Curk College, Wikipedia encyclopedia

TOM DE WALT/NEWS-PRESS

Structure of gecko foot

FORCE through van der Waal's attractions (for details see 'Intermolecular forces' explained below). This provides them with a FIRM FOOTHOLD. This greatly enhances the gecko's CLINGING ability and enables them to CLIMB AND MOVE QUICKLY OVER SMOOTH, VERTICAL SURFACES, or to HANG UPSIDE DOWN. The bristles do not act as suckers, so the geckos are UNABLE TO CLING TO SMOOTH WET SURFACES. Such extraordinarily CLOSE CONTACT is extremely DIFFICULT TO BREAK. Studies from slow-motion film of a moving gecko also reveal that it CANNOT DETACH ITS FOOT IN A SINGLE VERTICAL MOVEMENT. Instead it has to LIFT UP EACH EDGE so that the angle of the hairs to their attachment is changed. Only then it is able to PEEL the entire pad away.

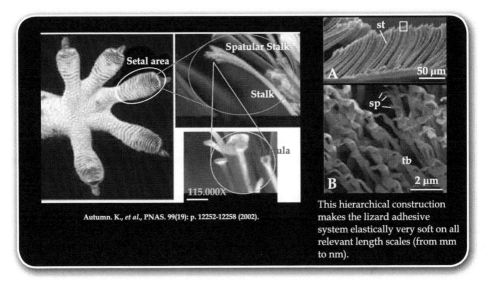

Autumn. K., et al., PNAS. 99(19): p. 12252-12258 (2002).

This hierarchical construction makes the lizard adhesive system elastically very soft on all relevant length scales (from mm to nm).

Intermolecular forces, are exerted by molecules on each other and affect the macroscopic properties of the material of which the molecules are a part. Such forces may be either attractive or repulsive in nature. They are divided into two classes: short-range forces and long range forces.

Long-range forces, or van der Waals forces as they are also called, are attractive and account for a wide range of physical phenomena, such as friction, surface tension, adhesion and cohesion of liquids and solids.

High-speed footage of this amazing movement also reveals that the gecko's tail harbors perhaps the most surprising talents of all. Their impressive tail makes them the world's MOST TALENTED ACROBATS by enabling them to perform

STUNTMAN-TYPE FEATS. They are able to CLIMB UP SLIPPERY VERTICAL SURFACES, as if they're wearing a parachute, or are IMMUNE TO THE EARTH'S GRAVITATIONAL PULL. Due to this extraordinary feature, scientists are now even contemplating outfitting future astronauts with robotic tails modeled after these lizards'.

Video footage of these elite lizard climbers reveals that under the best conditions, geckos GRAB ONTO SURFACES with hairy toes that UNCURL AND PEEL WITHIN MILLISECONDS. If they hit a slippery patch, their tails go into action. During RAPID CLIMBING, the tail functions like an EMERGENCY FIFTH LEG. If they SLIP with a front foot, the tail taps the wall and stops their heads from TIPPING BACKWARD. If this response is not enough, geckos use their tail as a bicycle kickstand against the wall to stop them from FALLING HEAD OVER HEELS. When a gecko is climbing upside down, on the undersurface of a leaf, perhaps, and there is strong wind, normally the lizard would fall upside down. This occurs since it doesn't have any gliding adaptations, and can cause injuries. But the gecko's tail, with an AIR-RIGHTING RESPONSE, will immediately SWING the animal WHILE IN THE AIR, TO RIGHT ITSELF. It does an EQUILIBRIUM GLIDE, QUITE IN CONTROL, by BEAUTIFUL MANEUVERS IN THE AIR, while SWINGING AND TURNING its tail. It actively moves its tail up and down like a dolphin. It actually SWIMS THROUGH THE AIR to reach its landing target. Geckos are truly one of nature's most amazing AERIAL ACROBATS.

Lizard tail

Lizards have a long tail which works as an aid to **balance during movement**, and as a storage of fat, which acts as a food source during periods of starvation and reproduction. The tail also maintains social status, as tailless males are less likely to find a mate, and tailless adolescents find it more difficult to acquire a home range. Losing the tail has serious consequences and does put the lizard in a more threatened state of existence.

Tail autotomy

The phenomenon whereby lizards **voluntarily or purposely break off a part** of their tail is called **'autotomy'**.

Meaning:

1. **Self-amputation:** the ability (of certain animals) to release part of the body that has been **grasped, seized or trapped** by an external agent, to **elude** the attacker.

In many species the tail is **fragile and detachable**. Some lizards have an unusual ability to **'amputate' when attacked or grabbed** by their tail by a predator. After **shedding** the tail, they will **escape to a safe hiding place**. Sometimes when threatened, the lizard will **wave** its tail, which is attacked instead of the body. They then break off the tail and run away, leaving only a segment of the broken tail **writhing** on the ground for up to five minutes. The lizard's tail has its own nervous system and may often continue to **wriggle** or move independently for several minutes after being severed. This is apparently to distract the predator, while the tailless lizard **scurries for cover**. This **amputation happens very quickly** and is almost **bloodless**.

The tail breaks at one of several predetermined **weak points.** These are called fracture planes, across (rather than between) certain vertebrae. The tendons connecting them can, **at will, be severed**. The muscles are also arranged in such a way that they too **come apart neatly**. However, not all lizards lose their tails easily. For example, the collared lizard has a sturdy tail that is rarely lost. Even tails of the agamids, varanids and chameleons do not break easily. These lizards have tough tails that usually cannot regenerate a very complete tail if their original is lost.

The lizards will sacrifice their body part, in return for an ultimate escape. The predator may even eat the tail, as the tails have good fat reserves. In some cases the lizard will return and eat its own tail in order to reclaim its fat reserves.

At times even a small bump or a tug will **break it off**. To add to the effectiveness of this strategy, sometimes the tail may be brightly colored. This **puzzles** the attacker and **draws its attention away** from the head and other vulnerable body parts. In most cases they are able to **regenerate** it very **swiftly**. The new extension will be strengthened not with bone, like the original, but with cartilage. Occasionally the initial severance is incomplete, and the tail remains connected to the body with flesh. Then the wound begins to heal and also the replacement tail grows. The result is a lizard with two tails!!

Some tree dwellers have a long **prehensile** tail. This allows them to **wrap or coil** around a branch 'monkey style' to give them an added measure of security, from their high vantage point. Tails of these species do not break off easily.

(Interestingly, the word **'prehensile'** means: **Able to grasp something, to take hold of things, especially by wrapping around them.**)

Food habits

A lizard's diet is quite varied. Most of them are insectivores. Some species are herbivores. For example, the Galapagos Island's marine iguanas feed on algae off the wet rocks. Spiny lizards are omnivores. They eat both plants and small animals. Some large lizards like the Gila monster are carnivores. They eat small animals, including other lizards. **Most lizards find their food visually through movement, but some can also trace with smell by flicking their tongue (like the snakes)**. Common lizards hunt insects, spiders, snails, and earthworms. They **stun** their prey by **shaking** it, and then **swallow it whole**.

Mating characteristics

Male lizards use a variety of tactics to attract a female's attention (given in detail on page 355 under 'Signal instincts').

In most lizards, **males declare their territories by performing ritualized displays**. This includes **postural displays, reinforced by ritualized movements**. Depending upon the species, it may include **'push-ups'** or **'head bobbing'**. The subordinate male usually assumes a submissive posture. A tail raise in females, who raise the base of, or the entire tail, generally indicates receptiveness to mating.

During the courtship of lizards, the male gets a **biting grip** on the female to hold her, while he brings the base of his tail into position for mating.

Most lizards reproduce by laying eggs, though there are some species that give birth after hatching their eggs inside the body. Others will give birth to live young.

Lizard eggs are usually **leathery shelled and porous,** and can expand by absorption of moisture as the embryos grow.

Once its eggs are laid, the lizard calls it a day. They are not caring parents. There are exceptions. Lizards generally don't stick around to protect the eggs from harm or keep them warm. Fortunately, the newly hatched lizards do not go through any stage of dependence upon adults, and are able to take care of themselves right away, without the mother's help.

Behaviour

Lizards like all other reptiles are ectothermic (cold blooded) creatures. They tend to assume the temperature of their surroundings. They enjoy dry, warm conditions and seek out warmth by basking in the sun. Basking is a very important feature for a lizard's survival.

Some species are most active during the daylight and summer hours. While some of them hide underneath burrows, rocks, or debris during extreme hot days, and emerge again as the temperature cools. Most of them hibernate through the winters. But there are a few species like the geckos that are mainly nocturnal.

Most lizards inflate their lungs with the same muscles that they use to walk, except for the monitor lizards. This is why they find it **difficult to run and breathe at the same time**.

Signal instincts

Lizards communicate via complex body movements to signal dominance over a territory, to signal courtship, or sometimes to accept defeat. Some signals are only for members of the same species, while other signals are used on other species. Using these species-specific, ritualistic signals, reduces the need for outright combat. It helps individuals recognize species related members for mating.

Elaborate displays evolved in lizards:

- **Gape**: an open-mouth display.
- **Lunge**: a brief and rapid movement towards another animal. Males may fight by lunging with each other until the weaker one gives up.
- **Chase**: a rapid pursuit.
- **Bite**: using the mouth to grasp another animal (used in aggression and during mating).
- **Inflate**: to puff up or enlarge body or throat (dewlap).

  Many lizards also make use of horns and crests. The use of impressive ornamentation is often restricted to males. The females of many species can also defend territories by stereotyped movements similar to those of males.

A blue-tongued skink sticking out its blue tongue

The lizard's puffing up to appear larger and more intimidating is an interesting act. It is similar to humans' putting shoulder pads into jackets, and lifts into shoes, or wearing high heels and big hair. Lizards can **inflate themselves with air, and stand high on their legs to look bigger and more imposing** to other lizards and potential enemies. The amusing part of this tactic is that it only works if you look at the lizard from the side view. If you look at them from the back or head on when they are displaying, they look very thin (laterally compressed). But from the side they look too big to mess with.

- **Arch (back)**: raise the back vertically, often accompanied by a sucking in of the sides of the body. The above two methods make them appear larger than they truly are.

- **Head-bob or shuddering nods**: up and down bobbing or nods of the head, or slights bobs of the entire body.

- **Push-ups or press-ups**: up and down bobbing of the body. This can be with all four legs or the front legs only. Just as human push-ups suggest strength and toughness, push-ups performed by lizards indicate a fierce, "get out of my territory!"

- **Color display, camouflage or warning coloration**: of brightest colors. Color is an important aspect of lizard biology for several reasons. Lizards are the most visually oriented of all the reptiles, and patches of color are important in communication between individuals. Color also helps a lizard to blend into its surroundings and thereby escape the notice of predators.

Some may use **warning coloration**. For example, the blue-tongued skink sticks out its blue tongue at predators. The appearance of its strikingly colored tongue, contrasted with a red mouth, and accompanied by a hiss, is enough to scare away a threatening bird or reptile.

- **Waves**: this is particularly done by a vanquished lizard, who acknowledges his defeat and waves to the victorious contender.
- **Sounds**: like hissing and squeaking.

If signaling fails, then the lizards can get into physical violence. Pregnant or unready females will at times signal males to discourage their approach for courtship.

Senses

A lizard's senses are adapted to its lifestyle.

- **Vision**

  Vision is the most important sense in all but a few lizards. **They have an ability to hunt fast-moving prey.** In many lizards, stationery objects are not observed as easily as moving ones. Many have highly acute color vision. There are some underground dwelling species that cannot see. Vision helps them to communicate by the external colorful body parts, gestures and movements, to distinguish male and female.

- **Hearing**

  Hearing varies greatly. But in geckos and snake lizards, sound is an important means of intraspecific communication.

- **Smell**

  Teiids and monitor lizards have highly developed Jacobson's organs, and they flicker their long, forked tongues to catch scent particles. This is similar to the snakes.

Locomotion

Among the various other survival features of lizards, some of the most fascinating are the characteristics associated with locomotion. Different forms of locomotion depend upon the various modifications of the lizard foot.

Lizards can:

- **Walk**
- **Climb; cling and climb over smooth vertical surfaces**
- **Glide**
- **Sprint**
- **Burrow**
- **Cling**
- **Jump from elevated places**
- **Few can even swim**
- They walk while throwing their weight from side to side, resulting in the characteristic **wriggling** motion. This also causes the tail to **swing** to provide a counterbalance. Some species also lift their front legs off the ground while **running at high speed**.

Some lizards are capable of **rapid acceleration** and possess **great ability to rapidly change their direction of motion**. Some species are able to use **bipedal locomotion**. While running at high speed, propelled by its powerful hind limbs, the lizard's front feet rise off the ground.

Studies have shown that lizards undergo **a rapid evolution after introduction to a new home**. The rapid evolution can affect not only the structure and function of a species but also influence its behavior and natural history.

Lizards, especially the anole lizard, signal their rivals with a visual display, which **'shouts' against a noisy background,** to get their point across. This signal needs to be strong enough for a rival to see, but not vivid enough to say "eat me" to a passing predator. Their forest home can be a visually noisy environment, with the branches and leaves waving in the breeze. In such a situation they have to have a strategy to get their message across. In such a noisy situation, even the lizard movements become faster and exaggerated.

Method of attack and defense

Method of defense

All lizards seem to be wizards at staying alive. They have adopted an arsenal of defensive strategies and some great ways of surviving. A lizard's world is full of danger and they have many enemies. Hungry snakes, birds, and other predators are everywhere, ready to pounce. To escape such enemies, a lizard needs to be **always agile, and ready to take off in a hurry and hide**. In fact, the lizards have one of the strangest strategies to ward off predators and make a run for it!

A good way not to be eaten is not to be noticed (camouflage). Once noticed, the next best thing is to try not to be caught, or to look as unappetizing as possible.

Defense strategies developed in lizards:

- **Camouflage and mimicry of inanimate objects** - such as sticks and leaves, is the first line of defense. **Color plays a major defensive role for many lizards.** Some species, like the chameleon and the anoles, can **change their colors** and blend seamlessly with their surroundings, becoming almost invisible. While others make themselves inconspicuous, by pressing their bodies close to rocks or tree trunks to avoid casting a shadow. The modus operandi here is; **"If you can't run away from an enemy, maybe you can disappear."**

  (Refer picture on page 86.)

- **Escape - when camouflage has failed, or movements have been detected and a lizard is noticed, it will usually resort to flight (running away).** Since lizards are unable to move rapidly over long distances, they usually forage in a well-defined area which contains one or more retreats. Escape then takes the form of a **rapid dash** to this retreat, although they may **pause one or more times en route**. The type of retreat depends largely upon their habitat.

  ▶ Open areas: Diving/digging into a burrow, slithering underground, or sinking.

  ▶ Rocks or outcrops: Dorsally flatten so that they can squeeze or wedge in a narrow crevice.

  ▶ Aquatic: Swimming, diving to the bottom, and hiding temporarily beneath rocks and debris (e.g. *Iguana iguana*).

  ▶ Desert: Swimming through sand; running for a short distance and then diving beneath the surface.

  ▶ Arboreal or semi-arboreal: Climb into higher branches, or make an effort to move around to the opposite side of the trunk, or move into the densest parts of horny vegetation.

- **Autotomy** – voluntary loss of the tail (as mentioned above).

- **Warning signals** – Some lizards surprise predators by doing something completely unexpected. When they feel that their position is being contested, they bring into play their different body morphology, **displaying a bold and intimidating threat**. They will very cleverly pass on the message **"I am as good as anybody else."**

(As explained under 'Signal instincts' on page 355.)

> - Some species like the horned lizards, when cornered, can **squirt** a thin stream of blood from a sinus beside their eyes. They're able to shoot from a distance into the mouth of an attacker. Studies also mention that this blood has a **repulsive** taste.

> - In some cases, a lizard's mere anatomy is enough to **repel** or discourage even the most famished predator. Some, like the thorny devil of Australia, are covered with such warts and knobs that they look like a miniature mountain range of 'chocolate chip' like horns.

- **Retaliation**

   When cornered, large species like the monitor lizards with their formidable teeth and claws, along with their whip-like tails, defend themselves aggressively.

Method of attack

Not all species are harmless fighters. When threatened by a predator or a rival, they are able to charge headlong into a battle, relying on strength, ferocity, or a bite which is definitely worse than any bark. Lizards can become aggressive and take the *"nothing ventured, nothing gained"* stance when confronted with an enemy. This is defined as anything larger than they are, which is pretty much everything else in the world, when you're only 23 cm/9 in long.

Lizards largely rely on sight and smell to hunt. This primarily depends on the type of food they eat. Herbivores **actively forage**, while insectivores can either **sit and wait to ambush** or go in search of the prey. The insectivores are **fast-moving and agile**. They can capture a wide range of prey and are the most successful of all.

Their various forms of attack are:

- **Biting and scratching** – especially by large species, like the monitor lizards. Many species are capable of vigorous biting, lacerating the victim's skin with their powerful jaws.

- **Lashing the tail**
- **Venom**– Only two species of lizard, the Gila monster and the Mexican beaded lizard, are overtly venomous. Other lizards thought to be without venom, may actually be mildly venomous and rely primarily on **speed, stealth and strength**.
- Some species have a specialized mode of hunting. The monitor lizards with their powerful limbs, will dig out crocodile eggs, at the same time keeping an eye on the ferociously defending mother crocodile.

Prey handling

This is done mainly by **grasping** and then **swallowing**. Lizards **shake their prey vigorously**, sometimes **bashing** it against a rock or on the ground in order to subdue it. Or they **chew it repeatedly to crush** it before swallowing it.

It's an endless game of **don't-get-caught** or **outcompeted** and 'evolutionary equipment' which makes the lizards fascinating survivors.

Expressions of lizards in a patient

Lizards in general will exhibit typical reptilian features like:

- Basking
- Hibernation
- Camouflage
- Hide or flee to escape
- No parental care

Along with some or all of these general lizard traits, lizard-remedy patients will display characteristics of their species' specific behavior, methods of attack/defense, body parts and functions.

Behavior:

- **Fast/speed and agile**

To be fast and agile is an important lizard feature. They could be still, absolutely motionless, and suddenly, in a frenzy, move very fast in sudden bursts. It's an ability to act quickly, to have presence of mind in a difficult situation, and to make your move out of it.

The concept of speed and agility in a lizard is not limited to its locomotion but can be found throughout the animal's functions and reactions. For example, the chameleons are very slow-moving, but they accurately attack a prey with their tongue at lightening speed.

Alert words that reflect the speed, quick and fast movements:

Be brisk	Lightening speed
Dart	Be quick
Dash	Accelerate
Hurry	Speed, speed up
Impulse to jump	Running at high speed
Jerky	Rapid motion, fast-moving
Jumpy	Move fast in sudden burst
Lively	Quickly change direction
Run	Sudden quick movement
Rush	Go fast
Scamper	Rocket
Scurry	Go like a bullet
Scuttle	
Skittish	
Sprint	
Swift	
Zoom	

Active

Alert

Attentive

Aware

Dexterous

Fast and agile

Lithe

Nimble

Observant

Quick thinking

Responsive

Supple

Vigilant

Watchful

• **Locomotion**

Alert words that indicate the various forms of locomotion:

Cling

Go upside down and all sorts of gravity defying acts

Burrowing, dig, force their way, rapid swimming movements

Wriggle, wiggle, writhe, squirm

Zigzag, twist and turn

Slide, slink, slip, swim

Climb, jump, glide, fly, leap, drift

Cling/Clinging

This is a characteristic symptom in lizard cases: to cling, hold on, remain glued. The ability to climb up the wall and go upside down can be observed.

Alert words that reflect this lizard ability to cling:

To cling to something

Hold onto something

Adhere

Stick, sticking to the wall

Grasp

Hang on

Hold on

Attached

Glued

Grounded

Stuck

Gravity defying acts

Going upside down

Climbing up the wall

Acrobatic acts

Communication via various signals

Lizards' communicate through various stereotyped behavior: color display, camouflage, change of colors and various body morphology. From these different displays we can understand many characteristic expressions in lizard cases.

– Color display: Display of, or an attraction for bright colors.

– Bluff, inflate, and the use of specific body parts to appear bigger or stronger.

– Distract or attract attention or threaten by different body gestures and functions like: performing autotomy, waving, changing colors, camouflage, gaping, head bobbing, arching, push-ups, shudders, etc.

Alert words that express the above features:

Autotomy or self-amputation (and the regeneration)

Cutting off or to cut off	Regenerate
Voluntarily or purposely break off	Renew
Break it off	Restore
Amputate	Redevelop
Shed	
Severed	
Come apart neatly	
Point of breakage	
Bloodless	
Fragile	
Weak points	

One also needs to know that this process of autotomy/breakage is very sudden like – sudden cutting off, sudden removal, break off suddenly, etc.

Bluff, inflate (to appear bigger than one is)

Blow your own horn	Appear bigger
Boast	Bloat
Brag	Enlarge
Con	Expand
Defraud	Puff out
Dupe	Puff up
Fake it	Swell up
Fly your own kite	
Mislead	
Pretend	
Pull a fast one	
Shoot your mouth off	
Show-off	
Sing your own praises	
Trick	
Try to make an impression	

- Acute vision and hearing

- Territoriality

Method of defense:

- **To escape and hide** – first line of defense common in reptiles, but in lizard cases one can observe the following specifics:
    - Run, running away, flee, to climb
    - Dive, diving, slither
    - Hide, wedge
    - Swim, submerge
    - Scurry for cover

Method of attack:

– Ability to catch a fast-moving prey: the combining of speed, agility, fast movement, acute vision and hearing
– To stun (the prey) (very specific for lizards)
– Bite and tear
– Thrash, shake vigorously
– Grab, hold, grip, grasp
– Crush, chew repeatedly

Alert words to describe their method of attack:

Charge	Batter	Compress
Dive	Beat	Crush
Leap	Flay	Squeeze
Pounce	Hit	
Spring at	Lash	
Swipe	Strike	
Thrust	Whip	

Stun

'To stun' is a very characteristic lizard behavior. This phenomenon of lizard behavior has been observed many times. When shining a torch on a lizard in the dark, its initial reaction is to remain still. It will not move for a few seconds, as if stunned, and then suddenly it scurries off.

Alert words that indicate 'to stun':

To zap

To freeze

Unable to move

Immobile

Completely paralyzed

Body parts and functions:

• Movable eyelid

   Ability to wink (as opposed to the snakes with immovable eyelids giving rise to their baleful stare)

- Tail

  Prehensile

  Wrap

  Grasp

  Coil

Characteristic expressions in a gecko

So far we don't have any remedy made from the geckos. But while studying lizard remedies we realised that these are equally interesting in their behavior. So here we summarise the possible important gecko expressions from what we studied about them under 'Lizards — Introduction'.

- Perform various acrobatic tactics:
    - To grip or move quickly over smooth, slippery and vertical surfaces
    - Hang upside down
    - Have a firm foothold
    - Maintain a close contact
    - Against the gravitational pull
    - Inability to cling to smooth wet surfaces
    - Adhesive force, clinging, remain glued
    - Grab, grip
    - Grip over irregular surface
    - Climbing
    - Tipping backwards
    - Falling head over heels
    - Aerial acrobatics with various air-righting responses — swing while in the air to right themselves, equilibrium glide, in control, maneuvers in the air, swinging and turning, swim through the air
- Increased activity in the night
- Very vocal (loquacious)

In the following section we will be studying remedies from the following families:

Suborder: Iguania	Suborder: Scleroglossa
Family: Agamidae Remedies: *Chlamydosaurus kingii* [Frilled neck lizard] *Calotes versicolor* [Bloodsucker] *Pogona vitticeps* [Central beaded dragon] **Family: Iguanidae** Remedies: *Iguana iguana* [Green iguana] **Family: Chamaeleonidae** Remedies: *Chameleo zeylanicus* or Chamaeleon (Divya) [Indian chameleon] *Furcifer oustaleti* [Oustalet's or Malagasy Giant Chameleon] **Family: Phrynosomatidae** Remedies: *Sceloporus occidentalis* [Western fence lizard]	**Family: Anguidae** Remedies: *Anguis fragilis* [Slow worm] **Family: Lacertidae** Remedies: *Lacerta agilis* [Sand lizard or Green lizard] *Lacerta vivipara* [Common lizard] **Family: Helodermatidae** Remedies: *Heloderma horridum* [Mexican beaded lizard] *Heloderma suspectum* [Gila monster] **Family: Varanidae** Remedies: *Varanus komodoensis* [Komodo dragon or Monitor lizard]

Suborder: Iguania

Introduction

The Iguania consists of the chameleons, iguanas, anoles and relatives. This group is named after the well-known American lizard, the green iguana or *Iguana iguana*.

Classification

Suborder: Iguania (includes the iguanas, chameleons and relatives)

    Family: Agamidae (Agamid lizards)

    Family: Chamaeleonidae (Chameleons)

    Family: Iguanidae (Iguanas)

    Family: Corytophanidae (Helmeted lizards)

    Family: Crotaphytidae (Collared and leopard lizards)

    Family: Hoplocercidae (Hoplocerids)

    Family: Opluridae (Madagascar iguanians)

    Family: Phrynosomatidae (Scaly, sand and horned lizards)

    Family: Polychrotidae (Anoloid lizards)

    Family: Tropiduridae (Tropidurids)

Generalized anatomy

The Iguania are the most COLORFUL of all lizards, and the males are more colorful than females. They grow up to 2 m/6.5 ft in length. They are SPLENDIDLY ORNAMENTED, especially the agamids and iguanids, with a fringe of flat SPINES along their backs, and CRESTS, SCALES, FRILL, and FLAPS – ALL ARE USED FOR COMMUNICATION.

An Iguania species-note the flat spines along the back

Food habits

Iguanas are unusual among lizards in that they are PRIMARILY LEAF-EATERS, though they also feed on insects.

Mating characteristics

The males use their bright color for display, both to attract females and to declare their possession of a territory. The color display is also frightening to rivals. Males are **highly territorial** and will chase off other males. They will mate with any receptive female that lives in, or strays into, their territory.

While occupying a prominent vantage point, they will NOD THEIR HEAD VIGOROUSLY, BOB UP AND DOWN, and do PRESS-UPS. SOMETIMES THEY EXPOSE BRIGHTLY COLORED SCALES ON THEIR THROAT AND CHEST. The males also approach females with PULSATING, JERKY MOVEMENTS.

Common behavior

Most species AMBUSH their prey and CAPTURE IT WITH THEIR TONGUE.

If they sense any threat, these ARBOREAL creatures will almost certainly LEAP from the branch into the water below, and SWIM away with powerful beats of their long keeled tails. Iguanids can SWIM FOR LONG DISTANCES BELOW THE SURFACE, to escape any danger.

Difference between lizards (in general) and Iguania:

Lizards	Iguania
Tongue that is forked or notched, flicks out constantly to detect scent particles that are deposited in the sensory organs situated in their mouths. Not an instrument of eating.	Most of the species have a tongue that grasps their prey.
Largely insectivores Meals are not picked up by tongue but with a turn of the head and a grab of the jaws which are armed with small cylindrical teeth.	Largely herbivores, feeding on leaves.
	Colorful and equipped with splendid ornamentation: crests, spines, flaps, and dewlaps.
	Specific signaling instincts are: head bobbing/nodding, press-ups/push-ups, exposing the brightly colored ornamentation (scales, crests, etc.)

Possible human expressions of the Iguania

<u>Behavior:</u>

- Climb, swim, leap
- Territorial
- Solitary
- Specific signals (expressions and possible source words) for communication include:
  - Display of bright colors: in human terms this is a desire for brightly colored clothes
  - Ornamentation: in human terms this can be expressed as a desire for ornaments, or jewelry
  - Head bobbing or nodding
  - Press-ups
- More herbivorous (vegetarian)

<u>Method of attack:</u>

- Ambush hunters, sudden attack
- Grasping (by the tongue)
- Captures/hunts visible prey

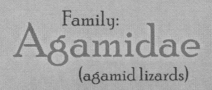

Family:
Agamidae
(agamid lizards)

Homoeopathic remedies

Chlamydosaurus kingii [Frilled neck lizard]

Calotes versicolor [Bloodsucker]

Pogona vitticeps [Central bearded dragon]

Introduction

The diverse group of Iguanians that inhabit the Palaeotropics and Palaearctic are called 'agamas'. The Agamidae family includes more than 300 species. They are generally terrestrial lizards, but some can be arboreal (tree dwelling) or rock dwellers.

Habitat

Most agamids inhabit the **warm environments** of Australia, southern Asia, and Africa. Members of the Agamidae family can also be found in southern Europe and on several Indo-Australian islands. They have also been introduced to regions where they are nonnative such as the southern United States and Madagascar. This has occurred through commerce and the pet trade. They inhabit warm environments, ranging from hot forests to tropical rainforests.

Anatomical characteristics

They usually have **well-developed, strong legs**. They're usually **diurnal** with **good vision**. They have dull rough scales which lie side by side and are well suited to desert conditions. The agamids (except the genus Uromastyx) **lack fracture planes** in the caudal vertebrae. **Tail breaks in this family of lizards are intervertebral and do not result in the regeneration of the long, tapered, pliable tails that lizards with such autotomy planes are able to regrow.** Agamid regenerated tails vary, from hard spiny clubs to tails that almost resemble the regenerated tails of species with autotomy planes, in size and shape, although not pliability. The eyes are small with prominent eyelids, while the tongue is broad and short.

One of the key distinguishing features of the agamids is their teeth. The teeth are borne on the outer rim of their mouth (acrodont), rather than on the inner side of the jaws (pleurodont). This feature is shared with the chameleons, but is otherwise unusual among lizards.

Possible common expressions in patients

- Preference for warm/desert conditions, and daytime
- Expressions related to the tail autotomy

Chlamydosaurus kingii [Frilled neck lizard]

Order: Squamata

Suborder: Iguania

Family: Agamidae

Genus: Chlamydosaurus

Species: Chlamydosaurus kingii

Common names: Frilled-neck lizard, Frilled lizard, Dragon lizard

Introduction

The frilled lizards get their name from the FRILL AROUND THEIR NECKS.

Habitat

Frilled lizards are members of the dragon family. They live in the tropical and warm temperate forests and savanna woodlands of northern Australia and southern New Guinea.

Chlamydosaurus kingii with its mouth wide open and neck frill flared out

Anatomical characteristics

The LARGE, LEATHERY FRILL normally lies folded around the shoulders and neck, like a cape. This frill is a large ruff of skin, and is supported by long spines of cartilage. The frill normally lies folded down on the animal's neck and shoulders and flares out when the lizard is frightened or agitated, allowing the lizard to escape. Some authorities believe that the frilled lizard cannot extend its frill without also opening its mouth. This frill also aids in thermoregulation. It helps the lizard in regulating its body temperature by allowing the heat to disperse.

Food habits

They eat insects, spiders, and sometimes small mammals and lizards (unlike the common herbivorous iguanian nature).

Characteristic behavior

They spend most of their lives in the trees, but descend occasionally to feed on ants and small lizards. Like other reptiles, the frilled lizard is active during the day and relies on the sun to warm its body. They generally **live alone** and are **territorial**.

Specific method of attack and defense

When the frilled lizard sees danger, it first SLOWLY CRINGES DOWN onto the ground looking like a stout stick, relying on its natural body colors to act as **camouflage**.

When this unique creature feels threatened, or when it needs to look fierce, it RISES ON ITS HIND LEGS, GAPES ITS YELLOW COLORED MOUTH WIDE OPEN, and UNFURLS ITS ENORMOUS, COLORFULLY PLEATED SKIN FLAP THAT ENCIRCLES ITS HEAD. IT SUDDENLY FLARES OR SPREADS THE FRILL LIKE AN OPEN UMBRELLA, DISPLAYING A BROAD AND ROUNDED EXPANSE OF BRIGHT ORANGE AND RED SCALES. This gives the appearance of a HEAD MUCH BIGGER THAN ITS NORMAL SIZE. To add to this **bluff**, they can **hiss loudly** and even **jump or lunge** at the predator. This entire spectacle is quite alarming, giving it a **misleadingly ferocious appearance**. This behavior can send many predators running for cover. It is also capable of frightening away large snakes and hunting dogs.

At times it even heightens the threat by repeatedly LASHING ITS TAIL on the ground. If this fails to ward off the potential predator, or if an attacker is unintimidated by these antics and continues to advance towards it, then his nerve will eventually break, and he will **run** for it. IT SIMPLY TURNS TAIL, MAKES A SUDDEN TURN, MOUTH AND FRILL OPEN, AND BOLTS, WITH LEGS SPLAYING LEFT AND RIGHT. THIS POSTURE ALSO MAKES IT APPEAR TALLER AND BROADER. IT CONTINUES ITS DELIBERATE RUN WITHOUT STOPPING OR LOOKING BACK, UNTIL ROCKETING OFF BIPEDALLY, IT REACHES THE SAFETY OF A NEARBY TREE. It is there in fact that he is most at home. This kind of a 'HASTY AND GANGLY RETREAT' is one of the quirkiest behaviors seen in nature.

In Australia the frilled lizard is also known as the *'bicycle lizard'* for this kind of behavior.

When on the tree it relies on **camouflage** to remain **hidden**. With its body and tail pressed against the bark, and the frill now folded back, held tight around its neck, it looks exactly like the stump of a broken branch. The only thing that gives him away is his need to KEEP HIS EYES ON THE PREDATOR. As the predator circles the tree, the lizard adjusts its position, SWIVELING millimeter by millimeter around the branch, checking on the position of the potential threat to be sure that he has no need to retreat still higher up the tree.

If forced to fight, this lizard can inflict a **painful bite** with its strong canine teeth. But they are not venomous. Their main predators are the birds of prey, larger lizards, snakes, dingoes, and feral cats.

Possible expressions of the frilled neck lizard in patients

Amongst the common expressions of the lizards and iguania, one can appreciate the speed, agility, camouflage, head bobbing, push-ups, running, climbing and solitary nature.

Specific to the frilled lizard is:

- Expressions and words pertaining to the frilled lizard's characteristic manner of expanding the throat flap when in danger or when they want to threaten or bluff.

  Possible source words related to this behavior are:

  - To spread out or flare open suddenly; like an open umbrella, unfurl, expand, display, open out
  - Run very fast, run without stopping or looking back, rocketing off, sprint, hasty, gangly, dash, race, speed, quick escape
  - Wide open gape
  - Hiss, jump, lunge, lash
  - Camouflage, keep an eye
  - Painful bite

- Climbing (since the frilled lizard is primarily arboreal)
- Meat eating

Calotes versicolor [Bloodsucker]

Order: Squamata

Suborder: Iguania

Family: Agamidae

Genus: Calotes

Species: Calotes versicolor

Common names: Bloodsucker, Oriental garden lizard

Introduction

Bloodsuckers get their gruesome but incorrect name from the tendency of males, in breeding season, to develop blood red throats. They don't really suck anyone's blood, but they may CHANGE COLOR TO REFLECT THEIR MOODS. The change of color is often confined to the head and shoulders, and on some occasions even diffused over the whole body and tail.

Habitat

Bloodsuckers are agamid lizards widely distributed geographically on the Asian mainland, in eastern Iran, across the Indian subcontinent, and throughout Indochina and Indo-Malaya. Naturalized populations are also found in both the New and Old Worlds. They are ESPECIALLY FOND OF GARDEN SETTINGS, AS THE LOW PLANTS AND HANGING VINES FORM AN IDEAL HABITAT.

Anatomical characteristics

These bloodsuckers are also known as crested tree lizards, as both males and females have a CREST from neck to tail. Like chameleons, bloodsuckers **shed** their skin, and unlike other lizards DO NOT DROP THEIR TAILS, which can be LONG, STIFF, AND POINTY. Bloodsuckers are capable of SEEING IN TWO PLACES AT ONCE BY INDEPENDENT ROTATION OF THE EYES. They have lateral body scales that point backwards and upwards.

Mating characteristics

During the breeding season, males become quite **territorial and chase away other male intruders by developing their** BLOOD RED HEADS. They do this by **doing push-ups and/or moving their heads to and fro.** This is quite a FIERCE DISPLAY BY THESE OTHERWISE SHY LIZARDS. The male bloodsucker tries to attract a female by handsomely BRIGHTENING HIS HEAD WITH RED COLORS. Immediately after mating the bright color disappears.

Characteristic behavior

Bloodsuckers, like the distantly related chameleons, are actually SHY and HARMLESS. They are known to LIVE IN THE SAME TREE OR BUSH FOR YEARS.

Calotes versicolor with the bright red head

Materia medica

Summary of a proving of *Calotes versicolor* **conducted by Sigrid Lindemann of Auroville**

Proving symptoms indicative of lizards in general:

- Immobile, feet glued to the ground. A total grounding feeling.

- Totally absorbed by sounds and vibrations. Feels the vibrations on the floor.

- Feelings of being able to change my face and personality very quickly.

- Vision: attentive, cunning, alert into the group, with immobile body. Still, only eyes moving, aware of eye sockets. Alert looks.

- Impulse to jump, jerky mood.

- Handstand facing the ground, body bent upward.

- "I do it all alone." "I will find my way." (to be independent)

- My teeth feel or are sharper, and I am biting my inner cheeks.

- Negative thoughts zooming by like a rocket.

Proving symptoms specific to the Iguania or the *Calotes versicolor*:

- Wonderful colors: paintings of Emil Nolde and even Vincent van Gogh come to mind.

- Head/forehead: Moving to and fro, in sync with my breath.

- I am in a room with a guy I hardly know, and want to have sex with him. I ask if he has a condom, and he says no. Immediately then the whole mood is completely gone and matter is over (sudden change of mood that reflects the sudden changing of the color of the chameleon which belong to the iguania).

- Dreaming of always going the same way that I know from the past, different scenes, but going always the same way as habit.

- I identified with a chameleon, because I felt I had the ability to adapt to any situation. Everything was good, everything was fine.

Possible expressions of the bloodsucker in patients

The common expressions of the lizards and iguania like having crests, performing push-ups, movement of head to and fro, and gripping. In addition the *Calotes versicolor* will possibly have the following characteristic traits:

- Change color—display of bright red color, reflects changing moods
- Shy, harmless
- Absence of autotomy/tail breaking phenomenon
- Shedding of skin, molting
- Able to see at two places at the same time
- Live in the same place

Pogona vitticeps [Central bearded dragon]

Order: Squamata

Suborder: Iguania

Family: Agamidae

Genus: Pogona (bearded dragons)

Species: Pogona vitticeps

Common name: Central bearded dragon

Habitat

This species is generally found in the **arid, rocky, semi-desert, and dry open** woodlands of Australia.

Anatomical characteristics

The bearded dragons vary in color from brown, grey, reddish brown to orange. They measure upto 2 feet, including the tail, which is at times longer than their body. The Pogona have SCALES ON THEIR THROAT, NECK AND HEAD WHICH FORM SHARP SPINES. The scales also extend to the sides of their body. The lizard gets its name from these SPINY PROJECTIONS THAT RESEMBLE THE HUMAN BEARD. This beard is darker in the males. During the mating and courtship period this beard turns even darker, almost black. Like all Agamids they have well developed legs that help them lift their body completely off the ground. This helps in reducing the heat intake and in the cooling of their bellies.

Pogona vitticeps

Characteristic behavior

Their specific behavior includes typical iguanian **head bobbing,** PUFFING UP THEIR SPINY THROAT, and WAVING THEIR ARM. They also exhibit at times **a partial color changing act**. These actions are performed by males to attract a potential mate, asserting dominance over a territory, typically for the highest sunning sites for basking or as defensive displays. The females perform this either to discourage or encourage a proposing male to mate.

The specific bobbing gestures that are performed for particular acts are as follows:

- Slow bowing motion: often used by adult females to signal submission to a male.

- Fast bob: used by males to signal dominance. This is often accompanied by an inflated and/or blackened beard.

- Violent bob: used by males just before mating. This bob is much more vigorous, and usually sets the animal's whole body in motion.

There are also arm waving gestures that can be displayed by both male and female:

- The male will only arm wave to show submission to a dominant male. The female will arm wave to show that she is ready to mate followed by a slow head bob.

- Juveniles will arm wave from the moment they are hatched to show that they are a bearded dragon, and also to show that they are not a threat to other bearded dragons. They are basically saying, 'Please don't hurt me, I'm a bearded dragon.'

They are **generally not social**, except the time they gather in groups on common basking or feeding sites.

Mating characteristics

The various acts displayed during the courtship period or mating are explained in the behavior section above. It is also observed that gravid females will often refuse the advances of a male, by chasing him and lying on his back.

Method of attack and defense

When feeling threatened, bearded dragons will FLATTEN ITS BODY AGAINST THE GROUND, PUFF OUT ITS SPINY THROAT, AND OPEN ITS JAWS TO MAKE ITSELF APPEAR LARGER.

Possible expressions of the *Pogona vitticeps* in patients

The bearded dragons will exhibit the common expressions of the lizards in general as well as the Iguanians, like the head bobbing, puffing up to appear larger, changing colors, climbing, solitary existence, and connection or preference or images of a warm habitat, specially deserts.

Their specific indications are as follows:

- Spines/spiny projections (possible source words/expressions)
- Arm waving (possibly seen as a very specific gesture)

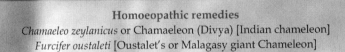

Homoeopathic remedies
Chamaeleo zeylanicus or Chamaeleon (Divya) [Indian chameleon]
Furcifer oustaleti [Oustalet's or Malagasy giant Chameleon]

Family:
Chamaeleonidae
(Chameleons)

Introduction

The name is derived from two Greek words: *khamai* (Gr) on the ground, near the ground, or dwarf; *leon* (Gr) a lion, hence 'a lion near the ground', a little lion.

Since the lizard **changes color according to its surroundings**, the term **chameleon** has come to refer to someone who changes his action or opinion. This is to **accrue benefit in a given situation, rather than expresses his true personality or beliefs consistently**.

The chameleons belong to the family Chamaeleonidae. They are a family of the Iguania suborder that has developed a range of **special adaptations, where each part of their body is radically modified for an arboreal (tree climbing) existence. They are characteristied by their grasping feet and long, extensible tongues.** A chameleon's tongue is usually one to one and one-half times as long as its head and body length and extends faster than the human eye can follow. It also has a **sticky tip on the end used to catch prey**. Chameleons can also cheat by hiding their whereabouts with their ability to **change color**. Sometimes, a shift in appearance is part of the lizard's visual communication. For example, when a chameleon gets angry, it turns red. A very, very angry chameleon will turn black.

Generalized anatomy

Chameleon species have in common: their foot structure, eyes, atypical lizard ears, and tongue. Chameleons vary greatly in size and body structure, with total length ranging from approximately 2.8 cm/1.1 in to 68.5 cm/27 in. Many have **head or facial ornamentation like crests or horns**, which are **hard and bony or hornlike appendages, which are flexible**. They also have **fringes** and **spikes**, which turn them into four-legged battering rams. Many species are sexually dimorphic (2 different forms). The males are typically much more ornamented than the female chameleons.

Their trunk is excessively flattened from side to side. This is a shape that absorbs radiation during early and late portions of the day, but avoids it during the hottest times. This narrow, leaf like profile makes them inconspicuous among foliage. Some even **sway from side to side** to mimic leaves blowing in the wind.

Chameleon feet are **bifid claspers**. The five toes on each foot are fused into a group of two and a group of three, giving the **foot a forceps, or a tonglike appearance**. This feature is characteristic of the chameleon, but absent in other lizards. This specialization of the feet helps the chameleons to **tightly grip** or **anchor** narrow branches. Each toe is also equipped with a **sharp claw to gain traction on surfaces such as bark when climbing**.

The **grasping** feet of the chameleon are supplemented with a **gripping, long prehensile** tail that is able to **curl up**. The feet and tail together are used to **balance** on the branches and allow chameleons to be remarkable **slow-motion acrobats**. The tail is sometimes used as a weapon. A chameleon can **coil its tail downwards** like a watch-spring and use it almost as a fifth leg. **Chameleons cannot lose their tails or grow new ones like other lizards (absence of tail autotomy).**

Their eyes are the most distinctive among the reptiles. The upper and lower eyelids are joined, with only a pinhole, large enough for the pupil to see through. They have the anatomical equivalent of 'rearview mirrors'. Each eye can **swivel and rotate independently, and is able to focus separately on two different objects simultaneously. This gives separate but coordinate views.** It allows them a full **360-degree arc of vision** around their body. It provides the unique ability to see ahead and upwards with one eye, and to look behind and downwards with another eye. It's like 3-D vision. Its only blind spots are directly above and below — eyes that are able to **spot danger in any direction**.

Closer view of a chameleon's eye

When prey is located, both eyes can be focused in the same direction, giving sharp stereoscopic vision and depth perception. While one eye looks to the right for prey, the other can look to the left, or even towards the rear, for oncoming predators. The turret like eyes do their work while the chameleon's head and body remain perfectly still. They have very good eyesight for reptiles, letting them see small insects from a long distance (5-10 cm/2-4 in).

A chameleon's tongue is its deadliest weapon. They have a very long, **lightning-fast** tongue that is sometimes longer than their own body length. The tongue is capable of **rapidly extending out** of the mouth, **fired at an extraordinary speed**. The chameleons first **slowly stalk** their prey. When the prey is within range, the chameleon gets a good grip on the branch, and then **flicks its tongue out at an incredibly great speed,** with **deadly accuracy**. It usually **strikes the target** at the centre of its defined mass, while catching it on the tip.

The tongue **shoots out in a fraction of a second**, faster than human eyes can follow, at around 26 body lengths per second. The tongue hits the prey in about 30 thousandths of a second. The tongue has a tapered rod encircled by muscles and a bulbous, **thick and adhesive tip**, which serves to catch the prey. As the sticky tip hits its prey, it **fastens** on, physically **grasping** it, and then **rapidly forming a small suction cup**. Once the tongue **sticks and traps** the unfortunate prey, it is **quickly drawn back** into the mouth, where it is **crushed and gulped**

The chameleon tongue projecting out

down by this master hunter. Even a small chameleon is capable of eating a large locust or mantis. The whole action is completed in a second or so. When the tongue is not in use, it lays neatly **coiled** in the floor of the large mouth.

They lack a vomeronasal organ. This is also known as a chemosensory, or the Jacobson's organ. Like snakes, they do not have an outer or a middle ear. This suggests that chameleons might be deaf, although it should be noted that snakes can sense vibration through their skull bones. Most chameleons can **communicate by vibrations** that travel through solid material like branches.

Food habits

Chameleons generally eat locusts, mantes, crickets, grasshoppers, and other insects. Larger chameleons have been known to eat small birds and other lizards.

Mating characteristics

Chameleons make best use of their '**ability to change colors**' to attract potential mates. The males are more brightly colored than females.

Common behavior

Changing color – 'The Master of Disguise'

All chameleons can **rapidly change their skin color**. They can become almost **completely invisible**. This ability to **rapidly change color at will** is used **to communicate, to express their physical and psychological condition, and to express their moods. It is not just to camouflage.** It is strange that chameleons do not choose background hues or patterns to guide their color changes and may not even be able to perceive color differences. Chameleons are naturally colored for their surroundings as a camouflage. When angry it may go black with fury. An amorous one may acquire colorful spots. A submissive one may turn pale grey. The particular range of colors available for these responses depends upon the species.

Hence color plays a part in:

- Communication
- Temperature control: they make themselves darker when they need to warm up
- Mood and emotional expression
- Territorial defense
- Mate attraction
- Protection: from predators

At the height of the breeding season the colors are spectacular, as males try to impress females. For some reason which seemingly contradicts the concept of camouflage, in the dark of night in a relaxed state, chameleons turn pale, almost white, while becoming darker in bright light. They are stimulated to react not simply to the light their eyes perceive, but also to the strength of the light that falls on their skin.

Chameleons change color by expanding or contracting pigment cells, called chromatophores, which are scattered in their skin. When the cells are expanded, the skin darkens due to the dispersal of melanin pigments in the cells. As the cells are contracted, the skin becomes lighter. A great number of different colors such as: pink, blue, red, orange, green, black, brown and yellow, and even patterns, can be produced in this way.

Ultraviolet light is part of the visible spectrum for chameleons. Chameleons exposed to ultraviolet light show increased social behavior and activity levels. They are more inclined to bask and feed and are also more likely to reproduce, as it has a positive effect on the pineal gland.

Chameleons are **solitary** animals (common to the iguanians). They are **shy and extremely nonsocial. They are reliant on their excellent camouflage to stay hidden**. Males and females space themselves out by displaying aggressively to other individuals, **opening their mouths wide, inflating their bodies, and hissing**. Males may interlock their horns and attempt to dislodge their opponent. They may eventually resort to **biting**.

Chameleons are very **territorial**. Not only does an individual claim and defend a three-dimensional space within a bush, it also has, within that territory, special places for particular activities. It has a space where it spends the night, another where it sunbathes to warm up in the morning, and yet another where it regularly hunts.

Locomotion

Chameleons are ergonomically suited to climbing thin branches. Chameleons are **much slower** in their movement than the other lizards (but they can attack an unsuspecting prey with their tongue with amazing speed). They are **incapable of rapid movements** and have a disconcerting habit of **releasing their hold and simply dropping** to the ground or to a lower branch. Once there they immediately assume their characteristic **motionless posture**. Most lizards walk with a sprawling gait, while a chameleon **advancing along a single thin twig must necessarily keep all four of its feet directly beneath it**. To help it maintain its balance under these circumstances, its body **flattens from side to side,** so that its centre of gravity is kept directly above the twig it is walking on. As a result of these adaptations, chameleons find it **hard to walk on a flat surface, and tend to totter awkwardly** if they are forced to do so.

On the ground, chameleons walk in a **slow, stilted fashion, each leg being waved in a curious vacillatory, hesitant manner before being set on the ground.** The whole effort is not unlike the **labored, unsteady gait,** of a person after a prolonged lay-up in a sickbed. The females of many species are compelled to descend to the ground, to lay their eggs, upto 40 at a time, in holes they make in the earth.

Method of attack and defense

The characteristic mode of defense amongst chameleons involves not only the use of gestures as signals, but also body colors – 'the camouflage' (as explained above).

Chameleons perch **motionless, patiently waiting** for prey to come within range. They are **continually scanning their surroundings by swiveling their eyes.** Once it has noticed prey, it will advance with **dreadful deliberation, moving extremely slowly, one foot at a time.** If need be, it can stand on its branch perfectly steady, using just one hand and one foot. It leans forward slowly, with both its eyes now focused on its target, so it can assess stereoscopically the precise range of the prey. To help in the process, it may **sway its head from side to side.** If the surrounding foliage is dense, it may only be able to get a clear view of its target with one eye. Even then, its assessment of range can be very **accurate.** With eyes that are like telephoto lenses, it can judge distance from their focus. It is very important for it to get the range exactly right. The blow that is coming must neither fall short nor overreach. It must hit the target with the accuracy and power of a boxer landing a punch on an opponent's chin. (Refer the action of their tongue on page 390.)

Common expressions of chameleons in patients

The chameleons differ from other lizards in the areas of: fast movement, clinging ability, and autotomous fracture planes in the caudal vertebrae. The only characteristic general lizard symptom is: to stun its opponent, as when its tongue hits with lightening speed, and the ability to camouflage (change colors). They will also express the common iguanian features.

Chameleons have their own specific traits:

Behavior:

- *Ability to change colors*

  When a person is described as a chameleon, the reference to the animal is generally a commentary on the person's ability to blend into various social situations. This often means the person has no true values, or that he quickly abandons them in company, if it's convenient to do so.

  Alert words that indicate this color changing ability:

  - Rapidly change colors, invisible, blend, camouflage
  - Change hue at ease and at will
  - Change colors that reflect their changing moods

- Locomotion
  - Incapable of rapid movements (specific for a chameleon)
  - Slow, acrobatic movements
  - Advancing along a single thin line, maintain the centre of gravity, maintain its balance
  - Difficulty walking on a flat surface: labored, unsteady gait
  - Walk slowly, totter, stilted, waving each leg in an oscillatory fashion before stepping

- Lack (or possibly it is not so prominent) of extra sensory perception (clairvoyance) (seen in the snakes and some lizards due to lack of the Jacobson's organs).

Method of attack:

The important words of their mode of attack that can be seen in patients along with the characteristics of the chameleon's long and extensible tongue:

- Motionless, remain still, immobile, stationary, frozen, unmoving
- Patiently waiting, stalk
- To continually scans their surroundings
- Moving extremely slowly
- *Expressions and words derived from the specific action of the tongue:*
  - ▶ *Lightning fast, rapidly extending out, fired at an extraordinary speed, shoots out in a fraction of a second, incredibly great speed*
  - ▶ *Deadly accuracy*
  - ▶ *Shoot or hit the target*

- ▶ *Sticky, adhesive tip*
- ▶ *Grasps*
- ▶ *Quickly drawn back, coiled*
- ▶ *Crush, gulp down*

This process can be summarized as a period of waiting and watching. Then at the right time, attacking with lightning speed, and then camouflaging. This can be compared to the pick pockets that wait for the right opportunity. When it arrives, they will quickly extend their hand and pull the object towards them, grasping, and then blending into the crowd.

Body parts and their functions:

- Eyes
  - Swivel independently, rotate
  - Separate but coordinate view
  - Focus separately on different objects at the same time
  - Ability to spot danger in any direction

In human beings this can be expressed as an ability to keep sight or focus at two different directions at the same time. One eye is looking out for danger and the other focuses on the target.

- Feet
  Alert words derived from the feet and its function:

  Bifid, claspers, forceps like, tong like

  Grasp, tight grip, anchor, traction, hold, clutch

- Tail
  - Curl up, coil downwards

Chameleo zeylanicus or Chameleon (Divya) [Indian chameleon]

Order: Squamata

Suborder: Iguania

Family: Chamaeleonidae

Genus: Chamaeleo

Species: Chameleo zeylanicus

Common name: Indian chameleon

Habitat

This is the only species of chameleons found in the Indian subcontinent.

Chameleo zeylanicus

Anatomical characteristics

One of the most interesting features of an Indian chameleon is its EXTREMELY LONG TONGUE. This at times may exceed its body length. The head has a BONY CASQUE (resembling a helmet), ornamented with CRESTS or TUBERCLES.

Case of *Chameleo zeylanicus*
By: Joanne Greenland

50-year-old female presents in August 2004, with depression following death of partner; who had years of lymphoma and then died from leukemia.

C/O:

Early stages of arthritis in joints, especially feet, numbness in toes, stiffness and aching in joints

Anal fistula (currently)

Obesity: 103-110 kg/226 – 242 lbs

Bothers most?

I get caught up; I cannot get out of it. I am upset unnecessarily. I lost my partner of 19 years to cancer. He was sick for nearly 10 years. It was not all bad but **the end was awful**. All the time in that hospital, **watching him suffer, nothing I could do**. I was so relieved when it all ended and I did **not have to pretend** to be OK anymore. I left the hospital for the last time and thought Thank God! Then the funeral kept me busy. We had discussed it so I knew exactly what he wanted, and it was quite involved and theatrical. That was good for me. Then the people stopped coming. No one rang and **I was left alone**. Miserable, in bed. **I curl up in the warmth**. I am running away from my problems. I am obstinate. I go to bed and stay there for days. **Hibernating** from life. **Buried under the covers, hiding.**

Did not have to pretend to be OK?

I am good at putting on a disguise. I can change my colours for my audience. I walk out and appear all happiness and joy. **I let them think I am strong and coping and in control.** Underneath I am a mess. **The part of me they cannot see, that hidden part is very sad, vulnerable, lonely, and afraid.**

(Here we see a specific behavior as her mode of survival. It is 'to change colors'. We see camouflage as a general reptile feature, which means to blend into the surroundings, but lizards have a specific ability to 'change colors', which is also very specific for a chameleon.)

Tell me more?

I am not good by myself. I am so depressed. I **hide** under my blanket. I don't want to deal with it.

I am not good by myself?

He brought out the best in me. I did not need to **pretend** in front of him. I could be me, and he was happy with that. He understood my achievements and desires. I do not like sharing my truths with anyone. **People use that sort of information against you.** Now I have no one.

Tell me more.

I was expelled from my Catholic boarding school for jumping the fence, staying out past curfew, and kissing a boy. I did not do anything really wrong. I was 17 and bored. The nuns had it in for me. They were **suspicious** I was up to something. They kept a **close eye** on me, I think they were just **jealous** because I was having fun and they were **trapped** in the nunnery.

I was sent home and a couple of months later, my mother died of kidney failure. She had been sick for a long time. It was a blessing in **disguise** really. It was good to spend those months with her before she died.

Tell me more.

I have always hated pessimists and I am becoming one of them. I am miserable, pessimistic and lonely.

Tell me more.

I have become **suspicious**. I see the bad in everything. I think people are **plotting against me**. I left my job because I thought my equal, although **he thought he was my superior, was always trying to bring me down. He would turn others against me because he was jealous of my capability.**

I was good and he knew it. He was crap and he knew that as well. **He made others think I was crap and he was good. He took my good ideas as his own, and belittled me in front of others.**

(This is at sensation level c: indicates the kingdom; animal.

We see here issues of 'me vs him', and 'he is doing…this to me'.)

I was so stunned I could not stand up for myself.

('They wait for the right moment and strike from nowhere, completely unexpected.'

This is at sensation level C2: indicates the subkingdom; reptile. But the feeling 'stunned' is very specific for lizards.)

Tell me more.

So I left. I had had enough. I was not over the loss of my partner. I was not coping. **I did not want anyone to see me like that. I was vulnerable. Because I am an independent powerful individual I did not want anyone to see how I was not coping. I was not winning and it was becoming obvious to others that I was not coping. I was vulnerable to their opinions and attack.** In my game there is always **someone wanting what you have**. I thought I would leave while I could still hold my head up. Now I have not worked for 1 year and I think I should go back but cannot get the motivation. If I go back to what I was doing it is a failure. A step backwards. I am sick of **feeding violence to people** (she is a movie director). I want to provide **amusement, fun, color, lots of changing colors, and joy** for the public. I think that is what they want as well. People have enough misery in their lives. We lose loved ones. Death is irksome. What is the point? Blackness. No one returns calls. **It feels like I have been expelled and rejected all over again.**

(We see here the violence on one side, and the amusement, fun, color, lots of changing colors, and joy on the other.)

Blackness?

No color. It just is. There is **nowhere to hide**. It is all the same. No change. It's awful, depressing.

('No color', this is very interesting, as chameleons are brightly colored. And earlier she says the opposite; that she wants to make movies which have lots of colors, lots of changing colors.

So 'it is black', 'no color' and 'there is no way to hide'. Hiding is very important for reptiles, as they perceive themselves at a position of disadvantage, weak and powerless. So their first line of defense is to hide.)

Anal fistula?

It hurts when I poo, (pass feces). Just when it is opening up. It feels **twisted and squished. The pain shoots up diagonally from the anus. It is very quick, sudden, and sharp.** Like a **needle piercing.** I cannot move. It is very painful.

Tell me more about the sensation of the pain.

There is not much more. It is sharp. It happens quickly. You know it is going to happen, because you have gone to the toilet to have a poo; but you wait, in trepidation, and then just as it starts, **wham, it gets you**. **A sharp, piercing pain.**

('Quick, sudden and sharp' 'Wham, it gets you', 'Sharp, piercing.'

'Squished' means to squeeze something.

At sensation level C3: specific to lizards.)

What bothers you most about it?

The pain. **You are focusing on something you cannot beat.**

Tell me about death.

All the hope gets taken out of you. The innocence about mortality goes. Death is a pragmatic/realistic part of life. But it takes the joy out of life. You ask yourself, **"How will I survive?"**

Joy?

The ability to adapt to any circumstance, any surroundings with ease.

The effect of that?

Safety, security, happiness, peace.

Tell me more.

I don't want to be rejected. I made my colleague's life a misery because I did not want to be kicked out. It is a burden to be ambitious. It means you are not like others. If I was the same as others it would be easy. Instead I have to know what they want, and then **I change my appearance to get what I want. I do my research, plan, and with the click of a finger I change to what is needed.** I am hard on myself. I am never satisfied. I am always pushing. **I must be bigger than them. I must be better than them.** I cannot settle. I must be **better than them.** Look at me, look at me. **I can change to suit their needs.**

Ambition?

For me it is inescapable. But others threaten you. They try to take you down. They stare you **straight in the eye** and say, 'don't you dare'.

(So in order to survive, to prove that she is stronger, bigger and better to others who belittle her and put her down and try to be superior, she needs to change her appearance. She will change her colors. It is very sudden, at the 'click of a finger I change'.)

Dreams?

The other day I had a dream of 6 helicopters flying in formation. I was one of the pilots. One helicopter pilot waved at me and then he crashed. He got distracted; **I would not cover for him. I would not lie for him.** I could not help him or his family with **deceit**.

Feeling in the dream?

I was better than him. I was not going to let him bring me down.

Dream #2.

I was panicking. **I had to go faster. I had to get out. I was being pursued and I needed to get to safety.** I had been given time. These people were holding me back. I was yelling. They did not want me to change. I was scared of **disappearing**. I would **not be seen**. I would not be heard. I would be completely **invisible**.

Feeling in the dream?

Fear. I knew I had to get out of there. It was a matter of **survival**.

Obesity?

I cannot really see it, though I know it is there. I eat properly. I exercise. Other people see me as fat.

Tell me more?

Fat people are lazy. I think that and I make judgments about people who are not as big as me. My father said I was lazy, but I am not. **Fat is not sleek. Loose skin.** It looks like the **whole skin could come off** and there is a normal person underneath. **Being fat is not sleek, not stylish, not sexy.**

Sleek, stylish and sexy?

I feel like that when I have a waist. I have an internal grin that no one else can see. I feel alive. You put out a face for others to see and you feel good. The real you is in your heart and brain.

Tell me more.

It is how people want you to be. It is your acceptable face. The one that stops the **demeaning and the back stabbing.**

Tell me more.

You feel clear headed. You can compartmentalize your thoughts. You have an external face. You feel 100% alive.

Tell me more.

You are behaving as others expect you to behave. **You are a different person for different people.** You have one face for friends, another for family and another for strangers. It is all me, but one group would not know the me that I show to another group. It is not my true self. None of them are. They are all **disguises**.

Tell me more.

I change the way I speak, the way I talk and the way I walk for different people.

I am like a chameleon. I can be in one room and as I walk through the door to another room I change as quickly as you click your fingers. I can change my accent, my image, everything about me. You would not know I was there if you had seen me in the room before. I am completely different.

(Speaks of the source. The need to change quickly is an important lizard theme.)

Effect?

I have a **camouflage** for every occasion.

Effect?

I feel more powerful, more in control, less **vulnerable**.

Tell me more.

I have perfected it. I really change my walk, my talk, my accent, everything.

Tell me more.

I do it to fit in to different groups. It is automatic now. I don't even need to think about it.

402

Fitting in?

I feel safe if I fit in. If I am one of the boys I am safer. That is why I carry weight. It gives me a more masculine appearance. **Men are more powerful than we are. I work in a man's industry and I have to be able to compete with them.** You are judged by your external appearance. You are judged by your looks.

(The need to fit in comes from an intrinsic feeling of being powerless, 'that men are more powerful, and I have to be able to compete with them'. This is an important survival theme, and how she perceives an attack is that is sudden, and it comes from nowhere (reptile). Therefore, she takes a disguise, becomes a completely different person each time, changes her appearance and camouflages. By camouflage she means to 'change colors' (chameleon) and she does this 'very suddenly, quickly, at the click of a finger' (theme of lizards).)

Tell me more about fitting in?

Just like the chameleon. To keep safe it can instantly change its colors to fit into its surroundings. That is what I do. I change my external appearance for what is required. I have always done it. Now I am not even really conscious of it, it just happens.

Tell me about chameleons.

I love them. I have one.

You have one?

I have a few, not real ones. **Little ornaments.** They fascinate me. I love the way they can just fit in. They change themselves so they fit in. You really would **not know they were there**.

Treatment: *Chameleo zeylanicus* 200C

Follow-up in September 2004 (one month later):

I don't feel the urge to run away anymore. My bowel is behaving. I have no pain and no difficulty passing poo. I had a colonoscopy and all is clear. My hemorrhoids are back to normal. I have been more motivated, able to go to the gym, exercise, walking every day. I have lost 3 kg/7 lbs.

I feel I want to clean everything out. All the extraneous rubbish. I feel divorced from the past and now I can start afresh.

Staying in bed?

No I have not gone back to bed once since I saw you. I am up and motivated and really changing. I feel so much better.

No treatment.

Second follow-up in November 2004 (3 months from original appointment):

Have been cleaning out my partner's stuff. Gave away his tools, clothes, etc. I have kept a few things but **felt the need to move on** and get rid of all the stuff.

I have now lost 5 kg/11 lbs, but it has slowed down. I am not walking or exercising as much. I have not gone back to bed at all, but my motivation is not as good.

I have stopped going to church. I am sick of them preaching. I don't want a dissertation. I do not believe what they are saying is true. They use **devious** ways to get money out of you. I do not mind giving money, but it is the **deceit** I do not like.

I feel I am not seen as an individual. I have been working but I am over it. It is a total distraction from my writing.

Distraction?

I am **hiding** from what I really want to be doing. I have had enough. I am there for the wrong reasons. I am so good at it. They need me. I am so charismatic. I can **perform on cue**. I can make people do whatever I want. I can charm people. I can make them **see me in a different light.**

I can turn it off and on at will. As I walk through a door **I change**.

I feel I am relapsing. I have been **withdrawing** a little. I am tending to go back to bed. My bowel is unhappy again. I only did that job to help them out, but **I feel they were using me.**

Treatment: *Chameleo zeylanicus* 200C

Follow-up May 2005 (9 mo. since 1st dose of 200C, 6 mo. since 2nd dose):

Fistula returned. I have been 110% better. Not as good in the last couple of weeks. I am in control of my life. Not wanting to go back to bed. Writing every day. I just don't want to slip back any further, so I came.

Dream

I met a man. (She names well-known Hollywood personality, called B. here for privacy reasons).We were at a Jewish festival. He liked me. I looked fat. We were at the synagogue. Another man let off a bomb. I **grabbed** him. I thought, 'am I saving myself or am I saving B?' "Am I trying to be the hero?" "Do I want B to see me as a hero, so he won't think I am fat and will want to be with me?"

(Again we see her need to be perceived as someone different, someone that she is not.)

Treatment: *Chameleo zeylanicus* 200C

Follow-up February 2006 (1.5 years since the 1st dose of 200C):

I have been good. Now, all I remember of that horrible time when my partner died is the end. Then I thank God it is over. The elation that it was all finished. I used to remember every minute of the last few days. I could say to myself, it is 10:00 am: I was feeling this at this time on the day before he died, etc.... Now I cannot remember any of that. If I really questioned myself I could find it, but I do not think of it. I think of the new life, the new me, the positive existence I can now live. Now I am able to live today. Getting all the stuff done I want done. I have a new mantra: **with or without you, I can be happy.**

(Her need and dependency on others has come down.)

I am focused but not ruthless. **I understand that we are all on a journey, and that I have skills in some areas, and others have skills I do not have.** This has enabled me to be able to get on with people better. If it is not done my way, at my speed, I can step back and reassess. I could never have done that before I saw you. I am really happy. I have lost 10kg (22 lbs) since I first saw you. I am happy with my weight now. I do not need to be any smaller. I can maintain this weight easily. I have been walking and exercising. Maybe not as much as I was, but I have a balance in how I am doing in life. I was writing a lot, really focused and clear and in that time I did not walk or go to the gym. Now I need a little more of your remedy so I can get back to it. I need something to re-fire my oomph. I feel nothing can touch me. I feel I am not quite as good as I was.

Fistula?

I have had no further problem with that. My poo is perfect. It is just the right texture, color, and weight. I am very happy with it. It sounds weird to be happy with your poo, but I get enjoyment seeing mine being just as the doctor said a good poo should be.

I have no pain.

Aches and pains?
I have none. I feel great. I just feel it is on the verge of returning and I want to catch it before it gets any worse.

Tell me more.
I have a feeling of wanting to **hibernate**, to curl up in bed again. It is not a good let's-do-nothing-day feeling. It is an escaping-from-the-world feeling.

Treatment: *Chameleo zeylanicus* 200C

She continues to do well.

Authors' comments:
Main themes of animal kingdom
- I let them think I am strong, coping, and in control
- People use that sort of information against you
- Plotting against me
- He was superior and trying to bring me down
- Turning others against me
- He was jealous
- He belittled me

Specific reptile features
- I curl up in the warmth
- Hibernating
- Buried under the covers, hiding
- I am good at putting on a disguise

- The part of me they cannot see, that hidden part, is very sad, vulnerable, lonely, and afraid
- Pretend
- Suspicious
- They wait for the right moment and strike from nowhere, completely unexpected
- I did not want anyone to see me like that
- I was vulnerable
- Change my appearance
- Cover, lie, deceit
- Loose skin, as if would come off (like molting)

Specific lizard features
- Quick, sudden and sharp
- I change as quickly at the click of a finger
- Urge to run
- Perform on cue
- Grab
- I was so stunned I could not stand up for myself

The need to be perceived as someone different than who they are in reality.

To be seen as someone who is stronger, powerful, and bigger.

Specific Iguania (suborder features)
- Lots of colors, colorful
- Ornaments

Specific chameleon features
- I can change my colors
- I change to what is needed
- Different person for different people

The indications will surmise the general features of lizards, iguanians and the chameleonidae. The specific indications are as follows:

- Extremely long tongue
- Bony casque, crests or tubercles

Furcifer oustaleti [Oustalet's or Malagasy giant Chameleon]

Order: Squamata

Suborder: Iguania

Family: Chamaeleonidae

Genus: Furcifer

Species: Furcifer oustaleti

Common names: Oustalet's or Malagasy giant chameleon

Habitat

Furcifer oustaleti is a very LARGE SPECIES of chameleon found in Madagascar.

Anatomical characteristics

Furcifer oustaleti grows to about 50-60 cm/20-27 in. It is primarily DULL in color, with some yellow, red, or greenish spots. It may have a white stripe on the sides, when lolling amidst foliage. When disturbed, a monster like this can TRANSFORM ITSELF INTO A MIXTURE OF STRIKINGLY DISRUPTIVE PATTERNS WITH BRIGHT YELLOWS, WHITES, AND BLACKS THAT ALMOST LOOKS LIKE A PSYCHEDELIC POSTER. It has NO HORNS. However, it has a LARGE, FLATTENED CASQUE over its head and neck.

Possible expressions in patients

Both the remedies will exhibit the common features of the chameleon. The only characteristic difference, between the *Furcifer oustaleti* compared to the *Chamaeleo zeylanicus*, is the ability to change to very strikingly bright colors from a completely dull appearance.

Furcifer oustaleti

Family:
Iguanidae
(Iguanas)

Homoeopathic remedy
Iguana iguana [Green iguana]

The Iguanidae includes lizards with **well-developed limbs, movable eyelids** and **tongues that are shorter and less protrusible** than the chameleons, that are remarkable for their long tongues.

Iguana iguana [Green iguana]

Order: Squamata

Suborder: Iguania

Family: Iguanidae

Genus: Iguana

Species: Iguana iguana

Common name: Green iguana

Introduction

The word 'iguana' is derived from 'iwana', meaning 'lizard' in Spanish-Arawak[1], the language of the Tainos[2] people of the West Indies.

The genus Iguana includes two species: the green iguana and the Lesser Antillean[3] iguana.

Habitat

Iguana iguana or the green iguana is a LARGE, ARBOREAL species, native to Central and South America. In Central America iguana meat is frequently consumed. They are often referred to as 'bamboo chicken', or 'chicken of the trees'.

Anatomical characteristics

The Green iguana has an EXOTIC APPEARANCE, WITH BEAUTIFUL COLORATION, LARGE SIZE, AND AN UNUSUAL DINOSAURLIKE APPEARANCE. It grows upto 1.5 m/5 ft in length from head to tail, although a few specimens have grown more than 2 m/6 ft and can weigh upto 5 kg/11 lb. An exceptional specimen may weigh up to 10 kg/22 lb. They are generally greyish or green, although some populations can be orange.

---

1   Arawak: Indians once widespread in the Antilles, now found primarily in NE South America.

2   Tainos: An extinct Arawakan Indian tribe of the West Indies.

3   Antilles: A chain of islands in the West Indies, including; Cuba, Jamaica and Puerto Rico.

The COLOR OF AN IGUANA MAY VARY, AND IT DEPENDS UPON ITS MOOD, TEMPERATURE, HEALTH, OR SOCIAL STATUS. This is similar to the chameleon. Color alteration also helps in thermoregulation. In the morning, while the body temperature is low, the skin color will be darker, helping the lizard to absorb heat from sunlight. As the day gets hotter and the sun radiates upon them, they become lighter or paler, helping to reflect the sun rays and minimizing the heat absorbed. Active dominant iguanas usually have a darker color than the lower-ranked iguanas living in the same environment. Six to eight weeks prior to and during courtship, males may acquire a bright orange or golden hue.

The iguanas have stout legs and a LONG SHARP WHIPLIKE TAIL. **Autotomy** is seen in these lizards. They also have a CREST OF TOOTHLIKE SCALES down their backs. Adults have a fleshy pendulous DEWLAP beneath the throat, which is quite large in males. Apart from self-defense and to attract potential mates, this fleshy structure also serves in heat absorption and dissipation when it is extended. Their STOUT build gives them a clumsy look, but they are FAST AND AGILE ON LAND (unlike the chameleon). They also have STRONG JAWS and RAZOR-SHARP TEETH. The iguanas have a third eye, the 'parietal eye' (refer page 348 & 1126).

Food habits

Juveniles eat a wider range of food than adults. Their diet includes insects, as well as fruits, flowers, and leaves; as their protein requirement is very high-needed for rapid growth. Older iguanas, that are close to their maximum growth, consume a low phosphorous, high calcium, leafy diet for their maintenance requirements.

Mating characteristics

Green iguanas use HEAD BOBS to court a possible mate, and also for a variety of social interactions. The frequency and number of head bobs have particular meanings to other iguanas.

Apart from head bobbing, a male iguana's long, erect spines and extended dewlap, which make his head appear larger, are other features that attract females. BATTERED AND CHEWED spines indicate a male with **a low position in the mating hierarchy.**

Adult males are highly **territorial**. They secrete pheromones and mark their scent on females, or over branches. During mating, the male approaches the female, climbs on her back, and straddles her. To restrain his mate, he grips her shoulder skin with his teeth, sometimes causing wounds. Copulation can last for several minutes. Female iguanas can save sperm for several years, allowing them to fertilize eggs at a much later date.

Specific behavior

Green iguanas are **diurnal** and **arboreal** (live in the trees), and are OFTEN FOUND NEAR WATER. They are ectothermic and **bask** in the sun to absorb the heat. They TEND TO LIVE ALONE, BUT ARE OCCASIONALLY FOUND IN GROUPS, where there are prime spots for basking in the sun. In the wild, most disputes mainly occur over basking sites. They spend most of their time high in the forest canopy, about 12-15 m/40-50 ft above the ground. They will descend infrequently, usually to mate, lay eggs, or to change trees.

Green iguanas are AGILE CLIMBERS. Their long legs and long claws are specially adapted to aid in **climbing.** They are quite STURDY, as they can fall from up to 15 m/50 ft onto the land unhurt! This happens because they use their hind leg claws to HOOK leaves, branches, or anything, in a CLASPING motion to break a fall. They are equally TOUGH TO LAND ON SOLID GROUND as well.

They have GOOD SENSES OF HEARING and SMELL. Their EXCELLENT VISION enables them to DETECT SHAPES AND MOTIONS FROM LONG DISTANCES.

During cold, wet weather the green iguanas prefer to stay on the ground for greater warmth. They are EXCELLENT SWIMMERS. While swimming, an iguana will often remain SUBMERGED and let its four legs hang limply against its side, as it propels itself through the water with powerful tail strokes.

The Green iguana can be EASILY TAMED and does not require constant attention. For this reason many consider them to be the ideal pet! They are, however, NOT AFFECTIONATE and should not be chosen as a pet to share love and affection. THEY DO NOT PARTICULARLY LIKE TO BE PICKED UP! Sometimes they can also be aggressive toward their owners. This is particularly true of male iguanas and female keepers. A sexually mature male iguana may make an unprovoked attack on an unsuspecting female human. This may be either because she has come too close to the lizard's personal space, or because human odors may convey unknown messages to iguana chemoreceptors.

Specific method of attack and defense

When threatened this lizard usually **freezes or flees**. Most commonly, since this lizard usually lives beside rivers or basks in trees overhanging water, it may DIVE into the water from overhanging branches to escape from predatory birds or mammals.

Their cryptic coloration provides excellent **camouflage** in the tall forest trees in which it lives. Because they look so much like their green environment, they can **remain immobile** when a predator is spotted, and manage to **go unnoticed**. YOUNG IGUANAS MAY BE FOUND IN SMALL GROUPS, AND USE THE 'SELFISH-HERD' OR 'MORE EYES ARE BETTER' STRATEGY TO AVOID PREDATORS.

If cornered by a threat, the green iguana will extend and DISPLAY THE DEWLAP, STIFFEN, AND PUFF UP its body, and BOB ITS HEAD at the aggressor. If the threat persists, and if caught, then it TWISTS AND ROTATES AROUND, and will WHIP or LASH its tail. It can also BITE and use its claws in defense. WOUNDED ANIMALS ARE MORE INCLINED TO FIGHT THAN HEALTHY ONES.

Green iguanas are GENERALLY PREYED UPON BY HAWKS, and this FEAR OF HAWKS is exploited by man as a ploy to catch them in the wild. The sound of a hawk's whistle or scream makes the iguana FREEZE and it becomes easier to capture.

Case of *Iguana iguana*
By: April Bowen of San Diego, California
Female, age 16

HISTORY: She was born to a white mother/black father, conceived after only a few weeks' acquaintance, and then they got married very soon after. Her mother again became pregnant, 2 months after her birth, so she was **weaned abruptly**. She has always been **jealous** of her younger sister. Her mother felt guilt about all this, so compensated by giving her whatever she desired, and allowing her to **make her own decisions** at a very young age

During her pregnancy, the mother had hired a **private detective** to check out her growing **suspicions** about her husband. She was angered to find that not even in her wildest imaginations, could she conceive of the many **huge deceptions and lies** that this man had told her. (e.g., he failed to mention the fact that he'd been married before, and had never bothered to get a divorce, making their marriage invalid). **He had changed his name twice.** He strung her along for quite awhile, with ever more **fabrications of the truth.** She felt very **cheated and betrayed** by him, and eventually left him. He has contributed very little in both money and attention to his girls.

As a young child, the patient was always very **clingy and needy**, especially for tactile experience. She **clung to her sheepskin rug** until her teens, **sucked her thumb** until 10, and would **drink from a baby bottle** as late as age 12. She **hated chocolate**, which is unusual for most children. **She hated going anywhere new, but preferred to stay at home with her mother**. She would not even want to go play at another child's house, or go to amusement parks or other fun activities. She refused to try anything new. Her inconsistency in attending school resulted in many **learning difficulties**, as well as an inability to read much beyond a 3rd grade level, or to do even basic math.

One curious thing she did until her teens, **was to run on all fours, (her feet and hands, not knees) very fast, and very gracefully. She would be very fast and agile, and could easily leap over obstacles quite effortlessly. She was very smooth, not clumsy or clomping.** People would often say she reminded them of a cheetah. At times that was the only way she'd get around.

Initial interview: 24 August 2007
(BG = Body Gesture)

Observation:

Very attractive, mixed race girl, age 16, wearing a black T-shirt with a white skull on it. Quite a bit of acne, on forehead and cheeks. She is a bit reluctant in being here, but came due to her grandmother's insistence. **She is very animated, chatty, witty, and quick to laugh.** Her parents are divorced, and her dad lives many states away from her. She has seen him only rarely in the last five years.

H: What's troubling you the most?
P: My dad; **I want to get over my dad and what he did to me.**

> *This is the first hint of the kingdom – animal. Also, from the mother's history we know the underlying story of deception, lies, fabrication, to change names, suspicious and jealousy.*

My mom bought a plane ticket, and I was going to fly down and see him. Then the day before I was supposed to leave, he called and said he couldn't do it. He said he couldn't afford groceries, couldn't take off work, and didn't really have a place for me to stay.

H: What was that like for you?
P: I was pissed off and sad and felt **betrayed**. I wanted to punch a hole in the wall.

H: Just describe more this 'betrayed'.

P: Like..he told me..got my hopes up. **He breaks me down, like a milk carton** (HG-fist pounding into palm).

H: What do you mean, 'breaks you down like a milk carton' (reflecting back HG)?

P: You know how when a milk carton is empty, there's nothing inside of it to hold up the sides? It just **breaks down very easily**. Like **beats me down**, he'd get my hopes up. I was really angry. It's like **he showed his true colors.**

Breaks me down, beats me down – animal indicators.

Then she says 'he showed his true colors' – this was the first hint towards a reptile – a lizard.

H: His **true colors**?

P: He always comes off as this nice guy to everyone, like he tries to make it look like he cares, especially about kids, but, he doesn't. Now I see him for his true colors, who he really is.

H: What was the experience of this for you?

P: Everything just kind of **sunk** (HG-down and outward gesture), like my world just sunk. It goes down – there's nothing that makes you happy. You're just completely unmotivated to do anything. **I could barely move.**

This feeling 'could barely move' is specific for lizards. They stun their prey before they chew them. Her first reaction on seeing her father's true colors is that she could barely move.

Spontaneously, very emotional, blurts out:

"He broke my heart! He BROKE (HG-flexed arm, fisted, brings elbow down vehemently) my heart!! He like…**ripped it out of my chest (HG-to chest, violent, ripping out motion)**, and smeared it all over (HG-shows smearing motion)!

To rip apart – is said with a prominent hand gesture. This is very strongly indicative of the source.

H: Describe this more?

P: **He ripped** (HG-ripping out of chest) **it out, like he physically tore it out!** I never had my heart broken before. I used to really like him. After he called, **I could hardly move. I was weak and I didn't want anyone to see me that way.**

417

H: What means 'weak'?

P: Not strong, the opposite of strong. I was mentally weak. You're like really sensitive to anything around you for a while. I was really **sensitive to light. I wanted to be in the dark.** I was also really **intolerant of other people** for a couple of months. I barely came out of my basement bedroom. **I just wanted to be alone, in the dark, in my cave.** I went through a huge **antisocial** phase after that. I was really serious, and didn't want to laugh. **It was just other people's presence, their energy, their vibes, were going into my bubble (HG- (   ) the parentheses are showing what the hand gesture looked like — she was defining a space around her with the hg.).**

H: Bubble?

P: You know, **it's like your space. It's just like a general space, like a foot and a half around you (1/2 meter). If people get in my face and in my bubble...I don't want to say claustrophobia. It's not like I'm scared of them, but I just don't want them in my bubble.**

H: What's the main effect all of this has on you?

P: If my dog died, I'd really miss her. I'd miss my dog more than my dad. He's nothing to me. So I'm not really missing anything. You don't feel anything after awhile. Now I just don't feel anything. If I saw him walking by in a mall, I wouldn't say anything to him, I wouldn't even say hello. I'd just walk by him like he was nobody.

H: What's the experience of having your heart ripped out?

P: It hurts. It's like **your 'mental' heart is ripped out**; your spirit, your Zen, gets really sad, like a fuse blew. It's like...**mend yourself back together** (HG-hands going up to a peak, together, fingers moving very quickly).

I equate this 'cutting off of feelings' with her father to the 'losing the tail', which the lizard does to survive. Both are defense mechanisms. Also, I notice that whenever emotions start to come up, she quickly and adeptly changes and avoids the subject.

H: Any dreams?

P: I was in my basement bedroom, and someone was trying to come in my door. I **grabbed** my machete **(HG-arm flexed and fisted like holding a knife defensively and on alert),** and I was hiding behind my bed, then **running** upstairs and **jumping** over furniture. For some reason, I had to go back in the house, and they were setting up a bomb. I felt really rushed,

418

like I had to get something, but I didn't know what it was. I felt **like a secret agent.** All I had was my machete to **whip around (HG-like swinging it back and forth),** and I **ran.**

I'll have random dreams where I try to find things that no one else can. **I'm often like a spy or a secret agent.** One dream I had was I was robbing someone's house, and I broke something on their microwave. The main feeling was that I was scared, but mostly **I didn't want to get caught.**

Grab, Hide, Run, Jump, Rushed, Whip.

All seem to be important source words.

H: Any fears?

P: I was scared of spiders when I was a kid. **I wasn't scared of snakes!** My older sister had a snake as a pet. I was never scared of dogs or cats. I have two rats.

I prefer being alone. I could be without friends for a week or more.

I don't pick very good guys to date. The last one was a parolee, just got out of jail, and he smokes. The one before that was a pushover. **I totally OWNED him!** He was such a pushover, such a girl, like borderline lesbian. But **if you buy me food, I'm like AHHH! (BG-swooning gesture)**

This body gesture was showing that she would do anything for food.

H: Say a bit more about 'totally owned him, pushover'?

P: **I toyed with him a lot, like dangling something in front of a cat. (HG-dangling a string)**

You have to understand that the patient's pace was very rapid, going quickly from one thought to the next. It was very difficult to stop and pin her down on anything. I got the impression that her relations were not based on love, but were more about 'what's in it for me?' She teased and toyed with his affections.

It was just so easy! But he got me into a car crash, and **almost killed me!** I like going **fast.** I think I jinxed his car. I had said before we left, "I hope I don't get in a crash with these child safety locks, because they don't let you open the door!"

When we crashed I felt like the car was going to keep on spinning, but **my instinct is to grab onto something.** I was just **clinging (HG) onto the handhold so tight.** When we finally stopped, I was just freaking out. **I wanted to RUN!** I had **a lot of adrenalin going,** was just pacing on my knees, like

crawling around really fast, felt dizzy. I was like (HG-both arms flexed and fisted, pointing forward, bringing them down forcefully), "Let's go! Let's go!!" **My instinct was just to run away as fast as I could.** My friends had to restrain me, were trying to calm me down. **I was itching to run. It felt like I was going crazy, like I was on speed or something.**

Grab, cling, hold tight, crawling fast, just to run away as fast as I could, on speed — very specific source words.

I have had bad back problems since, because I really tensed up. I got a very bad **whiplash**. I have problems with sitting up straight. When I went back to school, I was just like, STEP-STEP-STEP (BG-indicating very slow movements).

Whiplash, pinching, biting — important source words.

I sometimes have a stomachache, but just drink ice water and its better.

Appetite: It's like my stomach is an endless pit! I can eat and eat and eat!

Interests:

I like all the colors. I like things happening, like things busy. My favorite color is red, but switching over to green lately. I don't really like yellow, orange, or blue. I also really **like white and black**. (She is wearing a black shirt with a white skull on it.)

H: Any animals you particularly like?
P: I used to like cats, but now I hate them. I'm definitely a dog person. Tigers are cool. **I DON'T like BIRDS!!** (BG-shuddering dramatically) They totally freak me out, even in the wild! I don't know why. **I'm afraid they'll swoop down and attack me.**

I really like lizards. My dad had an iguana. I'm generally good with reptiles. My friend used to have a really cool iguana that was the size of a cat. He'd take it outside on a leash, and it'd really freak people out. One day, I want one for a pet.

H: What do you like to do?
P: **I LOVE music!** Anything that has a **nice beat, easy to dance to**. I like **hip hop and rap**, I like metal. One where there's a **strong beat and a chorus.** I like **cool beats, cool rhythms. They keep the beat, man!** (HG-beating out a rhythm with her hands) **I like the rhythm. I like music that you can bounce your head to** (BG-starts bouncing and bobbing her head as if to music). **I am ALWAYS 'doin' the head bob!'** (HG-more head bobbing). I just can't help myself, especially when I'm in a good mood and listening to music and dancing.

I LOVE to dance! I'll be dancing all over the house. I don't like to take dance classes, just like to be free. I want to learn to swing dance. That looks really fun to me. Whenever music comes on, I'm dancing and head bobbing!

If I could do anything at all, I'd be a pilot. I want to fly, so bad! You're just SO free! You've got the take off, you'd have complete power. Something about flying is really appealing to me. It's like moving to Miami...I don't know why, but I've always wanted to live in Miami, Florida. I definitely will, one of these days.

H: What about Miami is so appealing?
P: It's hot and humid there, and the days are long. I love that kind of weather. I NEED to be in the sun. Here I hate how there's hardly any sun. I'm not supposed to live where it's cold and rainy or hot and dry. I've never been there, but have always known that one day I'll move there.

I get this split personality. I just step outside myself to get outside my body.

H: Tell me more about flying?
P: It's just totally different. You're just always on land. When I was a kid, I was always living in the trees, always up in the trees, could climb anything. I like it there, just hanging out in the leaves, it's nice and cool and shady; nobody to bother you. It feels really free, and you have a better view of everything. I would climb up in our olive tree, and stay there for hours.

Flying would be cool, because you can take off in a giant tube of iron. My friend went in the air force, and is learning to work on planes and repair them, but I want to be in the cockpit. I'm a little afraid of heights. Being in an enclosed cage is better for me. It felt safe to be inside the cage of the Zipper (an amusement park ride), but it was scary on the Ferris wheel, because it was open. You never know when one of those crazed birds will attack you (laughs)!

H: Crazed birds?
P: You know, like that old movie, "The Birds", where they start attacking everyone.

H: How is school for you?
P: I go to an alternative school. It's so open. Public school, everyone was all in groups.

H: What was the difficulty for you?
P: It was SO structured. For me, it's so easy to get distracted. I have to have pennies or something I can touch or see. I get so distracted by other

things, like a cool car going by (BG-turns head as if looking at car). "That's awesome!" I like technology a lot, computers and cameras. History has no interest to me at all. You're just talking about some guy that's killed another guy in the past.

Spontaneously:

I HATE KIDS! I hate kids, so much!! (shudders). Oh! Just keep them away from me!! (HG-pushing palms of hands away from body, like, keep away!) It's not like they're obnoxious or mean, or will **beat you down with a stick.** They just take so much work!! **They're always clinging (HG-clinging gesture) onto you, hanging on you.** I don't know how to entertain them. They're expensive.

H: Tell me a time that created the maximum stress for you?

P: When I didn't have a dog. Having a dog just brings my life together (HG-arms flexed, fists being pushed together in front of her) It's nice, taking care of something. It's like, "You're my baby!" (HG-cradling a baby), ^without the baby. Having a dog taught me how to share. Before **I was pretty selfish. I was always thinking what I wanted, and never about anything or anyone else.** When I think about it, **I was really greedy, like I was never satisfied with what I had.** I always wanted more. I **would never share with anyone, ever.** With a dog, you have to think of someone else besides yourself all the time.

It was when I was 12, and we'd just moved onto a 48-acre lot (20 Hectare), and then found out we couldn't have a dog. **That just tore me apart; just ripping me (HG-ripping motion) apart,** because I couldn't have a dog. There'd be a void in my life. People and cats can't fill it. It's like an unconscious feeling. It wasn't just that I wanted a dog, it was I NEEDED a dog! I got really angry! One time **I threatened to kill my family. I was like bi-polar back then. I would seek revenge a lot.**

H: Revenge? Tell me more?

P: **I'd hold onto a grudge for a long time, and months would go by. But, I would be like, (HG-shaking finger in warning), "I'm going to get you later!"**

H: Tell me more about this time you threatened to kill your family?

P: There was nothing to do, literally, NOTHING to do on all this land.

I was just alone. I pictured myself playing with a dog, and I couldn't have one. **I wanted them all to die. I realized more about willpower.**

422

I KNEW I could take a knife to my mom while she was sitting there and she was sewing. It was like an epiphany that I had this willpower.

H: Tell me one more time that's created maximum stress for you?

P: **Losing my dad**, when he said he couldn't do it. He's an asshole! **He did this to me!** He's just **constantly lying and not holding up his end of it. Now, I think that NOTHING is better than HIM.**

In some ways, I'll feel relieved because I don't have to worry about him anymore. I feel like **I have stronger feelings for my dog, than my dad. I don't think I'll even tell people I have a dad anymore. I'll just say, "My dad got hit by a train."**

What's a dad, anyway? We'd watch NASCAR a lot (race car races). I can remember when I was real little. I'd sit on his lap, and **the noise of the cars going around would calm me down, put me to sleep. I still like to listen**

It kind of bothers me. **I try to avoid** people who make me feel bad inside. I just don't get a good feeling around him. I like to hang out with my friends. When I see their energy, I feel good. **I absorb it like a sponge, just bask in their good energy.**

I think it's bad for me to step out of myself. It's easy for me to put up walls. (HG-pushing palms out to side)

H: What do you mean, 'put up walls'?

P: **Like, trying to put it in simplest form, I'd like to be less emotional. I'd rather ignore, like push away feelings that could be there (HG-pushing palms away from body).**

H: Tell me more about 'push away' (reflecting back HG)?

P: **Just try to avoid it. I mend myself, really fast (HG-same gesture as before with 'mend'). If I'm being ignored, it's really easy for me to just walk away.** I'm **more independent than most** of my friends.

H: Anything that you're particularly sensitive to?

P: I like people who are really themselves, are **independent thinkers.** I gravitate to **people who're happy who they are.** I don't like the people who wear big sunglasses, who have the 'Rich Bitch' attitude.

I don't cling on to certain people. That's another thing; **I hate people who 'cling on'. (HG-clinging motion)** It's easier for me to make friends with guys. Girls are more **clingy.** This one girl likes to **CLING ON a lot (HG-like**

brushing something off frantically, to get it off, very exaggerated). It's like she calls me everyday, many times a day. She's always **very needy. I don't like that feeling of being needed all the time.**

History from her mother:

She amazed me by telling me that her daughter had told her; **"My love is like a lizard's tail. It can only be broken 4 or 5 times!"**

Now, why she never mentioned that to me, I'll never know, but of course she had talked about 'mending herself back together', which I did not follow in the moment, unfortunately.

Case analysis by April:

Animal kingdom indications

- It's always her versus her father
- What he did to her — break her, ripped apart, tore, etc.
- Betrayed, lying, deception, cheating, trust

Initially I gave her Chameleon based on the following symptoms:

- The need to camouflage or hide one's true colors
- The ability to curl her tongue up and she could touch the tip of her nose with it
- Her mother said, "She's like a lizard."
- Attraction to colors

Remedy given: *Chameleo zeylanicus* 1M one dose.

Nothing much seemed to have changed with the Chameleon, and I was rather disappointed. After having a conversation on 'insight-alliance homoeopathic' discussion forum (webgroup on www.onlinehmp.com) about this case, I began to study the other lizards in more depth. I read about chameleons that:

- They don't cut off their tails
- They move very slowly (she had elements of *fast, running*)
- They rarely take part in any physical fighting, but will only change color (there seemed to be a requirement of more violence in her)

424

I thought about her desire to move to hot, humid Miami, Florida, as well as her propensity for hanging out in trees, so a tropical jungle dwelling lizard seemed more plausible than a hot, dry desert dweller. And, iguana is the lizard she actually mentioned by name, though she said she was 'good with reptiles', in general.

Authors' comments:

Specific reptile features:

- Weaned abruptly (lack of maternal care), independent
- Sensitive to light and need to be in the dark
- Bask

Specific lizard features :

- Change his name, fabrication of the truth (camouflage)
- Show his true colors
- Cling and hold tightly
- Could barely move (to be stunned)
- Run away as fast as I could, speed
- Like a lizard's tail, chop it off
- Lose an arm, break off the tail

Specific *Iguana iguana* features:

- Head bouncing (head bobs)
- Climbing
- Fly out, jump out
- Bright colors
- Grab, hide, jump, run, whip
- Gripping, grab onto, holding on, can't let go
- Ripped apart
- Alone, in the dark, in the cave

Remedy: *Iguana iguana* 1M one dose

I didn't hear from her or her mom until one day, I got a call that she was in town again, and I could see her for an hour. I was quite surprised that she had come down to visit her dad, and was even staying with him.

First In-Person Follow-Up, October 24, 2008 (1 year, 2 months after initial consultation), 7 weeks after taking *Iguana iguana* 1M:

P: I've been having epiphanies lately, where things just seem to make sense. I realized about **the whole 'personal space' thing. I don't like anyone in my space** (HG-defining a 1 ½ foot boundary around her). Right now, I work at an upscale inn in housekeeping, and I LOVE it! It's weird that I want to go into the hospitality field, really. All day I'm socializing with people, but when I get home, **if anyone's in my space, I will rip them to shreds! (HG-tearing with claws)**. My sister's boyfriend practically lives at our house, and she's always got other people hanging out. This is my house! (HG-fist pounded into palm)

H: Tell me more about 'rip them to shreds'?

P: It's just an expression. I get really short-tempered, really irritated. **I like being alone, but I like people.** I get along with everybody at school, but I only have one good friend, and he's a guy. **I could easily go weeks without seeing people.**

H: I was really surprised to hear you were staying with your dad. What happened?

P: (Grinning) Oh! I do remember saying those things! **'He ripped my heart out and smeared it all over'** (HG-ripping and smearing motion). That was really intense (laughs)!

I was really betrayed (HG-forearm, bent at elbow, comes down forcefully) by him, but I got over it. He was just my father, just the one that 'made me' (HG-pulling from chest) be here in this world. He was never really there. Before this incident, he was just that guy that I'd see every once in awhile, or sometimes get a present from. When he did this, it just reinforced why I **shouldn't really trust him**. He kept calling me and tried to get me to talk to him, but I refused. Then **I got over it**, and finally he just left me alone.

I thought, I want to know my family, I wanted him to know me, and to know where I came from. I mean, I totally look like him. Everyone thinks I'm adopted, because I look nothing like my mom! (Her mother is a very fair Caucasian, and her father is a dark-skinned African-American) It's **hard to know who to identify with.** So I bought a plane ticket to come and see him (at 17 she bought it with her own money she had earned.) I told my sister, "You aren't coming! This is my trip!"

426

(Interestingly, her decision to see her father came about a week and a half after taking the dose of *Iguana iguana* 1M.)

H: So, what made you decide to come and see him?

P: When he quit trying to talk to me, just left me alone, and didn't talk to me for three months. And then the thought of maybe him dying suddenly. **It was very hard for me to trust him. I have a hard time trusting men again, like once bitten, twice shy.** He's my dad, so I have to talk to him. I told my mom that **my love is like a lizard's tail. (A few minutes into the interview this time, and it comes out.)**

H: What do you mean, 'my love is like a lizard's tail'?

P: **You know how if a lizard has its tail chopped off, it can grow back only so many times? If it keeps getting chopped off again and again, after awhile it just adapts, and it won't grow a tail back anymore. I felt like if he chopped off my tail one more time, it wouldn't grow back.**

He CHOPPED (HG-fisted, bent arm coming down) off my tail!! (Very vehemently, close to tears, the most emotion that she expressed in the entire case.) But then I started thinking he's my dad, and **I wanted him to know who I was.** He didn't have any food in the fridge. It's not a big deal, **I'm pretty good at feeding myself. I don't need anyone to take care of me. Yesterday and today have been good between us. I want him to know me, and I feel like that is finally happening after all these years. And I think I am starting to understand why he's done a lot of things like he has.**

H: How has your neck and back been from the accident?

P: My neck is absolutely fine now. It's like there was never anything wrong. My lower back is still bothering me. It gets stiff, real bad, it really hurts! It's mostly brought on when I'm leaning over the bathtub to shampoo my dog.

One big thing that I have noticed though, is now I can ride in a car with men, and I'm not freaking out about their driving like I used to.

H: What do you mean? (She had never mentioned this fear in the first interview)

P: I used to freak out driving, especially with men, after I was in that car crash. I'd really freak out at corners, like "SLOW DOWN!!". When I flew around the corner, I'd feel that pulling to the sides again. Lots of times, I'd actually ditch people if they'd drive like that.

H: Tell me more about this?

P: I remember my dad used to fall asleep at the wheel, he'd just doze off. I remember **I used to just stare at him. I wouldn't blink**, to make sure he didn't fall asleep at the wheel. Besides the fact that he's a guy. **I just don't trust men, in general. It's in their nature to show off.** Men always want to have the coolest, flashiest, and fastest car. They like to show off, thinking they'll impress us. I used to be impressed with that, but after the accident, I just wanted them to slow down. Now, it seems that whole feeling is nearly gone.

H: Just describe a bit what it was like, when you had that feeling?

P: I was always **skittish, wide-eyed**. I'd get very **twitchy (HG-twitching back and forth with her hand)** and stuff, especially in the traffic down here. I would **just jump out of a car** if I had to. I'd get really angry, like I'm going to **punch them**, like **I wanted to physically hurt them** to stop this! **Angry and panicky!** Like, **so angry, but the panic takes over, and I just jump out of the car.** I get angry, and I will literally throw something at the car, if they try to come back and pick me up.

H: Tell me more about jumping out of the car?

P: **I fling (HG------→ frantically) open the door and jump out.**

H: How was the 'panic' expressed in you?

P: **Like adrenalin.** Like, **I would lose an arm,** to get out of this vehicle! It's very **selfish. All I think about is me, me, me!**

H: What do you mean, you would 'lose an arm'?

P: **I mean, I would do anything to avoid losing an arm. It seems strange, doesn't it? I would lose an arm, to avoid losing an arm!**

H: What means 'losing an arm'?

P: **It's like what a lizard does. If they're in danger, they'll break off their tail or lose a toe, so that they can get away and survive. It's their defense mechanism. They mend themselves back together again in a few weeks.**

H: Describe more your experience when riding in this speeding car?

P: I'm like, **gripping** (claws hanging on), everything around me.

H: Gripping?

P: **Like grab onto, because I'm scared. Gripping means, holding on for dear life! It's like I can't let go, it's just my instinct when I'm in fear.**

H: I thought you told me before that you loved cars, especially fast ones?

P: I do like the way they look, **I love to ride in an awesome car.** But I don't like **revving engines**. It's really weird, because **I like watching car crashes, hearing the engines**. I'm always going on YouTube and watching car crashes.

H: How has your appetite been?

P: I haven't been eating as much, lately. It seems like I get full much faster. I don't feel as **ravenous** all the time like I used to. I would never get full before. I've been trying to eat a healthier diet than before, and I've lost a few pounds. [While she was never fat before, she is noticeably slimmer.]

H: How has your skin and acne been? (It looks quite good to me.)

P: I'm not having as much of a problem with it now. It seems to be clearing up. Probably as I'm getting older, I think. It's **smoother**. I used to have oily skin, but I had all these patches of **dry, scaly skin** that I was always picking at. Now, it's smoother, and more balanced.

H: Is there anything else that is troubling you now?

P: I can't think of anything, but maybe get my sister and all her friends out of my space. I do crave my own space! After being around people all day, I want to come home and relax in peace and quiet. I don't feel like being social. Other than that, things are going good right now.

PLAN: Wait.

Originally, her chief complaint was this:

"My dad — **I want to get over my dad and what he did to me.**" And it does seem that she's taken some action to do just that.

I feel she is doing quite well on *Iguana iguana* 1M, and doesn't seem to need another dose yet. Many things are shifting. Of her own volition, she decided to try and establish a real relationship with her dad, and she used her own money to make that happen. Before, she had completely cut off her emotions around him, denying that she felt anything for him, and had refused to speak to him for months. One week after taking the *Iguana iguana* she decided to

429

try and develop a relationship with him. She seems to have a little bit of empathy and understanding for him, where as before, she was only thinking of how things affected her. I am not so sure how this will turn out, as her father has a long history of deception and lies, and not following through.

The panicky fear when riding in a fast car has gone away, seemingly overnight. Her appetite is more balanced, and she's eating less. Her neck is no longer in pain, although she still has a stiff back after certain activities.

Her skin has cleared up significantly. She is more able to focus at school, and is being less distracted than before. Her studies seem easier to her.

She has matured in her thinking. Her selfishness and self-centeredness has been replaced by a bit more empathy for others, and at least the realization and awareness that she has been selfish. She does not seem to have made any connection between taking the remedy and having all these changes so soon after. For her, having her case taken was somewhat of a novelty, like having her astrological chart done.

Her mother told me by phone that within the last month or so, she has matured incredibly. All on her own initiative, she went out, applied for, and got a better paying job. She is taking two college-level classes that will count for both high school and college (very uncharacteristic of her). Her mom was very surprised that she's been researching colleges and what she has to do to get in, as she was never before even remotely interested in college. She signed up for driving school. Before she had said she didn't need to learn how to drive, as she could get around fine by public transportation, skateboard, or bike. Her mom said that her extreme moodiness is gone, and she's even been a joy to be around, which was not the case before. Her mom also did not attribute these changes in her as being related to the remedy.

Brief Phone Conversation, Early December, 2008 (12 weeks after taking *Iguana iguana* 1M):

P: My dad and I are at a high point in our relationship. He's been calling me twice a week lately. After I graduate high school, I'm going to live with him so I can be near a junior college I want to go to. He seems like he's really trying for the first time in my life. It's starting to feel like I have a real dad, like other kids. I'm starting to trust him sometimes. I feel good. I don't think there's much wrong at the moment.

Possible specific expressions of the green iguana in patients

Common lizard features:
- Camouflage, remain immobile
- Freeze or flee when attacked
- Performs autotomy (unlike the chameleon)

Common Iguania features:
- Climb, swim, leap
- Display of bright colors
- Territoriality
- Head bobbing, stiffen, puff up, throat flap (dewlap)
- Crest, spines

Along with the above lizard and Iguania traits, specific *Iguana iguana* features are as follows:

Behavior:
- Ability to change color that reflects their changing moods (like the chameleon)
- Locomotion
    - Agile climbers, excellent swimmers (very specific and unlike the chameleon)
    - Fast and agile on land (unlike the chameleon)
    - Can fall from heights and remain unhurt; tough to land on solid ground; sturdy
- Tendency to be solitary as well as the need to be with others in order to protect oneself from a threat
- Acute senses: hearing, smell, and vision
    - Able to detect shapes and motion from a distance
- Not very affectionate
- Don't like to be picked up
- More aggressive when wounded or injured
- A possibility that these patients might react to hawks, or may have dreams/ fear of hawks

Body parts and their functions:

- Unlike the other lizards, which tend to have a feeling of being small because of their size, the *Iguana iguana* will probably not have this feeling due to their large size.
- Powerful tail: whip, lash, strokes
- Claws: clasp, hook, grasp, grip, rip apart
- Razor sharp teeth: bite, chew, batter
- Exotic appearance, beautiful coloration
- Specific color: green

Family:
Phrynosomatidae
(Scaly, sand and horned lizards)

Homoeopathic remedy
Sceloporus occidentalis [Western fence lizard, Blue-bellies]

Phrynosomatidae is a diverse family of lizards, extending from Panama to the south of Canada. This family still holds debate with its order of placement. Some authorities still group them with the Iguanidae, while some classify them as a separate family. The preferred habitat by most of the species of this family is hot, sandy deserts. The spiny lizards (Genus-Sceloporus) prefer rocky deserts or even relatively moist forest edges. These lizards can be egg-laying or viviparous.

Sceloporus occidentalis (Western Fence lizard, Blue-bellies)

Order: Squamata

Suborder: Iguania

Family: Phrynosomatidae (Scaly, sand and horned lizards)

Genus: Sceloporus (spiny lizards)

Species: Sceloporus occidentalis

Common names: Western Fence lizard, Blue-bellies, Swifts

Introduction

Sceloporus from the Greek *skelos,* meaning leg and *porus,* meaning pores in reference to their femoral pores (a row of small holes) located along the underside of the legs. The name *occidentalis* refers to their western distribution.

It is the most common reptile in California. Six subspecies are recognized:

- Island fence lizard, *Sceloporus occidentalis becki*
- San Joaquin fence lizard, *Sceloporus occidentalis biseriatus*
- Coast Range fence lizard, *Sceloporus occidentalis bocourtii*
- Great Basin fence lizard, *Sceloporus occidentalis longipes*
- Northwestern fence lizard, *Sceloporus occidentalis occidentalis*
- Sierra fence lizard, *Sceloporus occidentalis taylori*

Habitat

Unlike the other species of Phrynosomatidae, this one enjoys a variety of habitats: from the forests, to high elevations, grasslands, and woodlands. They AVOID THE HARSH DESERTS.

Anatomical characteristics

The Western Fence lizard usually measures upto 15-23 cm (6-9 in), with brown-black color. Their peculiar physical attribute is the BRIGHT BLUE BELLY and the YELLOW VENTRAL SIDE OF THEIR LIMBS. Some species possess this blue patch even on their throat. This blue patch can be faint or absent in females or juveniles. The scales are SHARPLY KEELED.

Sceloporus occidentalis

Reproduction

This is an egg-laying species, and lays eggs every year at spring.

Characteristic behavior

This lizard is very COMMONLY SPOTTED BASKING ON PROMINENT SITES; perched on fences, rocks, and paths. They can be seen bobbing up and down or doing a push-up to display their bright blue bellies to rivals or potential mates. They are AGILE CLIMBERS and JUMPERS, JUMPING FROM ONE ROCK TO ANOTHER. They are HIGHLY ACTIVE and are frequently foraging for insects. In between feeding bouts they bask in the sun. They hibernate in the winter.

Like many species of lizards, this one is able to change its general coloration to match its background. Light colored lizards placed on dark rocks become a darker color. Interestingly, SOME LIZARDS REMAIN DARK WHEN PLACED ON A LIGHT BACKGROUND, MIMICKING A SHADOW cast by an imperfection or crack in the rock surface.

Interesting note:

Western Fence Lizards may reduce the incidence of Lyme Disease in their range! It has recently been discovered that when infected ticks feed on the blood of these lizards, the Lyme disease spirochetes they carry are destroyed. In areas with Western Fence Lizards, about 5 percent of ticks carry the disease, while in other areas 50 percent of ticks harbor the disease.

– Reported by the NY Times News Service, April 19, 1998.

Specific method of attack and defense

These lizards are also easy targets for predation since they so often venture out into the open. They usually defend by vigilance and a quick escape. They also perform AUTOTOMY of their tail. Unfortunately, its LOVE OF HIGH PLACES makes it easy prey for snakes, hawks, and predaceous mammals.

Studies have shown that FIRE ANTS ACTUALLY FORCE THE FENCE LIZARDS TO SPRING INTO ACTION. Fire ants seem to be one of the predatory creatures of these lizards, when they envelope and attack one moving on the ground. Normally when lizards meet a threat, they freeze and blend in with their environment. But in this case, the less the fence lizard moves when surrounded by the fire ants, the sooner it will be stung to death. The lizard will either TWITCH its body and shove off the ants, and then flee into its retreat or it simply LAYS STILL, WITH ITS EYES CLOSED, AND LETS ITSELF GET KILLED by the ants in much less than a minute. This is especially observed when lizards are attacked in an unfamiliar place.

Possible expressions in patients

In addition to the common expressions of the lizards and Iguania performing: the head bobbing, push-up, climbing, tail autonomy, ability to change color, the *Sceloporus occidentalis* has the following characteristic traits:

- Aversion/images of deserts
- Specific coloration: bright blue
- Very active; agile
- Climbing
- To mimic a shadow
- Love for high places/heights

Suborder: Scleroglossa

Classification

Suborder: Scleroglossa (includes the geckos, skinks, poisonous/venomous lizards, legless lizards, monitor lizards, etc.)

Superfamily: Gekkonoidea (includes the geckos)
- **Family**: Gekkonidae (Geckos)
- **Family**: Eublepharidae (Eye-lash geckos)
- **Family**: Pygopodidae (Australian flapfoots)

Superfamily: Scincoidea (includes skinks and relatives)
- **Family:** Lacertidae (Wall lizards or true lizards or lacertids)
- **Family:** Xantusiidae (Night lizards)
- **Family**: Scincidae (Skinks)
- **Family**: Dibamidae (Dibamids)
- **Family**: Cordylidae (Girdle-tailed and plated lizards)
- **Family**: Gerrhosauridae (Microteiids)
- **Family**: Teiidae (Macroteiids or whip lizards)
- **Family**: Gymnophthalmidae (Microteiids)

Superfamily: Anguoidea (legless and alligator lizards-includes the poisonous lizards and monitor lizards)
- **Family:** Anguidae (Anguids; glass and alligator lizards)
- **Family:** Helodermatidae (Gila monster and Beaded lizards)
- **Family**: Varanidae (Monitor lizards)
- **Family**: Lanthanotidae (Earless monitor lizard)

Scleroglossa—The name is derived from the Greek 'skleros', meaning *hard*, and 'glossa', meaning *tongue*. Lizards of this suborder exhibit **jaw prehension[1] for prey capture, a well-developed chemosensory system and wide foraging habit** provides them **access to more sedentary and hidden prey** than what's available or seen to other types of lizards, the iguana for example.

---

1   Prehension: the ability for grasping or seizing.

Possible common expressions of the Scleroglossa in patients

- Increased jaw mobility; more prominent images of swallowing much bigger objects

- Biting more strongly (than tongue movement)

- Highly developed chemosensory system that may include abnormal olfactory sensitivity and/or a curious tendency to perceive smells via the mouth

- Hunt, to look for, search

- Ability to capture something that is hidden and sedentary/slow moving/ inactive

Family:
Anguidae
(Anguids; glass and alligator lizards)

Homoeopathic remedy

Anguis fragilis [Slow worm]

Introduction

The word 'glass' in the term 'glass lizard' is derived from the **tail autotomy** of some species, that can **shatter their tails like glass,** to escape predation.

Generalized anatomy

'Alligator lizards' are **heavily scaled, almost armor-plated**, with a **thick osteodermal skin**. Rectangular scales are characteristic on some species.

Anguidae encompasses a large diversity of body types. Several species of Anguidae are quite small and limbless. *Anguis fragilis* is completely limbless, while others are limbless and rather long. Yet both resemble snakes. Some have strong but short limbs, and relatively large triangular heads with powerful jaws. Anguids range in size from less than 10 cm/4 in up to about 1-1.5 m/3.3-5 ft.

They may have a **pleat or fold along each flank, which allows for distention of their otherwise inflexible skin**. This adaptation is needed while carrying eggs or after having eaten a large meal.

Behavior

They are mostly **terrestrial**, except Anguis fragilis, which is semi-burrowing.

Possible common human expressions of the Anguidae

- A possible expression or feeling: 'To shatter like a glass'
- Armored, inflexible (Specific source words)

Anguis fragilis [Slow worm]

Order: Squamata

Suborder: Scleroglossa

Superfamily: Anguoidea

Family: Anguidae

Genus: Anguis

Species: Anguis fragilis

Common names: Slow worm, Blind worm

Introduction

Slow worms are actually not SLOW. If you tried to catch one, it would GLIDE AWAY SWIFTLY. (Ref: 'Life in Cold Blood' by David Attenborough)

Anatomical characteristics

The slow worm grows from 30-40 cm (12-16 in), with a maximum of 50 cm (20 in).

Compared to the other anguids the slow worm has a SMOOTH, SCALY AND SHINY SNAKE LIKE BODY. It has an indistinct head with a flickering tongue. It is not like the slimy worms. They are LEGLESS lizards, though internally there are remnants of the pelvic bones and vestigial[1] girdle to which their ancestors legs were attached.

Anguis fragilis coiled up

---

1   Vestigial: A bodily part or organ that is small and degenerated, or imperfectly developed; relating to a body part that has become small and lost its use because of evolutionary change.

This legless lizard superficially looks much more like a snake than a worm. At close quarters it is easily distinguished from snakes by the following features:

- Eyelids that can close/blink.

- Small ear opening (absent in snakes).

- Tongue is notched in the centre (rather than completely forked like in snakes).

- Shed their skin in patches like other lizards (rather than the whole skin as most snakes do).

- Ability to shed tail when threatened.

Once shed, the tail is very slow to regenerate, leaving many adults with a truncated appearance.

Young slow worms are often BRIGHTLY COLORED, with a METALLIC SHEEN and a central stripe. Females tend to keep the stripe as adults, but males are usually plain coppery brown or grey. Some may have ELECTRIC BLUE SPOTS, particularly in the breeding season.

Slow worms have GROOVED TEETH which allow them to **grab and swallow whole** soft invertebrate prey — such as slugs, hairless caterpillars and earthworms. This is a characteristic of the Scleroglossa lizards. Snails are usually avoided, except when they are still very young and the shell can be easily broken.

Food habits
Slow worms **feed on slow-moving prey** such as slugs, snails, spiders, insects and earthworms.

Mating characteristics
During breeding season, males become fiercely territorial and will fight by grasping at one another with their jaws.

Characteristic behavior
It is not uncommon, for these highly ELUSIVE legless lizards, to spend much of their time **burrowing** through the soil. Slow worms prefer HUMID HABITATS including grassy meadows, gardens, farmland, woodland margins and open fields. The slow worms BURROW IN SOFT SUBSTRATES, where ONLY THEIR HEADS ARE VISIBLE. They are generally SECRETIVE animals, and are NOT OFTEN

SEEN BASKING. They live in habitats that offer plenty of cover and warmth, HIDING under logs, flat stones, or piles of rubbish, while GOING COMPLETELY UNNOTICED.

Slow worms have an exceptionally long lifespan, but up to half of it is spent in hibernation. They are known to HIBERNATE BOTH COMMUNALLY AND SOLITARILY, and sometimes share their hibernating sites with other reptiles. It has been said that a slow worm is the longest living lizard. They live about thirty years in the wild, and up to fifty-four years in captivity!

Specific method of attack and defense

One of the biggest causes of mortality in slow worms, in suburban areas, is the domestic cat, from which it has no defense.

Method of attack

They rear up beside the slug, STABBING DOWN with their heads to seize it in the middle of its body, then SLOWLY ENGULF it.

Method of defense

Slow worm defense tactics include; attempting to move away quickly, DEFECATING, **autotomizing**, and FREEZING TO REMAIN UNDETECTED VIA CAMOUFLAGING.

Possible expressions of the slow worm in patients

Slow worm lizard patients will express general lizard features, such as; the ability to lose the tail, hibernation, territoriality, camouflage, remain hidden, elusive and to escape quickly. They will also express the common Scleroglossan features.

Specific slow worm characteristics:

Body parts and functions:
- Legless, cylindrical (like snake)
- Specific color: bright color, metallic, electric blue

Behavior:
- Fear of cats (possibility)
- Locomotion
    - Being limbless one will not see the common lizard expressions of locomotion like: climbing, running, clinging, darting, etc.
    - Burrowing

Method of attack/defense:
- Glide away swiftly
- Stabbing, grasping
- Engulf slowly

Family:
Helodermatidae
(Beaded lizards)

Homoeopathic remedies
Heloderma horridum [Mexican beaded lizard]
Heloderma suspectum (Helo.) [Gila monster]

Introduction

The family Helodermatidae consists of only two species:

- *Heloderma horridum* (Mexican beaded lizard)
- *Heloderma suspectum* (Gila monster)

Unlike snakes, their close relatives, **very few lizards have the ability to deliver a venomous bite,** either to subdue prey or in self-defense. The world's only two species of lizard with well-developed VENOM glands are also the only two members of the family Helodermatidae.

These are the Gila monster and the Mexican beaded lizard. Their poison is similar to that of a familiar snake, the Western diamondback rattlesnake *(Crotalus atrox)*. Their bite is quite painful, but seldom fatal to man. THE BITE PRODUCES A BENUMBING PARALYSIS, LIKE PARALYSIS AGITANS OR LOCOMOTOR ATAXIA. The venom of the helodermatid lizards differs from that of the snakes, because it is alkaline, while snakes' venom is acidic.

Genus: Heloderma

Introduction

'Heloderma' comes from the Greek words 'Helos', which means the *head of a nail or stud* and 'derma' or 'skin'. Therefore Heloderma means 'studded skin'.

No other lizards have been so immersed in myth and mystery as these two. This aura of mystery surrounding these two enchanting lizards may arise from their rather **secretive** lifestyles. They spend a good deal of their time in **burrows**, and are found only in **remote** habitats. They are the sole living representatives of an ancient group of lizards called Monstersauria.

Generalized anatomy

The Heloderma are **heavy-bodied, clumsy-looking** lizards with **short, thick tails** that store fat. Unlike the poisonous snakes that use hollow upper teeth (fangs), the venom glands of Heloderma are located in their lower jaws. The teeth are grooved but not hollow. The venom empties into the mouth through several ducts that open between the teeth and the lips.

The Heloderma's skin consists of tiny beads called osteoderms. Each bead contains a tiny piece of bone that gives them an almost **armor-plated** skin.

Food habits

Prey is restricted to nestling animals, ground nesting birds, and bird eggs. They **eat relatively large meals** and also have very low resting metabolic rates. This, along with their ability to store fat in their tail, makes frequent searching for food unnecessary. They can probably survive on 3-4 meals per year!

Behaviour

The Heloderma are **lethargic** lizards with a **slow, lumbering, and sprawling gait.** They are **diurnal and solitary.** Both species have **sluggish** habits: **hiding in burrows, emerging only for food or to mate.** The species are oviparous. They methodically search for food above and below ground throughout their home ranges, as they are both **strong diggers and good climbers.** This is aided by their **keen sense of olfaction.** Their **thick and powerful limbs aid in burrowing.**

Mating characteristics

In the spring, rival males fight according to a very specific set of rules. They use neither their sharp powerful claws or their poisonous bites. At first they **grapple** rather wearily to asses each other's strength. Then they begin to **wrestle** in earnest, each one trying to **pin down** the other. This **arm wrestling** bout can continue for several hours. The eventual winner is the one who ends on top most frequently. It's a control to test their strength while no one is seriously hurt, despite their lethal weapons.

Method of attack and defense

Venomous bite – lethal weapon

They both have a **strong, fierce and a tenacious bite, with their sharp, grooved teeth,** they **retain a firm grasp while they chew,** as this enhances the entry of the **venom** into the wound. It is like a **'bull-dog' attitude, not wanting to readily let go.** Both species **relentlessly chew the venom into their prey** or antagonists, rather than inject it through hollow fangs, as do the venomous snakes. The bite of these beaded lizards is so tenacious that the two suggested ways to free the victim are:

1) To force a stick into the mouth, to pry it open, while holding the lizard to the ground.

2) To immerse the lizard underwater. This is a rather crude delivering device!

The bite is **extremely painful,** and the venom delivers a **painful toxic shock,** making it an effective defense. In rare cases it can be potentially fatal to a human.

Possible common expressions of the Heloderma in patients

Body parts and functions:
- Specific words related to the skin: beaded, armor-plated, studded

Behavior:
- Slow, sluggish, lethargic
- Solitary, remote
- Eats large meals

Locomotion:
- Clumsy, lumbering, sprawling
- Digging, burrowing, climbing

Method of attack:
- Strong, fierce and tenacious bite, like a bull-dog attitude, not wanting to readily let go or leave

Tenacity:

1. Determined or stubborn; tending to stick firmly to any decision, plan, or opinion without changing or doubting it

2. Tightly held; difficult to loosen, shake off, or pull away from, like a tenacious grip

3. Persistent; persisting for long time and difficult to change, destroy, or get rid of

4. Sticky or clinging

5. Not easily disconnected

Few synonyms:

Stubborn

Obstinate

Resolute

Firm

Persistent

Insistent

Determined

Steadfast

Inflexible

- Firm grasp

  <u>More words:</u>

  Grasp

  Seize

  Clutch

  Take hold of

  Grip

  Clasp

  Snatch

  Clench

- Grapple, wrestle, arm wrestling, pin down

- Chew relentlessly

- Venomous, poisonous

- Painful bites

Symptoms of poisoning

- Benumbing paralysis

- Paralysis agitans

- Locomotor ataxia

- Swelling

- Nausea

- Vomiting

- Hypertension or hypotension

- Tachycardia

- Respiratory distress

- Perspiration

- Lymphangitis and lymphadenopathy

There seems to be confusion between the two remedies in our materia medica. Edward Anshutz's <u>New, Old and Forgotten Remedies</u> mentions:

The Gila monster is a native of Arizona, New Mexico and Texas. It is smaller than the Mexican variety, and is called, by Cope, Heloderma suspectum.

The provings and the clinical cases that follow were from the virus of the Gila monster obtained by Dr. Charles D. Elden, of Phoenix, Arizona, in 1890, who suggested it as a possible remedy for paralysis agitans and locomotor ataxia. He obtained the virus from a captive monster by irritating it and then letting it strike, or bite, a piece of heavy glass; by this means he obtained a few drops of a pasty yellowish fluid.

All the information that we have in our materia medica, indicative of Heloderma horridum, is actually indicative of Heloderma suspectum.

Heloderma horridum [Mexican beaded lizard]

Order: Squamata

Suborder: Scleroglossa

Superfamily: Anguoidea

Family: Helodermatidae (Beaded lizards)

Genus: Heloderma

Species: Heloderma horridum

Common name: Mexican beaded lizard

Subspecies
- *Heloderma horridum horridum*
- *Heloderma horridum alvarezi*
- *Heloderma horridum exasperatum*
- *Heloderma horridum charlesbogerti*

Introduction
'Horridum' means *'horrible'*, the *'horrible studded lizard'*! A close relative of the Gila monster, the Mexican beaded lizard, is also poisonous.

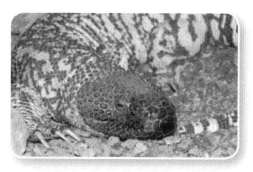

Heloderma horridum - note the beaded skin

Anatomical characteristics

It grows upto 70-100 cm (28-39 in), is SUBSTANTIALLY LARGER THAN THE GILA MONSTER AND HAS MORE SUBDUED COLORS than the Gila monster.

Characteristic behavior

They are EXTREMELY TOLERANT OF LOW TEMPERATURES. Even at 50°C/41°F they are able to move about and hiss if disturbed.

Case of dragon *Varanus komodoensis* (*Heloderma horridum* was given as zoological simile)

By: Michael Rutledge

Mother of 2 children, 35 years old with psychotic depression and **self-injuring behavior**. Her first major crisis occured in 2003. She was hospitalized for several months and was given antipsychotics. It took a few years for her to recover from the side effects. During that time some homoeopathic remedies from the leguminosae family seemed to help her, but she said the psychotic state remained there, lurking in the background. On 15-8-09 she asked me for help, because her psychotic state flared up and she again started cutting her arms for relief. It felt very risky to explore her experience, so repeatedly I told her nothing could happen if we go there together.

First interview, 15 August 2009:

P: Four days ago I had a major breakdown. Going to university I realized myself falling apart.

   I started cutting my arms again. The cutting brings it outside, because otherwise it would hurt too much. It allows me to sustain the pain. The pain is in my belly and it feels wounded and sore.

   I lose my balance. I fall out of this world, but I must stay here, there is no way I could go. **The other world grabs me, they tear me.**

   My **façade** works pretty well. It´s worse when I´m alone, no matter where. It pushes itself in the fore, sneaking, not suddenly. **My image is that of a tightrope act. I try to keep my balance. Beneath the rope is an abyss and monsters with teeth and claws.**

D: *Tell about the other world.*
P: I feel pressure. The air pressure is much higher. **A swamp, a marsh, fog, and poisonous gases. A place where dragons live, with poisonous teeth and claws. There is no sun and it´s cold. There is a sudden deadly threat.**

The monsters eat you, bite your leg, tear you apart and I must watch. I can´t come out of it, I have to give up everything up there. It´s terrible, a loss of all that keeps a human alive. Only desperation and sadness remain and the pain of losing all.

D: *Monsters and dragons (in German: Drachen)?*

P: **They are merciless, not very big, pointed everywhere, they have sharp claws and teeth. They tear the flesh apart and poison it.** They are as big as hippopotamuses and have an awful smell. **They have claws like a tiger but without fur, scaly skin like a lizard.** You know dragons (in German: Waran)? **With points on the skin**.

(The word she uses denotes not dragons in general but specifically the monitor lizard.)

D: *Fog of the swamp?*

P: The fog is dense, and lies on the earth like a veil. It is cold, dark and suffocating, no air to breathe. The fog makes you destroy your safe area of retreat. It destroys my safety suit that protected me going to this place. White fog is poisoning me without touching, only by looking at it. It is murmuring and singing lullabies. How beautiful it is to forget and give up. One ear is listening: he´s right, it is easier just to sit here, fall into sleep and wait for the dragons (in German: Drachen). The other half of me shrieks in panic, remembers how beautiful it is back in this world and why it is absolutely necessary to go back there.

The fog rising from the swamp consists of inconsolable sadness.

I also feel a great calmness. It feels cool, soft, and endless. No more tension, no more fighting, I put up with it. It feels agreeable; only the thought that it can´t stay that way is bothering. A dragon would also fall asleep, but in the background **destruction is lurking**. A lulling, lurking calmness. I should defend myself, but it´s easier to give in.

D: *The poison of the dragon?*

P: **It destroys tissue, dissolves it, so it can´t heal any more. It also changes the blood quality.**

D: *The poison of the fog?*

P: The poison of the fog has a different effect. It poisons the thoughts, changes the consciousness, changes your will, speaks to your mind. The only thing that helps is to close your eyes and try to think of something else very hard.

When pressure increases I see images of war. The sorrow of the humans touches me most. There is no escape, only death and destruction, loved ones are killed. Worst of all is that humans are the cause of all this.

D: *Where can all this be found?*
P: **Cold volcanos, uninhabited places, mountains, wild animals in the mountains. Coldness and missing sunlight. The warmth comes from the blood that flows out of the wounds.**

Rx: *Heloderma horridum* 1M single dose.

The remedy I would have preferred is *Varanus komodoensis*, but it was not available. Heloderma is phylogenetically the nearest I could get. The poisoning experience of the fog reminded me of an injured victim of the dragon, slowly dying from the infection, knowing it will be killed and eaten when it becomes too weak to run away.

Follow-up on 25 August 2009 (a week later):

P: It got better very quick. I took the remedy on Saturday afternoon. I was terribly tired and was glad lying in bed, giving in to that heavy feeling. In the evening I went to bed early. The night was strange, like a roller coaster ride, up and down. I slept in swinging movements. It was strange; I couldn´t sleep, although I was very tired. I opened the window looking out and almost fell back into sleep. I had an urge to breathe fresh air and to be outside and was so very tired at the same time. Like sleeping and being awake. Very tired and confused because of the vertigo. On Sunday I felt like I was on sedatives, tired, slow and soft, like a crabfish, who just got rid of his old layers. Calm, sad, and amazed. The pressure is gone, it dissolved like a pink cloud, it just disappeared. The tiredness left me during the following days. Yesterday I went to a family funeral which made me lose my balance, but in a very different way than before. (She tells a story with lots of emotions, but I have the impression of a normal human reaction, which she confirmed: touching, but no problem).

D: *What is the main difference?*
P: Before the remedy I couldn´t find my limitations. I ignored and stepped over them. I was firmly maneuvering all catastrophes, which has always been followed by a major breakdown.
Now I´m intolerant when I reach my limitations. I can´t step over them any more. I feel them much more clear and unequivocal.

Follow-up on 15 November 2009 (three months later):

P: The lurking feeling, which I have known for 10 years now, disappeared for a period of 6 weeks after taking the remedy. In the beginning I had wild dreams, but no nightmares.

For four to six weeks now I am having a lot of intense and often unpleasant dreams. Also the general feeling, of being exposed and not being able to keep out the suffering which happens all over the world, has increased. But this time I didn´t fall apart and it´s easier for me to accept my limits, but I have to be careful.

The other world "movie" is less intense. It is easier to step back so that the images can´t take hold of me as much anymore. I now realize that my state can be traced back to outside pressure. I take the images as symptoms which makes me have options now. Last week I took a day off. Also I made an appointment with a dietitian. The need to take care of myself has increased. I sleep well. Altogether I feel better by about 30% right now.

Rx: *Heloderma horridum* 1M one dose

Follow-up on 19 November 2009 (another four days later):

P: I felt the effect of the remedy immediately, like when I took it the first time; a feeling of softness and being tired, finally I can sleep! It would be nice to just give in to that feeling, but I can´t because of my obligations towards my family and my job. It feels as if a curtain was drawn between myself and the general suffering in the world. I feel better, because the fear is gone. I´m more in contact with myself and don´t feel so open and vulnerable any more. Before I took the remedy I fell apart and **parts of myself were drawn towards the abyss**. The remedy pulls me away from it.

Email from Michael Rutledge on 24 September 2010:

So far the case seems to be a homoeopathic happy end. Recently I asked her if there were any general changes for her in the long run and she replied: "Other therapies never gave me such long lasting and profound amelioration. The dragons have disappeared." She had no repetition of the remedy other than the times indicated in the case.

Interesting facts about *Varanus komodoensis* relevant to the case

* Small (young) Komodo dragons are **accomplished tree climbers**. (*"Tightrope act" to avoid being eaten by the adults.*)

- The dragon's teeth are large, curved and serrated and arranged so that the maximum amount of **flesh can be bitten off** and swallowed whole.

- The Komodo dragon is powerful and agile, and yet **surprise is still the method of choice** for capturing larger prey.

- By striking quickly and knocking the deer off its feet, the Komodo dragon begins **tearing it to pieces using its powerful claws and large serrated teeth. Animals that survive this initial attack are likely to die from infection from the bite,** as the Komodo's saliva is particularly infectious, with as many as 50 strains of bacteria *(also venom)*.

Possible specific expressions of the Mexican beaded lizard in patients

There will be common expressions of the lizard and the scleroglossans; along with the specific expressions of the *Heloderma horridum* as given below:

- Tolerance to lower temperature, a hot thermal modality

Heloderma suspectum (Helo.) [Gila monster]

Order: Squamata

Suborder: Scleroglossa

Superfamily: Anguoidea

Family: Helodermatidae (Beaded lizards)

Genus: Heloderma

Species: Heloderma suspectum

Common name: Gila monster

Subspecies

- *Heloderma suspectum cinctum*
- *Heloderma suspectum suspectum*

Introduction

The name 'Gila monster' refers to the Gila River Basin in Arizona. 'Suspectum' comes from the Latin: 'mistrusted' or 'suspected'. This refers to a venomous nature which was suspected but not proven at the time of naming.

Habitat

Heloderma suspectum is a species of venomous lizard native to the southwestern United States and northern Mexico.

Anatomical characteristics

A BRIGHTLY COLORED LIZARD WITH: CONTRASTING SCALES, BRIGHT SALMON PINK, YELLOW, WHITE BANDS OR RETICULATIONS ON A JET BLACK BACKGROUND, laid down in INTRICATE PATTERNS. This color scheme WARNS potential aggressors that it has a toxic bite or may also act as a camouflage. The teeth are loosely anchored, which allows them to be broken off and replaced throughout their lives.

Heloderma suspectum – note the bright colored contrasting bands compared to the subdued Heloderma horridum

Heloderma horridum (Mexican beaded lizard)	*Heloderma suspectum* (Gila monster)
Larger; of the two Heloderma species	Smaller; of the two Heloderma species
Subdued colors	Bright colors

Specific behavior

The Gila monster produces only SMALL QUANTITIES OF ITS NEUROTOXIC VENOM, which is secreted into the lizard's saliva. THEY CANNOT WITHHOLD VENOM; ENVENOMATION OCCURS EACH TIME THEY BITE. They often chew their prey to put as much venom into the bloodstream of the victim as possible. They can give serious bites, potentially fatal to humans.

Materia medica

Excerpts of *Heloderma suspectum* proving by Todd Rowe:

The central idea of this remedy is expressed in the following: I am busy or industrious, centered or balanced, and speeding in my space. Don't bother me or I will get irritable and lunge.

The theme of **aggression** was also present. For the most part, this took the form of irritability and the need to protect one's space. However, a number of provers had violent dreams, and one prover described aggressive feelings of wanting to punch others in the jaw. The aggression and irritability seemed to be without remorse or much emotion.

Another theme was that of **increased energy**. This took on many forms which ranged from apprehensiveness and anxiety to mania. Key words that provers used to describe this state included: anxiety, busy, industrious, working constantly, rushed (as opposed to the lizard's sedentary habits), not able to shut off the flow of ideas, insomnia, and agitation.

Three of the provers felt more social by the end of the proving. One of the prover's in particular noted a significant change from isolation and being a loner to greater socialness and calmness. For several provers, this also took the form of connecting more to deceased relatives. One prover described feeling as if she were much closer to her patients after the remedy and could see more clearly. We know that this animal is known for its solitary habits.

Animal themes were present throughout the proving. By the end of the exit group proving, participants predicted that the remedy was an animal, which had a tail, was involved in some type of construction, like burrowing, and had the potential to be aggressive. The colors red, white, black and yellow also came out, which match the colors of the lizard. The craving for eggs is also interesting, in that this is one of the primary foods that the lizard eats. Reptilian themes were also present, involving a lack of maternal feeling, striking out, and aggression.

The physical center of the remedy seems to revolve around: the upper respiratory system, nervous system, and gastrointestinal system. Many of the participants developed upper respiratory symptoms. One participant also experienced a cured symptom of chronic severe stabbing stomach pain.

Symptoms also were generally worse in the morning. Chilliness was noted by several participants. This was the leading keynote of this remedy prior to the proving. One prover had a dream of being in snow and woke up with intense shivering.

Phatak's Materia Medica:

- **INTENSE ICY COLDNESS; as if frozen; from within outwards.** This is the most peculiar symptom of this poison.

- **Breath and tongue cold.**

- **Cold feeling in lungs and chest.**

- **Coldness across scapula.**

- **Burning in spine. Cold creeping ring around the body.**

- Patient **staggers while walking. Steps high and puts down heel hard.**

- **Sensation as if walking on a sponge, or as if with swollen feet.**

- **Turns to right when walking.**

Few rubrics from Reference works:

- HEAT: FLUSHES OF: ALTERNATING WITH: COLDNESS, ICY. {0> 1> 0} [85]

- THOUGHTS: INTRUDE AND CROWD AROUND EACH OTHER: MORNING, ON WAKING. {0> 1> 0} [264]

- THOUGHTS: RAPID, QUICK: MORNING. {0> 1> 0} [264]

Possible specific expressions of the Gila monster in patients

The Gila monster patient will express all the characteristics of the Heloderma, along with a few specific features:

- Specific color:
  - brightly colored
  - *awareness of the colors red, white, black, and yellow* (color range of Heloderma skin)
  - intricate patterns (functions to warn and camouflage)

- – a possibility that these patients prefer bright colors in clothing or accessories like jewelry, etc.
- Increased aggression:
  - – particularly pertaining to territoriality
  - – a feeling of not wanting one's space invaded or disturbed
- The aggression ranges from; irritability to a desire to strike out with physical violence, but lacks feelings of remorse or emotion
- Irritability often takes the form of a desire to lunge
- INTENSE ICY COLDNESS:
  - – as if frozen; from within outward
  - – cold creeping ring around the body
  - – chilliness (also appears in the proving)
- Flushes of heat alternating with icy coldness
- Thoughts intrude the mind, especially in the morning, on waking
- Increased energy:
  - – ranging all the way from industrious to manic
  - – workaholics
  - – feelings of business
  - – apprehension, anxiety, rushed
  - – uncontrolled thoughts, and insomnia

This is particularly interesting because the helodermatids are generally sluggish, slow-moving lizards which rest when not foraging for food.

- Steps high and puts heel down hard:
  - – sensation as if walking on a sponge
  - – as if with swollen feet
  - – staggering gait
- Desires egg

Family:
Lacertidae
(Wall lizards, true lizards, lacertids)

Homoeopathic remedies

Lacerta agilis (Lacer.) [Sand lizard or Green lizard]

Lacerta vivipara [Common lizard]

Superfamily: Scincoidea (includes skinks and relatives)

(The Lacertidae lizards belong to the superfamily Scincoidea.)

Introduction

The Scincomorpha form the largest group of lizards. They are primarily **ground dwellers (terrestrial)** or **burrowers**, though some are tree climbers. Most skinks are **secretive** lizards that **spend most of their time under leaf litter**. Some species are known to **live inside holes** made by trapdoor spiders. Living **safely snuggled inside the holes makes it extremely difficult to find them**.

Generalized anatomy

They are mostly **long and slender**. They **lack the skin modifications** present in many of the iguanians. These species also have **varying degrees of limb reduction**: from completely formed limbs to completely absent limbs.

Reproduction

The skinks are known to **look after their eggs**. They bask in the sun, then go back to their underground nests, **transferring their body heat to the eggs**. When the eggs hatch, the young skinks are capable of finding their own food. Within a day or so the newborns will leave their mother, capable of exploring out of the nest. In some skinks the family life lasts even longer. Some of these lizards have a unique way of reproduction, where the female nourishes the developing young via a placenta.

Common behavior

Skinks do not pant as other lizards do to cool off. Instead, these lizards beat the heat by **resting in a shady spot or a cool underground burrow**.

Most skinks are **nervous animals that take cover if they feel even slightly threatened**. For this reason, people often have only short glimpses of them, before the lizard **darts** into a pile of brush or under a log. If an attacker is able to catch a skink before it can take cover, many of them will **drop the tail**, which continues to wiggle for several minutes.

- Burrowing, living hidden inside holes

- Shy, nervous

- Dart off into a hiding spot

- Secretive, hidden

- Parental care is present

- Drops tail (autotomy)

Family: Lacertidae (Wall lizards or true lizards)

Introduction

The lizards that belong to this family Lacertidae, from which the name 'lizard' is derived, are **'typical' lizards**. They are green, long-tailed, cylindrical, scaly, **agile** animals. They **dart** across the rocks and buildings in the warmer parts of Africa, Eurasia, the Middle East, and several northern Oceanic islands. They are in every sense, the classical lizards.

Generalized anatomy

These lizards are distinguished by a **collar of large scales on the underside of their necks**.

Life cycle and reproduction

All lay eggs, except *Lacerta vivipara*.

Behavior

Color changing ability in these lizards is minimally present in only one species. *Lacerta agilis* males become darker green during the mating season. **The structure of their tail supports fast zigzag movements and an accurate jump** that is needed to catch their insect prey. They are all insectivores.

Males are highly **territorial** and aggressive towards one another.

Possible common expressions of Lacertidae in patients

Of the general features of the lizards this group will have the following specific expressions:

- Agility
- Quick movement
- Zigzag movement
- Accurate jump
- Dropping of the tail
- Dart off quickly when in danger

They will also show the following expressions along with the common expressions of the skinks:

- Unable to change color (only seen in *Lacerta agilis*)
- Burrowing, living hidden inside holes
- Lacks various body modifications like crests, and spines

Lacerta agilis (Lacer.) [Sand lizard or Green lizard]

Order: Squamata

Suborder: Scleroglossa

Infraorder: Scincomorpha

Superfamily: Scincoidea

Family: Lacertidae (Wall lizards or true lizards or lacertids)

Genus: Lacerta

Species: Lacerta agilis

Common names: Sand lizard, Green lizard

Introduction

The sand lizard is a STOCKY, **terrestrial** lizard.

Habitat

The sand lizard is common in Europe and Asia, and it's habitat sometimes extends north of the Arctic Circle. A typical habitat of the sand lizards is lowland dry heathland[1], and the coastal sand dunes which reflect its name. They may also occur at low densities and in other habitats as well. They need a variety of structural and temperature conditions for thermoregulation and to seek cover from predators. A key requirement is UNSHADED SANDY HABITAT TO DIG BURROWS FOR EGG-LAYING AND SHELTER.

Anatomical characteristics

The sand lizard measures from 18-22 cm (7-9 in). Females are generally longer than males. They have a short head, blunt snout, and relatively SHORT LEGS AND SHORT TAILS. Sand lizards have an attractive pattern of DARK SPOTS WITH LIGHT CENTRES (OCELLI), OVER A BROWN OR GREY BACKGROUND.

Food habits

Sand lizards mainly feed on invertebrates such as slugs, spiders, and insects. They also feed on a variety of other foods, including fruit and flower heads.

---

1   Heath land: a tract of level wasteland; uncultivated land with sandy soil and scrubby vegetation.

Mating characteristics

THE MALES DEVELOP A VERY VIVID GREEN COLORATION ON EMERGENCE FROM HIBERNATION AND IN PREPARATION FOR THE BREEDING SEASON. OFTEN THEIR FLANKS TURN GREEN DURING THE MATING SEASON.

Lacerta agilis male displaying green flanks

The males enter into elaborate displays to attract a mate. Male sand lizards fight vigorously for females. They GRAB THE NECK OF THEIR OPPONENT WITH THEIR JAWS AND THEN ROLL OVER EACH OTHER, UNTIL ONE, USUALLY THE SMALLER LIZARD, RETREATS. The female of this oviparous species lays a clutch of 3-14 eggs in a burrow that she digs in loose sand. Exposure to the sun will help keep the eggs warm.

Specific behaviour

Sand lizards, like other reptiles, are ectothermic or cold-blooded. They need to bask in the sun, or be in contact with warm surfaces to raise their body temperature. They hibernate from October to March, the winter months. The males tend to emerge some time before the females.

Even though sand lizards are FAST-MOVING and ACTIVE DURING THE DAY, their **shy secretive** nature makes them difficult to spot. They **retreat into a burrow** or other **refuge** by the time the sunlight fades, and are INACTIVE DURING THE NIGHT. In some conditions, they may also remain inactive during the day, spending much of their time underground in their burrows, especially during very hot days. They often form small **colonies,** and sometimes they share the same burrows.

Sand lizards engage in a striking behavior that protects their feet from hot sand. The sand lizard 'DANCES' BY LIFTING ITS LEGS UP QUICKLY, ONE AT A TIME, OR BY RESTING ITS BELLY ON THE SAND AND LIFTING UP ALL FOUR LEGS AT ONCE!

Specific method of attack and defense

These lizards **rapidly shed their tail** when attacked by one of their usual predators; snakes, birds, or mammals.

The sand lizard is so rare, it is strictly protected by law in some countries.

Case of *Lacerta agilis*
By: Joanne Greenland

Past history:

Recurring chest infections

Pneumonia

Bronchitis yearly

Flu yearly

Asthma/ hay fever

Fracture of the left arm when 8 years old

Rotated right knee bone

Numbness in both arms; from wrists extending up to elbows

P: 17 years of Tae Kwon Do training.

Now involved in Tai Chi. At sunrise and sunset, or thereabout, I like to do my ritual of Tai Chi movements.

At present the ligaments in my legs are not strong, even after 17 years of exercise with Tae Kwon Do and Tai Chi.

Numbness in fingers extending up the arm.

Cramping in the right side of back, the muscles are not able to release.

Difficulty in horse riding. I cannot get my feet to sit correctly. It feels as if a solid rod is in the legs or my legs are in a plaster cast. My legs feel knotted up and tight. **They simply cannot bend to where I want them to go.**

I do long warm ups with my martial arts and I still cannot touch my toes, I can only reach mid-calf. I feel stiff up the back of my legs.

I am not flexible. It feels like it is pulling my hips down.

I am knotted up. It is very tight and it won't release.

Describe this more.

I am weaker. It feels like I have been stretched out of place. This makes me feel weaker.

Describe this more.

It feels like the muscle is at its limit. It is on the border line. It has gone as far as it can go. If I twist, then it is aggravated. It feels like it has been taken too far. It is under pressure, overextended, **taken further than it wanted to go**. Then it feels as if it is tearing or pulling. The muscles feel tight. They become inflexible (Hg like a stop sign).

Describe this more.

It is pulling. Stretching helps to improve it. It hurts but makes it feel better. However, I can only stretch so far. **I cannot get any further.** I cannot get any more. I cannot improve, the muscles won't let me.

Describe this more.

It is like elastic stretched as far as it can go. The muscles are rock hard. It is not the surface muscle that is the problem; it is the underlying muscle, closest to the bone. The masseur has to get in very deep. She cannot budge these tight, hard muscles. They are bunched up, one and another and another. They are extended to their maximum. The effect of that is that they start pulling on something else, causing other problems. It is the deep layers that are the problem.

Describe this more.

All the way in **there is no give.** They are hard and knotted. It is as if they are **grabbed**. There is no release. There is no flexibility. There is no stretch. It is all so tight. I have to work twice as hard as anyone else to achieve less. The muscles will not relax. They will not go floppy. They do not allow me to be nimble (Hg stop sign and a fist).

Describe this more.

I have to work twice as hard as anyone else to achieve less. I have to put in a hell of a lot more effort. **They make it harder for me. They are not supple.**

Describe this more.

I put more effort in than most people. I am trying so hard, but not getting anywhere. Why can't I? **Why won't they let me?** I try and nothing is happening. My coach says, just bend them, or just stretch them, but they will not stretch. They will not give. They are inflexible.

Describe this more.

It is like hitting a brick wall. I cannot talk to people and explain what I want.

Where did this come from? Unrelated to the discussion she associates the hard, inflexible muscles with her inability to talk to people.

Describe this more.

A barrier. I hit another barrier. I have hit a dead end. I try a different angle of approach. I try to manipulate my body into a position that is successful, but **the muscles are stronger than me** and will not let me stretch. They will not bend, they are not supple.

Describe this more.

What, about the barriers?

Whatever comes to mind?

I was harassed and bullied as a kid.

Again, we jump from tight muscles to I cannot talk to people, to I was bullied. I allow her to continue as she feels.

Describe this more.

I was picked on. I shut everything out.

Describe this more.

There was me and there was the person everyone else saw. They were totally opposite. **I had my own little world. A world where nobody could get through. A place where nobody could hurt me. My place was impermeable. I was isolated. I like it like that. I was always on the look out for intruders. I was vigilant and wary. I liked my own place without people who could hurt me.**

Describe this more.

I had no friends. **I did not match** what a girl should be. I was different.

I am a daddy's girl. I was called a tomboy and I think that was a compliment. I was not pretty or petite. I did not wear ribbons and frilly dresses. I did not play with dolls. I was my own person. **I created my own world within my own barriers.** Myself and I kept good company. My animals kept me company. I ignored everyone else. My animals were my friends. I played with frogs, snails, mice, snakes, and lizards. Lizards were my favourite, but I like all animals.

Describe this more.

People did not understand me. They were cruel, so I would push them away. I would block out all feelings, so eventually there was nothing there (weeps). There was me, and then there was everything else (stop sign Hg). It was my space behind the barrier, and everyone else was on the other side.

Like an invisible brick wall. Like a glass panel.

I could see the other side, but I was not part of it. **I kept everyone out of my space. They could not get in, they could not hurt me. My own private space. It was warm.** There was only what I wanted or needed to survive in my place. It was private. I could be me.

Like my home now. I only have in it what I want. I keep it 16°-18°C (60°-64°F) because that suits me. **I like that temperature in the winter**. Others think it is too cold, but I like it that temperature. **My reptiles like that temperature as well. They need it that temperature. When the warmth comes they are stimulated to breed. When the sun comes out *we* like to bathe in the sun.**

Hobbies?

I love fishing. I understand animals. Animals work in patterns. They have a predictable pattern of behaviour. I understand them. I enjoy horses and horse riding. I breed reptiles. I have a pair of goannas (iguanas), a water dragon, turtles, and carpet pythons. **I understand reptiles and they get me. We understand about respecting boundaries. We understand about *bending* to each other's needs.** If I am out of sorts, they leave me alone. If they are out of sorts, I leave them alone. I love their individual characters, the different markings they have and how they know how to defend themselves. (She has had 17 years of martial arts lessons, learning how to defend herself.)

Describe this more.

Animals have a standard predictable pattern of behaviour. If you do a certain thing then there is an expected reaction going to happen. It is a cause-and-effect principle. You know what will happen, and if you do not want that outcome, then don't initiate the behaviour. So you can **adapt to the situation**, accommodating each other, without overstretching yourself. **This means you can control the situation.** You can create the outcome that you want. This is a little like when my partner comes over to my place and starts moving things around, I get so mad and I tell him. If he doesn't want to see that side of me, then don't move my things.

(She had previously said, "It feels like I have been stretched out of place.")

She compares herself with her animals.

And your Tai Chi?

I love Tai Chi. It is good self-defense.

Describe this more.

Defending yourself against attack. It teaches you to know **how to react and how to get out of an undesirable or dangerous situation.** So you can **protect yourself** and be self-reliant. The **world is not a safe place** and after 17 years of Tae Kwon Do and now Tai Chi, I can defend myself well in most, if not all, situations.

Describe this more.

I am defensive.

I am **instantly ready to react** (clicks fingers). **I am vigilant at all times, always expecting attack, so I am prepared to defend myself. I like to keep my distance and I like you to keep yours.** If someone just turns up at my place **I am ready for attack.** I do not like strangers. They can f....k off, and I tell them.

Describe this more.

I won't let them come too close. Firstly I am rude, **to scare them off**. I give them an instant dismissal. If that doesn't work, I will strongly suggest that they back off. **I puff myself up, hold my shoulders high, thrust my chin forward, warning them that, that is enough now. If that does not work,**

I will strike, slap, lunge at them, or I may even drop them. I can be quite aggressive and can give what is required. **However, usually I just run away.** I prefer to escape than fight, but I will fight if I have to.

471

Describe this more.

I am independent and like my own company. I like my place to be as I like it. I do not like anybody changing anything. Don't interfere with my territory. It makes me really cross. My partner is the opposite of me, he is gentle and passive. He wouldn't hurt a fly, I'd snatch it up and eat it for breakfast! (She grabs the air with her hand as if grabbing the fly.)

Analysis

I would like to have treated this young woman with lace monitor goanna. She has a pair of these goannas and they are very dear to her. She describes them as she describes herself and even refers to them as *'we'* at times. I tried to find the goanna in potency but was unable to source it from anywhere.

I was certain she needed a lizard. *Lacerta agilis* has the rigidity of muscles, and the numbness experienced in the limbs, so I gave her *Lacerta agilis* with good effect. I wonder whether she would have done even better on lace monitor goanna.

Remedy: *Lacerta agilis* 200C

Follow-up 4 weeks later:

The moment she walks in, with a big grin on her face, she stands up and touches her ankles. She can wrap her hands around her ankles, whereas before she could only reach half way down her calf muscles.

How are things?

Two weeks ago a huge muscle release happened. My buttocks, hamstrings and hips all just let go. My masseur cannot believe it. She can get right into the deep muscles now. I am able to ride my horse properly. When my instructor says just place your legs against the horse I can do it. Before they were like stiff boards and I did not have the flexibility to bend them around the horse. I had no control. Now I have control. I can now improve and advance in what I am doing, instead of putting in so much hard work and not getting anywhere. It is much better. I can concentrate on other aspects apart from the simple, but previously impossible, task of being flexible.

What else is different?

I am not as grumpy. I feel lighter and happier. I am learning to tolerate my partner coming over to my place and putting things down, or moving things. I still do not like it, but I don't attack him for it. Instead, I breathe to myself and think it does not really matter. It doesn't, does it? We get on really well. It is silly to get defensive because he moved my mug.

Anything else?

My whole body just seems so much more flexible. I can stretch a lot more. I would not call myself a flexible person, but I am making change.

Tell me more.

I find I can do things I could not do before. In the physical realm with my Tai Chi, but also in my emotional world. I used to get very tense when my partner brought any friends over, even if I knew them well. I just don't feel comfortable with people. Now I seem better with that. Even my partner said I seem less on edge about it.

How is the numbness in you arms?

It is 50% better. I am still aware of it, but it has not bothered me as much lately.

Any dreams?

I cannot remember any.

Treatment: *Lacerta agilis* 200C

Follow-up 2 months later:

Still going well. Can now touch her toes comfortably. A second large shift happened after the repeat of the remedy. Feels 'nearly normal' and is excelling with her martial arts and horse riding. Feels more relaxed and happy in all aspects of her life. The numbness is barely noticeable.

Possible expressions of the sand lizard in patients

It is important to understand that, since homoeopathic pharmacies around the world have few Lacertidae remedies, and no skink ones, a patient expressing the common features of the skinks as well as the family Lacertidae (listed above) should be sufficient to warrant prescribing Lacerta agilis. This is irregardless of whether the specific features of Lacerta agilis are present or not.

The sand lizard will express the common features of the Lacertidae: quick movements, darting off in their hiding spots, ability to lose their tail, digging and burrowing, shy and secretive nature.

These *Lacerta agilis* characteristics will also be expressed:

Behavior
- Live in colonies, or in groups (reptiles in general tend to be solitary creatures)
- Color-changing ability (unlike the other lacertids who are unable to change their color)
- Characteristic dancing
    - ▶ lifting one leg at a time or all at once
    - ▶ jumping

Method of attack of rival males during mating season
- Fight vigorously
- Grab the neck with jaws, biting
- Rolling over each other

Symptoms from Materia medica
- *Delirium: alternating with: mental capacities heightened. {0> 1> 0}*
- *Industrious, mania for work. {6> 18> 107}*
- *Numbness, insensibility: lower limbs: feet: extending upward. {0> 1> 0}*

474

Lacerta vivipara [Common lizard]

Order: Squamata

Suborder: Scleroglossa

Superfamily: Scincoidea

Family: Lacertidae (Wall lizards or true lizards or lacertids)

Genus: Zootoca

Species: Lacerta vivipara

Common name: Common lizard

It is also known as the Viviparous lizard. It derives its name from its ABILITY TO BEAR LIVE YOUNG. This is an adaptation that helps it to SURVIVE IN REGIONS THAT ARE TOO COLD for eggs to develop. This species has one of the largest continuous ranges of any terrestrial reptile, reaching well into the Arctic. Young viviparous lizards are born in an egg membrane, from which they escape almost immediately.

Lacerta vivipara shedding its skin

Family:
Varanidae
(Monitor lizards)

Homoeopathic remedy
Varanus komodoensis [Komodo dragon or Monitor lizard]

Introduction

The monitors are the *king of lizards,* being the **largest of all lizards; the largest existing Varanus lizard is the Komodo dragon**. They have a general uniformity of appearance with an elongate head and neck, relatively heavy body, long tail, and well-developed limbs. They also have deeply **forked tongues, flicking in and out constantly,** similar to the snakes. They are all **carnivorous** species and active foragers, **consuming both live prey and carrion**.

2 subfamilies and 2 genera:

- Lanthanotus: subfamily Lanthonotinae
  - a single species (*Lanthanotus borneensis*)
- Varanus: subfamily Varainae
  - contains 50 species

Possible common expressions of the Monitor lizards in patients

- Huge, large, gigantic
- Tongue flicking in and out
- Carnivorous, cannibalistic

Varanus komodoensis [Komodo dragon, Monitor lizard]

Order: Squamata

Suborder: Scleroglossa

Superfamily: Anguoidea

Family: Varanidae (Monitor lizards)

Genus: Varanus

Species: Varanus komodoensis

Common names: 'Ora' or Land crocodile, as they are easily confused with crocodiles, Komodo dragon

Introduction

We know that the closest thing to a dragon lived millions of years ago in the prehistoric age. There is a creature that exists in today's modern world, not towering in height, yet powerful and mighty enough to be given the title of **"dragon"**.

Reaching 3 m/10 ft in length, and an average weight of between 68-90 kg/150-200 lb, the Komodo dragons are the HEAVIEST, LARGEST, AND THE MOST POWERFUL LIZARDS ON EARTH.

Komodo Island

Komodo dragons have THRIVED IN THE HARSH CLIMATE of Indonesia's Lesser Sunda Islands for millions of years. Their existence was amazingly unknown to humans, until about 100 years ago. They live on scrubby hillsides, in open woodland, and on dry river beds, where they feed entirely on live animals or carrion.

KOMODO ISLAND IS ONE OF THE HOTTEST PLACES ON EARTH, WITH TEMPERATURES that can reach over 38°C/100°F. The dragons, being cold blooded, regulate their temperature by HIDING IN BURROWS. Komodo and its neighboring islands are rampant with earthquakes, tidal waves, and volcanoes. Komodo itself is a national park.

Anatomical characteristics

Varanus komodoensis – the forked tongue flicking in and out

The Komodo dragon's FEROCIOUS nature is matched by its quite awesome appearance. It has a long body, well developed bowed legs, and a deeply forked tongue, which it flicks out as it searches for food. They have a relatively small head with wide jaws and a rounded snout.

They have a large muscular tail that can be used as a weapon. It can also be used as a prop, when standing on its hind legs. While they walk, the tail will swish back and forth to help them stay balanced. The males are much bigger than the females. ·

They have large muscular throats, which they use as bellows to pump air. They can do that even while they are running, unlike other lizards.

Their SHARP CLAWS are used for DIGGING burrows, UNEARTHING food, and HOLDING ONTO PREY TO DELIVER DEVASTATINGLY LETHAL EFFECTS.

They have RAZOR-SHARP, serrated teeth, resembling the flesh-eating shark's, but they are UNABLE TO CHEW. The dragon's teeth are its most dangerous weapon. They efficiently TEAR OFF CHUNKS of their prey and throw them backwards into their mouths. There are 60 teeth that are frequently replaced. They have **highly flexible jaws** (common to the scleroglossans) that allow them to SWALLOW LARGE PIECES of flesh with ASTONISHING SPEED, while large carcasses are RIPPED OFF. They are also known for their COPIOUS DROOLING.

Food habits

The Komodo is **carnivorous** and **cannibalistic**, and has an ENORMOUS APPETITE. It can eat any type of meat. It has a HUGE CAPACITY FOR FOOD, eating upto 80% of its own weight in a single meal! It often gorges to such an extent that it has to rest in the same position for several days, before it is able to move away. Large mammalian carnivores, such as lions, tend to leave 25% to 30% of their kill unconsumed. They'll leave behind the intestines, hide, skeleton, and hooves. Komodos eat much more efficiently, and leave behind only about 12% of their prey. They eat bones, hooves, and swaths of hide. They also eat intestines, but only after SWINGING THEM VIGOROUSLY TO SCATTER THEIR CONTENTS. This behavior removes feces from the meal.

Young Komodo dragons attack snakes, lizards, and rodents. The adults, due to their large size, are able to tackle much larger live prey, including—wild pigs, water buffalo, and deer. They are opportunistic feeders and will eat anything they can overpower, including small dragons and small or injured humans.

LARGE KOMODOS OFTEN CANNIBALIZE YOUNG ONES. THE YOUNG WILL OFTEN DEFENSIVELY ROLL IN FECAL MATERIAL, IN ORDER TO ASSUME A SCENT THAT THE LARGE DRAGONS WILL AVOID. YOUNG DRAGONS ALSO UNDERGO RITUALS OF APPEASEMENT, WITH THE SMALLER LIZARDS PACING AROUND A FEEDING CIRCLE IN A STATELY RITUALIZED WALK. THEIR TAIL IS STUCK STRAIGHT OUT AND THEY THROW THEIR BODY FROM SIDE TO SIDE WITH EXAGGERATED CONVULSIONS.

Mating characteristics

Komodo dragons are usually LONERS. They live their lives in SOLITARY until it is time to mate or gather in a group around a meal. Males are extremely cautious of their territory and they will patrol up to 2.5 km/1.5 mi a day. During the breeding season, males compete for the chance to mate. They "STAND" IN AN UPRIGHT POSITION on their hind legs and WRESTLE each other to the ground, with their tails acting as props. The one who gets PINNED DOWN loses. The winner then SCRATCHES his claws in slow, long strokes down the length of the loser's body.

The male Komodo produces a scent, which helps him find a female, who produces no smell. The dragon presses his snout to the female's body, and flicks her with his long, forked tongue to obtain chemical information about her receptivity. He then scratches her back with his long claws, making a loud SCRAPING noise. If unreceptive, she raises and INFLATES her neck and HISSES loudly. After mating, the females dig nests in sandy ground, laying clutches of upto 25 eggs.

TERMITE NESTS are often the Komodo's PREFERRED EGG LAYING LOCATION. Termites are able to keep a constant temperature and humidity in their nests, thus making it a perfect incubator. The nests are difficult to break off, and the hatchlings are often IMPRISONED or TRAPPED INSIDE. For days they go without food, until eventually either their own mother recalls the nest and frees them, or they are released by another mother lizard looking for a nest.

The dragon eggs are 7.6 cm/3 in long and are RUBBERY and TOUGH. They are also ELASTIC and EXPAND as the baby inside grows. This is so true that the dragon eggs are about 50% bigger when hatched than when laid. Typically it takes about 8-9 months for the dragons in the egg to develop. They then hatch out by use of a special tooth called an egg tooth. This razor like tooth falls out as soon as the lizard breaks free.

Characteristic behavior

They have a KEEN SENSE OF SMELL, SIGHT, AND HEARING. They are also **very intelligent.** The Komodo relies more on its sense of smell than sight. Its keen sense of smell enables it to detect the scent of decaying remains or carrion from upto 8.5 km/5 mi. Like snakes, it 'tastes' the air with its tongue, constantly FLICKING IT OUT to collect scent molecules from the air.

They are MOST ACTIVE DURING THE DAY. While walking, its body is held off the ground. Normally they move about SLUGGISHLY, SLOWLY, and STROLLING LEISURELY AROUND IN A CLUMSY, AWKWARD MANNER, on their pillar-like legs. They look quite ungainly, but despite their weight, they are also **fast, agile** and capable of **running** at upto 18 kph/1mph, in short bursts. They can run as fast as humans but they tire more quickly. They are also good SWIMMERS and can even CLIMB trees.

Specific method of attack and defense

The Komodo is powerful and agile, yet hunts by ambush. It relies on camouflage and PATIENTLY LIES IN WAIT for a passing prey. When a victim wanders by, the dragon springs onto its feet and charges with a quick sprinting burst. It then BRINGS THE PREY DOWN, USING ITS POWERFUL LEGS AND SHARP CLAWS. IT WILL CLASP THE PREY WITH ITS SHARP, SERRATED, SHARK-LIKE TEETH. While RIPPING ITS PREY APART, IT WILL EVISCERATE IT. The Komodo usually GOES FOR THE THROAT FIRST. A KILL IS USUALLY SHARED BY MANY DRAGONS. Adults are even capable of bringing down and DISMEMBERING animals as large as deer and pigs. Adult Komodos also have **a nasty bite** (a common scleroglossan feature).

Animals that escape the jaws of a Komodo will only feel lucky briefly. Dragon saliva is rich in toxic bacteria[1] that thrive on flesh. This bacteria contaminates the wound, and within 24 hours of the initial attack, the stricken creature usually dies of blood poisoning. Dragons CALMLY FOLLOW AN ESCAPEE for kilometers/miles as the bacteria takes effect, using their KEEN SENSE OF SMELL TO HONE IN ON THE CORPSE.

(Refer case by Michael Rutledge on page 451.)

---

1   In 2009, Dr. Bryan Fry, a venomous animal expert, published further evidence demonstrating that Komodo dragons possess a **venomous bite**. MRI scans of a preserved skull showed the presence of two venom glands in the lower jaw. They extracted one of these glands from the head of a terminally ill specimen in the Singapore Zoological Gardens, and found that it secreted a venom containing several different toxic proteins. The known functions of these proteins include: inhibition of blood clotting, lowering of blood pressure and muscle paralysis. The proteins also produce the induction of hypothermia, leading to shock and loss of consciousness in envenomated prey. As a result of the discovery, the previous theory that bacteria were responsible for the deaths of komodo victims was disputed.

Possible specific expressions of the Komodo dragon in patients

The Komodo dragon energy in patients will be very characteristically different than that of the other lizards, due to its large size, powerful musculature, strong feet, sharp claws and teeth. Possibly the patient will exhibit the general reptile and lizard features like the ability to ambush attack, chase, spring out from a hiding position, short bursts of rapid activity, etc. The Komodo dragon patients will exhibit violence and aggression to a much greater extent than the other lizards. They don't lose their tail. They don't perform any rituals like the other lizards, but they are fast, agile, and possess a keen sense of smell, sight, and hearing. Komodo dragon patients share certain characteristics with the snakes. They must be distinguished when we see these symptoms: flicking of the tongue and a propensity to dig and burrow. Komodos also exhibit a tendency to scratch using their sharp claws. Komodos will have all the common expressions of the monitor lizards in addition to their specific characteristics which are as follows:

Methods of attack and defense:
- Lie in wait
- Ambush attack
- Charge with quick sprinting burst
- Wrestle, pin down, bring it down
- Attack the throat
- Nasty bite
- Tear off, rip apart, eviscerate, tear chunks, dismember
- Venomous, poisonous
- Swing vigorously, scatter
- Chase or trail (as Komodos calmly follow prey that has escaped)

Body form and functions:
- Heavy, large, powerful, ferocious
- Armored
- Ability to move or swishes back and forth, to balance
- Drooling
- Rubbery, tough, elastic, expand

Other behavioral traits:

- Enormous appetite, gorges, huge capacity for food
- Carnivorous, cannibalistic, carrion, rotting
- Hiding in burrows
- Imprisoned, trapped
- Solitary, loners
- Bellow, hiss
- Languid, slow, ambling, clumsy, shambling, ungainly
- Connection with termites

Difference with crocodiles

In crocodiles the main action is to pull down or bring down the prey under the water and kill it inside the water. Crocodiles are also highly territorial and show parental affection.

Lizard (Divya) (species unidentified)

The specie from which the remedy Lizard (Divya) was made remains unidentified. Hence we cannot derive the specie specific expressions for a patient. One can apply the general themes of lizards for this remedy.

Case of Lizard (Divya)
By: Laurie Dack

Asthma for 16 years. My daughter was about to be born when it started. I would wake at 3-4:00 am and cough and cough and cough. Now it is in attacks. I can't breathe.

Tight, wheezing, constriction in my chest. Tickle in the throat.

Trying to get mucous out; a quick little tickle in my throat and the cough starts. The mucous builds and it adheres to the bronchi and I can't breathe.

< In a cold room

< In the winter

Work in a veterinary surgery and the room is kept cold. Feel chilly all the time. Tightness in the chest. Like breathing through a straw. I can't exhale very fast. Coughing and a fast tickle in my throat. I start to cough and then the mucous sticks there and it won't come up.

When it is cold my nose is completely blocked.

Gets blocked up. Completely blocked up.

Waking at night 2-4 times. Wheezing in the night.

The tube is constricted and I can't breathe. Need to use the nebulizer to open the bronchi. Then in the early morning I need to get up. Many, many attacks and I need to use the nebulizer sometimes 6-7 times/day.

Very deep and very tight in my chest. The mucous sticks in there and constricts my chest and my breathing. The inhalers don't work deeply enough. Need the nebulizer to open up my lungs so I can breathe freely.

Yellow mucous; bright yellow. Sticky, disgusting. Globs of thick, viscous mucous.

< Cold temperatures. I can't survive much longer.

Don't want to live like this anymore. Sometimes wish I was in an accident. It has been bad for too long. Have suffered so long. I feel embarrassed. I hide that

485

I use the nebulizers. No one at work knows about my condition. I work with sick animals, so how can I be sick. How can I help animals when I am sick like this?

When I am angry my breathing gets worse. The only person I am angry with is my husband. In fact we never argue because I am not able to say anything. My chest becomes so tight immediately when his mood becomes angry. It all sticks in my chest. Obstructing the bronchi. Can't breathe. Coughing and coughing and coughing and it doesn't get better.

Obstructing. A fast tickle in the throat (HG). Coughing and coughing and then wheezing. The mucous is stuck in there and it is in there (points to throat pit).

Dust really makes things worse. I have to run in and out of a dusty room to try to avoid breathing in dust, or even picking it up on clothes. Race in and out of a room that is dusty to avoid it (HG).

With the wheezing I can't last much longer. I will die. Severe constriction and wheezing. Won't make it. Afraid I will die. When I have an attack I need to get to the nebulizer at lightning speed. Can't wait, as I feel I will die. Constricting; all the mucous sticks to the tubes and I can't breathe.

Tightness in the bronchi. Fast tickle in the throat pit.

It goes right here in the throat pit, a fast tickle (HG) and wheezing is there. Tightening and constriction in the throat pit. Completely obstructed. Very difficult to breathe.

Movement of air is difficult…to get it out.

Have to jump up (HG) and quickly sit forward immediately or I will choke and die. < Lying down, as no air can get through, and I have to immediately sit up (HG). Will die if I don't move quickly enough. It is almost impossible. I have to move so fast to survive, or the bronchial tubes will close completely.

It moves very, very quickly and I have to move even more quickly to stay ahead of it. In seconds I could be in a severe situation and not be able to get out. I have to jump out of bed to get to the nebulizer at lightning speed (HG). Any hesitation, can't breathe, I just can't breathe.

< In the cold. I hate the cold. Everything moves more slowly in the cold, and I can't breathe. I avoid getting cold because it slows my breathing and the mucous buildup begins. Then there is the cough and the wheeze. I can't warm up.

The attacks are very bad when I feel angry. It is most often because my husband is angry or stressed. I can't talk, and I keep all my anger and feelings inside. It all sticks together in there (HG). I can't say anything. It sticks in here (points to throat pit).

My husband is strict. He puts very high expectations on our daughters. He wants my daughters to be the best, perfect. I feel helpless because I feel for them. I try to intervene, but I don't get far. My husband gets so angry. We all just disappear. Can't talk back, and can't say anything.

Speechless. Can't say anything. Can't argue. I lose my voice and I can't talk.

Everything builds up and sticks here and then I start to wheeze. Keep quiet and all the feelings are trapped inside. Don't utter a word, and just scurry off to another room. With my husband I literally cannot utter a word. Can't talk. Choked by him. Everything sticks in here and I can't breathe. End up at the hospital emergency. Need steroids.

My husband doesn't love me. No affection between us. He doesn't notice me. Since my daughter was born he ignores me. He doesn't see me. Avoids me. He stays away from me. He changed at that time, and he stopped looking at me. Stopped seeing me. The affection disappeared suddenly (changed suddenly).

He completed his education and now teaches at the university. He is well respected at the university. I supported the family while he went back to school. He wants me to prepare meals for him and take care of the household. But it is as if I am not there. Then he looks away, and he doesn't see me. He doesn't even notice me.

I am very, very busy, and I have to move very fast (HG). Keeping the children, the house, my office, my husband. Scurry here and there to organize everything. But I am invisible to him. I am there but he doesn't see me, except when he gets angry. Then he yells, and I am struck dumb.

I can't open my mouth. The children and I disappear when he starts to yell. We just run and hide when he gets angry.

When he starts to argue I can't say anything. I have to get out of there so quickly because I can't breathe. I feel so angry, and I want to tell him to shut up and to get out of here and stop being so hateful, but I can't. Then I get so angry at myself that I am not capable of expressing myself to him. I let him put his expectations on the children. I am not able to stand up for them.

I feel so inferior and small. I have to run into the bathroom and use the nebulizer because I can't breathe. He sees what happens, and he doesn't care. He treats me like nothing. Like a servant, but a servant you don't even see. You can have a servant who prepares your meals and takes care of the house and the laundry. You are grateful, and you say thank you, even though you are at a different level. Even though you are up here and they are your servant, but you can be happy they are there and part of your life. But he doesn't even see me, and it is as if I am not there. Yet I do all the things; cooking, the children, and the house.

We came to this country when we were very young. We had to flee Vietnam and we were stowed on tiny boats leaving our country, our families, and our world behind. It was an impossible journey, and there were many who did not survive. I clung to him for survival (HG). I was 13, and my father told him to take me. I fixed on to him, and that was my survival.

I will be with him until I die. To remember those times and think of our life now, we could never have imagined our lives like this. He is teaching at the university and I am working with animals. This life is beyond our imagination. I always loved animals and now I am working in this area.

I am helping people with their pets. My colleagues like to work with me. I love my children.

I am careful to listen to people and appreciate their feelings. Patients like me. It is easy for me to get along with animals. Get a lot of good feedback about my way with the animals. This makes me feel better about myself. But my husband knows nothing about this part of my life. With him I am insignificant, I am nothing. I feel like I am worth something to my colleagues and the animals. With my husband I am low, small, and insignificant compared to others. I feel smaller, worthless, and I don't deserve a high position, and I'm less than other people. I'm of no value.

I do so much, so that people will like me and I'll feel I am worth something. Even with people who are in a lower position than I am, I try to win over. I help others who are lesser, so I feel worth something. So I have some value.

I worked very, very hard and I was always in the top percentile of the class. Always felt others are so much better. Language and my educational background meant I have been at such a disadvantage. Not smart enough, not able to express myself in English.

Education was important in my family. Even though our lives were hard, my father pushed and pushed. Father was never satisfied with my accomplishments and would shun me. When he would get upset, I would disappear faster than lightning out of his sight. There was no way for me to respond. I just disappeared faster than you can imagine.

So the pattern is the same. My brothers and sisters used to tease me about how fast I could get out of sight when my father was looking for someone to yell at.

I had to be the best in the class. But even when I brought home perfect scores I was still told to do more. I feel this is there still now, my always feeling less than others, and never feeling accepted. I never feel I am part of this world, always feel as if everyone else looks at me and watches me to see if I am doing it correctly. I feel at a low level.

Small, very small.

Some colleagues at work I find very arrogant. I don't like people who step on others. They step on me sometimes to get ahead. They use my knowledge and advice to solve their clinical problems. When they don't know what to do with an animal, they ask me and I give them suggestions. Then they are successful, but they never come to me and see how I have helped them. Feel used and never acknowledged.

Feel stepped on. Get out of the way quickly, or I will be stepped on.

My husband tells me what to do. He is of course always right. I feel like doing something just to show him that he is not always right. Maybe take revenge. I am not able to. He pushes me away, and I feel I am hiding myself more and more.

I was receiving an award for a procedure I had developed in veterinary surgery and he didn't even know about it.

I am so invisible to him. When I am having an asthma attack, he sleeps through undisturbed. He wouldn't care if I died.

We have no sex life. It is not there, he isn't interested in me. When we do have sex, it is just sex; there is no closeness. Feel used, like I could be anyone or anything. He told me that I am abnormal. That I am 'perverted' because I wanted to have a sexual life. I feel I am abnormal and immoral somehow. He takes advantage of me all the time.

Inferior. I hate the way he makes me feel. Treated like a 'thing'. Used and abused with no thought. Like I am low, so low.

It is so hard because when we were young he was my lifesaver. I clung to him for life. I literally stuck to him, as that was the only way I survived. He gives me a place to stay and he is the father to the children. I am trapped and stuck. Can't change anything, can't express anything. I just hide and get out of the way as quickly as possible when his mood starts to change. Asthma attack when he gets angry, and I know it is starting to constrict. It moves so fast, (hand gesture of fingers moving on both hands) in my throat. It happens quickly, like lightning speed (HG).

Want to say something that would kill him, but I can't utter a word.

(Many lizards freeze when confronted by a predator.)

Just disappear so fast and race for the nebulizer. I move out of his way so quickly.

He gives me the walls around us; our home, and now I feel trapped. He doesn't want me to interfere with anything that he says or wants for them. He overpowers me, and my only recourse is to escape.

I have always leaned on him for encouragement and advice. He is powerful and articulate. I am the small one, and the weak one who escapes. I was always the one who leaned on him for everything. He is always the winner.

I worked outside the home and then ran home and took care of the children, prepared meals, and put them to bed. I did all the household things so that he could study. Then he graduated and now he is at the top of his profession. Everyone looks up to him.

I could be an ant under his shoe, I am nothing to him. An ant has no value, no respect, and no intrinsic usefulness.

Useless and worthless. Dirt, I'm treated like dirt. He doesn't respect me as a human being. He doesn't see me as his wife. I am a nuisance that sticks to him. He thinks of me as a prostitute if I want to have a romantic evening. He never wants to touch me. He says there is something sticky about my skin and he doesn't want to touch me.

I also had this feeling in my family. With my siblings I always followed what I was told. I felt weak and small, I couldn't say anything in my family either. I was teased and taken advantage of. I couldn't fight back, as I wasn't strong enough or articulate enough. I was always hanging around with my older brother. He used to try to get rid of me. I remember feeling pushed away. I would follow him and stick on to him, because I wanted to be with him. They teased me and tried and tried to get rid of me. Making plans with me and they would send me to the wrong location. I felt stupid, weak, used, pushed away, and angry. But I was too small and too frightened to say anything.

Dreams of robbers. They enter the house and are taking our things. I am sitting somewhere up above them and watching them. They don't see me. Want to call out but am afraid and too small to do anything against them. Helpless, powerless, small, and very cold. I remember in the dream feeling very cold. Like looking from a vantage point that is up above and looking down. I am hiding. The feeling is powerless, helpless, with nothing I can possibly do to stop them. I am frightened and want to stay hidden.

Dreams of having sex with other men, sometimes more than one man. I am admired and sought after, desired and wanted.

Fear of snakes - especially poisonous snakes.

Don't like cockroaches, centipedes, or scorpions.

Hate lizards. I can't bear lizards. They will stick to you. The worst part is that they adhere to you. They are sticky and cold. When you touch a lizard they are so cold. I can't bear lizards, that stickiness. They move so quickly like lightning and they will come on you, and stick, and you can't get it off. You try to brush them away and they will stick to you. Disgusting. They are so small and insidious.

Ohhhhhhhhhhhh!!!

They move faster than you know (HG).

One reason I was happy to come to Canada is that there are no lizards here. In Vietnam they are everywhere, sticking to the walls. I used to be so, so upset going into a room and turning on the light and then the lizard would scurry (HG) across the wall. It was so fast, you couldn't see it really, but it was there. I couldn't even scream, I was so startled and scared it would drop on to me, and stick to me. That cold sticky creature, you can't brush it away, as it sticks to you, like..... (HG). It has something it produces that sticks to you, and you are trapped and you can't get it off.

My siblings used to tell me I hated lizards so much because I was just like them; so frightened, small and weak, always running and hiding. I was always sticking to them and they couldn't get rid of me.

Very, very sensitive to the cold. I can't stand the cold. Everything is worse in the winter if I get cold. They need to keep the surgical room chilly and I am always in there. It makes me have to run out and use the nebulizer often. If I stay warm I feel much better. I don't generate my own heat - I can feel very cold, cold in the blood.

Follow-up:

I will briefly synopsize the history of her treatment over the last 4 years.

She returned 2 months after taking her remedy in a 200C dose (the only potency we had in stock). She experienced a 'flare up' of her asthma after the remedy.

She suffered an unusually severe asthma attack which was difficult to control with her regular steroid medications. She was in bed for several days and not able to go to work or do her daily activities around the house. She considered going to the hospital but increased the use of the nebulizers. After 4-5 days she started to feel better, and from that time she began decreasing her medication.

Over the first 1.5 - 2 years of treatment she had weaned herself off the daily use of asthma medication, now only using a ventolin inhaler when needed. (Approximately every 3-4 months.) She has reduced the use of medication from: sometimes up to 7-8 nebulizers per day with daily steroid use, to using only a 'short term' bronchial dilator once every 3-4 months. Throughout this time she experienced 2 other big asthma attacks, both brought on when she 'had to scurry away and hide', because her husband was angry and she just 'couldn't say anything'. Both of these episodes were times when the remedy was repeated and her breathing was relieved and she found a way of expressing herself. 'I found my voice'.

While the asthma has become almost nonexistent, she developed a skin eruption on the soles of her feet. The skin was extremely dry, with thick calluses, and deep, painful cracking of the skin. The skin was 'like leather' and the deep cracks would bleed and become very painful making it difficult to stand or walk at times. The worst part for her was the discharge from these deep cracks which she described as 'so, so sticky' she could hardly bear it. Her complaint was always about the 'sticky disgusting discharge'.

It was very tempting to consider different remedies for her as she struggled with these skin eruptions, but she was improving so dramatically with her respiration and energy and her inner sense of herself, that I continued with the Lizard remedy repeating when her 'state' was aggravated.

In the 4+ years of treatment, she has received 3 doses of Lizard 200C, and 2 doses of 1M.

Her skin has settled down and does not cause her the pain and discomfort that it did. She continues homeopathic treatment and feels she is able to breathe freely and express herself much more fully.

Summary and chart illustrating differences

Most lizards are **active during daylight hours**, when their **acute binocular vision** can be used to its greatest advantage, and vision is necessary for most non-burrowing species. Lizards spend considerable time obtaining food. The Iguanians **perch motionless** at familiar sites such as rocks, shrubs, and trees while **waiting for their prey**. This feeding method results in **fierce territoriality**, as prime spots offering abundant prey supply and camouflage are **constantly in contention**. They detect their prey using **visual cues**. They then **dash from their perches** to where the prey item is, and **capture it with their tongue,** in a process known as lingual prehension.

In contrast are the Scleroglossans that **actively roam over the ground, foraging for prey by searching, probing, and digging**. They use their well-developed chemosensory system in a process called vomerolfaction, as well as visual cues. Since this hunting method makes them **more conspicuous**, the Scleroglossans rely on **wariness, speed, agility, and camouflage** to escape predators. The Scleroglossan lizards do not use the tongue to capture prey. Instead, they **grab** their prey in their jaws (jaw prehension). As a result, the tongue is free for use as an organ of chemoreception, a sensory method more developed in the Scleroglossans than the Iguanians. Their enhanced vomerolfaction allows Scleroglossans to identify and **avoid dangerous prey** which harbor metabolic poisons or defensive chemicals. Since most Scleroglossans are highly mobile, they encounter greater numbers of prey than do Iguanians and thus have a greater need to **distinguish between the noxious and the delectable**. The enhanced chemosensory ability has allowed **some Scleroglossans to become subterranean dwellers and others nocturnal foragers**. These modes are unavailable to Iguanians that rely on vision as their primary hunting and defense device.

Lizards have a variety of **defensive** strategies to draw upon. In addition, the tails of many lizards break off easily. This is referred to as **autotomy**. This broken-off section **wriggles rapidly,** and often **distracts the predator**, as the tailless lizard **scurries for cover**. Autotomized tails are often **regenerated quickly**. Lizards can even **mimic or bluff,** by **showing a false show of strength,** to **mislead, deceive, or instill fear or doubt** in the mind of a potential predator. This may occur by appearing much bigger by inflating or by exhibiting color display. Lizards show a bold, intimidating threat, such as a bluff, or façade of strength, and then flee, run, burrow; or just escape without a display of false strength. They also exhibit an ability to cling and move on vertical smooth surfaces.

Many lizards defend certain areas against intruders of the same or closely related species. **Territorial** defense does not always involve actual combat. Presumably to avoid physical harm, elaborate, ritualized **displays** have evolved in many species. These presentations often involve the erection of crests along the back and neck, and the sudden increase in the apparent size of an individual through puffing and posturing. Many species display bright colors by extending a throat fan or exposing a colored patch of skin and engage in stereotyped movements such as push-ups, head bobbing, and tail waving.

Large, colorful horns and other forms of conspicuous head and body ornamentation are often restricted to males. Females of many species also defend their territories by employing stereotyped movements similar to those of males. A displaying male that stands out against his surroundings is vulnerable to predation. This is evidently advantageous for territoriality, and has evolved through natural selection. Territories are usually associated with limited resources, such as nest sites, food, and refuges from predators. A male that possesses a territory will more likely attract females. Thus, he will have a higher probability of reproductive success than one living in a marginal area.

When threatened by a predator or rival, some lizards charge headlong into a battle. They are relying on strength, ferocity, or a bite, which is definitely worse than any bark.

Characteristics of lizards

Suborder: Iguania

Grasps prey with their tongue (lingual prehension).

Tongue movements more pronounced.

Largely herbivorous, but can also be insectivorous.

Various skin modifications: crests, spines, flaps.

Beautiful coloration.

Head bobbing/nodding.

Press-ups/Push-ups.

Solitary.

Territorial.

Ambush predators.

Captures/hunts visible prey.

Climbing, swimming, leaping.

Family: Agamidae	Family: Iguanidae	Family: Chamaeleonidae	Family: Phrynosomatidae
Inhabit warm environments. Well-developed with strong legs. Dull, rough scales suited to desert conditions. Atypical intervertebral autotomy.	Display of bright colors. Head bobbing, stiffen, puff up, throat flap (dewlap). Faster and agile on land (unlike the chameleon). Some live in groups. Well developed limbs. Movable eyelids. Performs autotomy.	Ability to change color that also reflects their moods. Primarily arboreal. Forceps-like feet for grasping, gripping. Slow-moving on the trees; rocking back and forth locomotion. Unsteady gait on the ground. Long, prehensile and coiled tail to maintain balance. Specialized ability to capture prey with propulsive tongue that is often longer than body. Independent movement of both eyes; separate but coordinated view; ability to spot danger in any direction. Absence of autotomy. Insectivorous. Absence of Jacobson's organs; extra sensory perception is less or not seen.	Hot sandy deserts. Agile climbers.
Remedies: *Chlamydosaurus kingii* [Frilled neck lizard] *Calotes versicolor* [Bloodsucker] *Pogona vitticeps* [Central beaded dragon]	Remedies: *Iguana iguana* [Green iguana]	Remedies: *Chameleo zeylanicus* or Chamaeleon (Divya) [Indian chameleon] *Furcifer oustaleti* [Oustalet's or Malagasy Giant Chameleon]	Remedies: *Sceloporus occidentalis* [Western fence lizard]

Specific features of the Iguania species:

	Characteristic body feature	Dwelling	Locomotion	Characteristic behavior & Type of attack/attacked feeling
Chlamydosaurus kingii [Frilled neck lizard]	Throat flap—a large leathery frill that normally lies folded around the neck	Primarily arboreal (tree climbing)		Meat eaters Sudden expansion of the throat flap, hissing loudly, rocketing off to a nearby retreat Solitary Painful bite
Calotes versicolor [Bloodsucker]	Crest on the neck to tail	Fond of garden, low plants, hanging vines Lives in the same place/ bush		Changes to blood red color— the head and sometimes extending to the neck (reflects their changing moods) Shy, harmless No autotomy Independent rotation of both eyes
Iguana iguana [Green iguana]	Sturdy, tough, large size Powerful tail—whip, lash, strokes Claws—clasp, hook, grasp, grip, rip apart Razor sharp teeth—bite, chew, batter Exotic appearance, beautiful coloration Specific color—green	Arboreal Often found near water	Agile climbers, excellent swimmers Fast and agile on land (unlike the unsteady gait of the chameleon on land)	Fall from heights and remain unhurt; tough to land on solid ground Changes color depending on their mood, surrounding temperature or social status (like the chameleon) Generally solitary (but when young remain in groups) Acute senses: hearing, smell, and vision Able to detect shapes and motion from a distance Autotomy Battered and chewed spines indicate lower social status Can be tamed Not very affectionate Don't like to be picked up More aggressive when wounded or injured Commonly preyed by the hawks

	Characteristic body feature	Dwelling	Locomotion	Characteristic behavior & Type of attack/attacked feeling
Chameleo zeylanicus or Chameleon (Divya) [Indian chameleon]	Extremely long tongue Bony casque, crests/ tubercles			
Furcifer oustaleti [Oustalet's or Malagasy Giant Chameleon]				Ability to change to very strikingly bright colors from a completely dull appearance compared to the *Chamaeleo zeylanicus*
Pogona vitticeps [Central bearded dragon]	Spiny projections on the throat, neck and sides of the body	Arid, semi-desert regions	Climbing	Head bobbing, arm waving, color changing Puffing the spiny throat to appear larger during defensive displays or while attracting a potential mate or asserting dominance over a territory
Sceloporus occidentalis [Western fence lizard]	Bright blue belly in males; yellow color on the ventral sides of the legs Sharp keels	Avoid harsh deserts Perched on high places, fences, rocks, etc.	Agile climbers, jumping	Highly active Mimic a shadow Head bobbing, push-ups, autotomy Ability to change color Twitching

498

Suborder: Scleroglossa

Increased jaw mobility; grasp prey with their jaws (jaw prehension).

Bites stronger than tongue movement.

Highly developed chemosensory system that
may include abnormal olfactory sensitivity and/or a curious tendency
to perceive smells via the mouth.

Wide foraging.

Captures hidden and sedentary/inactive prey.

Family: Anguidae	Family: Lacertidae	Family: Helodermatidae	Family: Varanidae
Limbless or limbed.	Long, slender, lack body modifications like crests, spines, etc.	Skin-beaded, armored, studded.	Large, powerful, ferocious.
Tail autotomy.		Slow, sluggish, lethargic.	Strong feet, sharp claws and teeth, armored skin.
Thick skin, heavily armored, inflexible.	Collar of large scales.	Solitary.	Muscular tail: swishes back and forth to balance.
Terrestrial.	Unable to change color (except *Lacerta agilis*).	Eats a large meal.	Drooling.
		Acute sense of olfaction.	Clumsy, languid.
	Shy, nervous, darts off into their hiding spot.	Clumsy, lumbering, sprawling gait.	Dragon egg: rubbery, tough, elastic, expand.
		Digging, burrowing, climbing.	Do not lose tails nor perform the other characteristic lizard rituals.
	Secretive, prefer shady places, underground burrow, under litter.		Fast and agile.
		Strong, fierce, tenacious bite.	Keen sense of smell, sight and hearing.
			Flicking of the tongue.
	Show parental care.	Will hold on, a firm grasp.	Dig, burrow and scratch (using their sharp claws).
			Hiding in burrows.
		Grapple, wrestle.	Imprisoned, trapped.
		Venomous.	Solitary.
		Painful bites.	Connection with termites.
			Increased appetite.
			Violence, aggression.
			Lie in wait, chase, trail, ambush attack, charge with quick sprinting burst.
			Attack the throat, nasty bite.
			Tear off, rip apart.
			Carnivorous, cannibalistic.
			Wrestling.

Family: Anguidae	Family: Lacertidae	Family: Helodermatidae	Family: Varanidae
Remedies:	Remedies:	Remedies:	Remedies:
Anguis fragilis [Slow worm]	*Lacerta agilis* [Sand lizard, Green lizard] *Lacerta vivipara* [Common lizard]	*Heloderma horridum* [Mexican beaded lizard] *Heloderma suspectum* [Gila monster]	*Varanus komodoensis* [Komodo dragon, Monitor lizard]

Specific features of the Scleroglossa species:

	Characteristic body feature	Dwelling	Locomotion	Behavior Attack/Attacked
Anguis fragilis [Slow worm]	Smooth, shiny, scaly, snake-like Specific color – bright color, metallic, electric blue	Humid habitat		Fear of cats (possibility) Glide away swiftly Burrow in soft substrates with only heads visible Hidden, elusive, secretive Hibernate in a group or alone Tail autotomy Freeze to go unnoticed/ camouflage Stab
Lacerta agilis [Sand lizard, Green lizard]	Strong legs and stout body make it appear more solid and robust than many other lacertids Specific pattern – dark spots with light centers (ocelli)	Sandy habitat	Digging, burrowing	Live in groups Limited color changing ability: males turn green Characteristic dancing: lifting one leg at a time or all at once (jumping) Fight vigorously Grab the neck with jaws, biting, rolling over each other Specific symptom in materia medica: Delirium: alternating with, mental capacities heightened Industrious, mania for work Numbness, insensibility of lower limbs and feet, extending upward

500

	Characteristic body feature	Dwelling	Locomotion	Behavior Attack/Attacked
Lacerta vivipara [Common lizard]				Bear live ones (viviparous)
Heloderma horridum [Mexican beaded lizard]	Larger with subdued colors (in comparison to the smaller and brightly colored Gila monster)	Tolerance to low temperature		
Heloderma suspectum [Gila monster]	Specific color: bright colors, contrasting bands of black and pink, yellow or white, intricate patterns			Specific symptom in materia medica: Intense icy coldness; as if frozen, from within outwards Cold creeping ring around the body Flushes of heat alternating with icy coldness Thoughts: rapid, quick, crowd around each other
Varanus komodoensis [Komodo dragon, Monitor lizard]	Same as the family Varanidae features mentioned in the previous table. In addition the Komodo dragon are also venomous			

Family:
Amphisbaenia

Homoeopathic remedies:

Amphisbaena alba [white-bellied worm lizard]

Amphisbaena vermicularis (Amph.)

Introduction

Amphisbaenians, which are usually limbless, are the smallest suborder of the squamates, and very little information is available about them. They are sometimes called **'worm lizards'**, though they are neither worms nor lizards. They have features which link them both to lizards and snakes.

Their name is derived from 'Amphisbaena'; a mythical serpent with a head at each end. 'Amphisbaena' is a Greek word derived from the word 'amphis', meaning **'both ways'** or **'both sides'**.

These are creatures that can **'go both ways'**. They are so adapted to a subterranean life, that their heads, with both eyes and ears covered by skin, look very much like their tails.

The amphisbaenians are locally, but erroneously, considered poisonous. They are called 'ant-kings' from the widespread belief that they are **raised by ants or termites.** Recent observations confirm the connection with these insects, but the exact relationship remains a mystery. IT DOES APPEAR THAT AMPHISBAENA ALBA MAY HABITUALLY LIVE IN THE NESTS OF THE LEAF-CUTTING ANT *ATTA CEPHALOTES*. *Amphisbaena alba* is able to follow *Atta* trail pheromones. Once inside ant nests, the amphisbaenian may feed primarily on arthropods, notably beetles, which are also inquilines [1] in ant nests.

Classification

There are 4 families comprising 23 genera and a total of about 160 species.
Kingdom: Animalia
Phylum: Chordata
Subphylum: Vertebrata
Class: Sauropsida (Reptilia)
Subclass: Lepidosauria
Order: Squamata
Suborder: Amphisbaenia
Family: Amphisbaenidae (Worm lizards)
      Bipedidae
      Rhineuridae
      Trogonophidae

---

1   Inquiline: an animal, usually an insect, which lives in the nest or abode of another, with or without harm to the host.

Bipedidae is the only family of the Amphisbaenia characterized by two stubby, mole-like forelimbs. The two remedies from this group belong to the family Amphisbaenidae.

Habitat

Their ability to regulate body temperature is limited, which confines them in tropical to temperate regions.

Generalized anatomy

Amphisbaenas have **long cylindrical bodies** and **look remarkably like earthworms**, with their **rings of rectangular, juxtaposed scales that encircle their bodies and tails.** They are **exclusively burrowing in their habits and spend almost their entire lives beneath the ground.**

Close up of Amphisbaena alba

Most species are less than 6 inches (150 mm) long.

They are usually **legless**, although some species have small front legs, positioned close to the head and ending in long claws for burrowing.

Many lack pigmentation and are **pinkish brown** in colour, though some are more colorful. They are **encircled** by **rings of smooth, roughly square shaped vestigial scales** that look like segments. Unlike the scales of snakes which overlap each other, those of amphisbaenians are arranged in **concentric rings**. Because of these scales, they resemble earthworms. They **shed the entire skin in one piece**, similar to the snakes.

The shape of the snout varies according to the method of **tunneling**. There are three amphisbaenid head shapes:
– blunt-cone/bullet-headed
– spade-snouted
– keeled-headed

The burrowing techniques associated with the different head shapes are as follows:

blunt-cone/bullet-headed	spade-snouted	keeled-headed
burrow by head ramming followed by head twisting to compress the soil	burrow by tipping the head downward, thrusting it forward, and then lifting it upward to compress the soil into the roof of the tunnel	burrow by ramming the head forward and then swinging it left and right to compress the soil into the sides of the tunnel

Most of the skull is solid bone with a **large gape** (common to the squamates). The upper jaw has five to nine teeth on each side, with a single central egg tooth that fits between the enlarged teeth of the lower jaw. The amphisbaenians can therefore exert **powerful crushing bites**. The tooth in the upper jaw is used to **pierce** the eggs when hatching.

They have rudimentary eyes and smooth heads that look wedge-shaped in side view. The eyes lack eyelids (like snakes) and they are covered with translucent skin. Like many **burrowing** animals, they have **poor vision**.

Reptiles that live underground tend to lose the external eardrums and sometimes even their middle ears. This suggests not only that their ear openings are protected from predator or parasite attack, but also that they rely more on their other senses. The amphisbaenians have specialized scales on the face which function as substitute eardrums in an auditory system, unique to the worm-lizards.

The tail truncates in a manner that vaguely resembles the head.

Food habits

Their diet ranges form small insects to small burrowing mammals.

Behavior

Amphisbaenians have adapted themselves to an **underground life**. They are **highly modified burrowers. They are seen above ground only after heavy rain has flooded their tunnels, similar to the earthworms.**

Tunneling/Digging

The amphisbaenians **construct their own burrows**, when they move in search of worms, insects and larvae. They burrow not by excavation but by **compression**. They use their specialized thick, heavy skulls as a **ram** to **dig tunnels** through the soil, which can be quite hard in some instances. Their nostrils point backwards, which prevents them from being clogged up with soil while burrowing. The amphisbaenian drives its head, with its recessed lower jaw, through the soil with **considerable strength. Forcing it's head from side to side, or up and down**, with it's mouth tightly closed, it is able to create a tunnel. It **moves along the tunnel by sliding its rings of skin forward, over the body itself, bracing them against the walls of the tunnel. It then pulls the body forward, by means of muscles that connect the body wall to the inner surface of the skin. Digging can be slow and laborious. Once a tunnel is constructed, they move through it very rapidly.** Sometimes they take over burrows of ants or termites. Their heads are **heavily armored and strengthened** because of their use as digging tools.

Locomotion

The skin of amphisbaenians is loose around the circumference of the body, and muscles connect pairs of segments, so that these can be narrowed or widened. There are three sets of muscles on each side of each segment. Two reach backward and one reaches forward. These allow the animal to propel itself by **rectilinear progression, or an accordion-like motion**. The skin then moves, and the body seemingly just drags along behind it. As they slide forward, the scales ahead are able to get a grip on the ground, and allow those behind to be released and hitched up. **Uniquely, they are also able to perform this motion in reverse just as effectively.**

Amphisbaenians are also capable of moving by **concertina (accordion-like)** and **lateral undulatory** movements.

Like many advanced snakes and limbless lizards, **an amphisbaenian will use whatever movement is best suited to the soil and the shape of the tunnel. They will utilize different propulsive patterns with different parts of their body.**

Hearing underground

Amphisbaenians can detect sound of a prey in the tunnel ahead of them. They also sense it by collecting its scent with their **flickering tongue**.

Method of attack and defense

They are effective, formidable predators with their sharp teeth and powerful jaws, capable of exerting **powerful bites**. Their **interlocking teeth** can **cut and tear out** pieces from larger prey. They have been observed in their tunnels **biting and then spinning their body** to free the portion of flesh.

Amphisbaenians are threatened by many animals, but their **main enemies are the venomous coral snake, Elaps.**

Difference from snakes and lizards:

–   Ability to move both ways.

–   Snakes fix the skin tightly near the middle of the back, whereas amphisbaenians have the skin free around the circumference.

508

- Amphisbaenians have a reduced right rather than left lung.
- They have a uniquely shaped egg tooth.
- Annular, ring like segments.
- Specially adapted to burrowing habit.

Materia medica

Rubrics of *Amphisbaena vermicularis* **from Reference Works:**

Mind
DELUSIONS, IMAGINATIONS: BODY, BODY PARTS: FEET: BRAIN, ARE IN, WITH HEADACHE. {0> 1> 0}

Generalities
Weather: wet: agg.

Head
FEET ARE IN BRAIN, AS IF, DURING HEADACHE. {0> 1> 0}

Proving of Amphisbaena vermicularis from Metcalf:
HEAD: Heaviness in the forehead and parietal regions. Heaviness in the forehead. Great confusion and vertigo with swinging sensation, which seems to tend to one side, by a series of successive impulses, and then to the other by a similar operation.

Authors' comment:
This indicates exactly the concertina movement of the amphisbaenians.

Understanding of Amphisbaena by Dr. Divya Chhabra:
From her clinical experience she has understood the main symptom in these patients is 'an ability to move both ways'.

Amphisbaenian summary by Linda Johnston:
Linda has established this summary from cases seen in practice.

What is particular for Amphisbaena are the sensations of always feeling dizzy and unstable. He doesn't know whether he is going forward or backwards. This characteristic sensation for Amphisbaena is noted in the following rubric: Mind; delusions that his feet are in his brain. Which end is his head, and which is his feet? Among all the other typical Lizard themes, Amphisbaena will be dizzy, not knowing which end is up, especially when having to make decisions.

Possible common expressions in patients

One can see the characteristic reptile symptoms along with the symptoms of squamates. The difference between these and the other squamates is the amphisbaenians' 'ability to move both ways'. Another difference is the burrowing and tunneling that characterizes the worm-lizard species. Possible source words related to various body forms and functions are as follows:

Behavior:

- Locomotion
    - *Going both ways, or moving both ways*
    - *Rectilinear, accordion-like or concertina, and lateral undulatory movements*
    - Sliding, propulsive movements
    - Skin moves forward and the body drags behind
- Burrowing
    - Ramming, digging, tunneling
    - Force their head
    - Shovel, spade, scoop, dig
- Live underground, beneath the surface
    - Burrows, tunnels
- Construct their own burrows
- Emerge in flood, rains
- Poor vision and hearing
- Flicking of tongue, like snakes and some lizards

- Fear/aversion/affinity related to coral snakes, *Elaps*
- Relation to ants

Method of attack and defense:
- Powerful crushing bite
- Cutting, tearing, lancinating
- Biting and spinning

Body parts and function:
- Annular rings
- Leglessness
- Shed entire skin in one piece
- Flexibility of jaw and large gape (common in squamates)
- Loose skin (a sensation)

Amphisbaena alba [white-bellied worm lizard]

Order: Squamata

Suborder: Amphisbaenia

Family: Amphisbaenidae (Worm lizards)

Genus: Amphisbaena

Species: Amphisbaena alba

Common name: white-bellied worm lizard

They are STICKY, PLAIN WHITE, and about 75 cms (30 in) in length. These GIANT Amphisbaenians live in the tropical rainforests of South America. They are usually INSIDE THE HUGE NESTS OF THE LEAF-CUTTING ANTS, POSSIBLY USING THESE NESTS FOR EGG LAYING, OR FOR THE INQUILINES FOUND THERE AS A FOOD SOURCE. They have powerful jaws and can eat any small animal that they can overpower, as well as dead fish.

Specific indications or source words for *Amphisbaena alba*

- Sticky
- Specific color: white
- Giant
- Connection to ants

Amphisbaena vermicularis

Order: Squamata

Suborder: Amphisbaenia

Family: Amphisbaenidae (Worm lizards)

Genus: Amphisbaena

Species: Amphisbaena vermicularis

Not much information available.

Made in United States
Troutdale, OR
03/27/2024

18731086R00311